The Azar-Hagen Grammar

TEST BANK for

UNDERSTANDING AND USING

English
Grammar

FOURTH EDITION

PEARSON
Longman

Kelly Roberts Weibel

**Understanding and Using English Grammar, Fourth Edition
Test Bank**

Pearson Education, 10 Bank Street, White Plains, NY 10606

Staff credits: The people who made up the ***Understanding and Using
English Grammar, Fourth Edition, Test Bank*** team, representing
editorial, production, design, and manufacturing, are Dave Dickey,
Christine Edmonds, Ann France, Amy McCormick, Robert Ruvo,
and Ruth Voetmann.

Text composition: S4Carlisle Publishing Services
Text font: 10.5/12 Plantin

ISBN 10: 0-13-205214-8
ISBN 13: 978-0-13-205214-6

Printed in the United States of America
2 3 4 5 6 7 8 9 10—CRS—14 13 12 11 10 09

CONTENTS

INTRODUCTION

This test bank accompanies *Understanding and Using English Grammar, Fourth Edition.* Instructors can choose from nearly two hundred and fifty quizzes and tests to use for assessment. Teachers familiar with the third edition of the test bank will find that a great deal of new material has been created for this fourth edition.

QUIZZES

Each chapter contains a series of quizzes keyed to individual charts in the student book, followed by two chapter tests. The quizzes are intended as quick checks of student understanding for both teacher and student. Mastery of a quiz is a strong indicator that students are ready to progress to the next section.

CHAPTER TESTS

The tests at the end of each chapter are comprehensive, covering as many points from the chapter as possible. The formats of the questions in the chapter tests follow those used in previous quizzes. The two chapter tests are identical in format so that one may be used as a practice test if desired.

EXAMS

Two midterm exams covering chapters one through eleven and two comprehensive final exams are included in this test bank. They can be used in conjunction with the other quizzes and tests, or used separately.

FORMAT

Because students bring a variety of learning styles to the classroom, there is a wide selection of test formats, including sentence completion, sentence connection, multiple choice, and error analysis, as well as more open completion. To maximize the use of the answer key, open-ended writing practice has been kept to a minimum. Teachers wishing to incorporate more writing into the tests are encouraged to add their own material at the end of the chapter tests.

ANSWER KEY

An answer key for all quizzes, tests, and exams can be found in the back of the text.

DUPLICATION

The material has been formatted so teachers can easily make copies for their students. Permission is granted to duplicate as many copies as needed for classroom use only.

Acknowledgments

Much love and many thanks to Chris and Josh, who I hope will always use good grammar, for their patience with me during this project, and to Pat, whose support and belief in me have never wavered. Much appreciation to Ruth Voetmann and Stacy Hagen, for their direction and friendship, and to Cathy Costa, for trying out materials and giving valuable feedback. Finally, thanks to my many students for the inspiration and for teaching me how to teach grammar.

Overview of Verb Tenses

QUIZ 1 The Simple and Progressive Tenses (Charts 1-1 and 1-2)

Directions: Answer the question with a complete sentence. Use a simple or progressive verb.

Example: What is one thing you do every day before you leave home?

<u>*I feed my cat every morning before I leave home.*</u>

1. Where does your English class meet?

   _____

2. What did you bring to class with you today?

   _____

3. Where are you going to go after you take this quiz?

   _____

4. What did you do last weekend after you finished your homework?

   _____

5. Which teams are playing in the game this week?

   _____

6. What were you doing at this time yesterday?

   _____

7. Where will you be living ten years from now?

   _____

8. What do you want to do in the future?

   _____

9. When you fell asleep last night, what were you thinking about?

   _____

10. What time did you wake up this morning?

    _____

Directions: Complete the sentences. Use the present perfect, past perfect, or future perfect form of the verbs in parentheses. More than one answer is possible.

Example: Adam (*use*) _____*has used*_____ a computer since he was ten years old.

1. By the time the TV program ended, Pat (*fall*) _____ asleep.

2. That family (*live*) _____ in the house across the street since 1980.

3. By this time next year, Jessica (*finish*) _____ her degree.

4. Steve (*work*) _____ for the city of Milwaukee for fifteen years.

5. Hannah (*visit*) _____ Venezuela, Scotland, and France.

6. Maddy's friend arrived at 7:30, but Maddy (*finish, not*) _____ her homework yet.

7. When I finish reading this book, I (*read*) _____ all of the Harry Potter books!

8. Elvis Presley (*be*) _____ dead for years, but people around the world still enjoy his music.

9. By the time we arrived at the concert hall, the performance (*begin, already*) _____ _____ .

10. Joan (*drink*) _____ three cups of coffee since she arrived at work this morning.

Directions: Complete the sentences in the paragraph. Use the present perfect, present perfect progressive, past perfect, or past perfect progressive form of the verbs in parentheses. More than one answer is possible.

Nancy and Heather are identical twins. They look exactly the same. They (*enjoy, always*)

_____*have always enjoyed*_____ being twins because they like to confuse people. They are
1

high school students. Nancy and Heather (*attend*) _____ Brookfield
2

High School for three years. Last year, they had the same history teacher, Mr. Monahan. By

the end of the first semester of school, Mr. Monahan (*get*) _____ the
3

girls mixed up many times. Every time he said the wrong name, their classmates laughed.

Until last year, Mr. Monahan (*teach, never*) _____ identical twins in
4

the same class before. The twins' other high school teachers (*have, not*)

_____ so much trouble. This year Nancy and Heather
5

(*wear*) _____ identical clothes to confuse their teachers and
6

classmates. By the time the twins graduate from high school next year, they

(*have*) _____ a lot of fun being twins.
7

A. *Directions:* Write the *-ing* form of the verbs in the correct column.

begin	invite	serve	study
cut	✓learn	shop	supply
forgive	plan	stand	write

Double the consonant	Drop the *-e*	Just add *-ing*
		learning

B. *Directions:* Write the *-ed* form of the verbs.

Example: walk _____*walked*_____

1. marry _____

2. delay _____

3. permit _____

4. dance _____

5. hug _____

6. control _____

7. study _____

8. point _____

9. intensify _____

10. close _____

Directions: Use the given words to make a clear sentence. Pay attention to expressions of time. Add necessary punctuation. More than one answer is possible.

Example: last week \ Mary \ buy \ a CD \ for her brother

<u>   *Last week Mary bought a CD for her brother.*   </u>

1. yesterday \ Clara \ send \ an email \ to her friend in Hungary

   _____

2. by the time I pay my phone bill \ I \ spend \ most of my money

   _____

3. Maria \ live \ in Stockholm \ for three years

   _____

4. last Monday \ Mr. Williams \ call me \ at 6:00 A.M.

   _____

5. since Jon moved to Montreal \ he \ make \ many new friends

   _____

6. what \ you \ do \ after the concert \ tomorrow night

   _____

7. last night \ while \ I \ cook \ dinner \ I burned the meat

   _____

8. Mrs. Kita \ offer \ me \ a job in her shop

   _____

9. when I got to the restaurant \ they \ finish \ their meal \ already

   _____

10. by this time next month \ we \ be \ in our new apartment

   _____

CHAPTER 1 – TEST 1

Part A   *Directions:* Complete the sentences. Use the simple present, simple past, simple future, present perfect, past perfect, or future perfect form of the verbs in parentheses. More than one answer is possible.

1. Three weeks ago José (*eat*) _____ Italian food for the first time.

2. Tomorrow morning Max (*take*) _____ an exam in science class.

3. Kevin (*ride*) _____ his bicycle for exercise every morning.

4. Michelle (*work*) _____ in Paris since 2003.

5. By this time next year, Julie (*finish*) _____ her PhD.

6. I (*study*) _____ at the library yesterday when the fire started.

7. The students (*wait*) _____ for the bus for a long time. Here it comes now!

8. Willy (*visit*) _____ his mother next week.

Part B   *Directions:* Correct the errors.

1. What did you ate for breakfast?

2. Right now I am rideing the bus and talking on the phone.

3. Ruth has traveled to Paris three times last year.

4. My brother is seeming tired this morning.

5. Grandma falled down and broke her arm.

Part C   *Directions:* Use the given words to make a clear sentence. Pay attention to expressions of time. Add necessary punctuation.

1. I \ take \ a test \ right now

   _____

2. my brother \ live \ in the same apartment \ for seven years

   _____

3. computers \ work \ much faster \ in ten years

   _____

4. Ms. Thompson \ go \ to a play \ last weekend

   _____

5. the students \ eat \ lunch \ at this exact time yesterday

   _____

6. by the time I am 80 \ I \ live \ in Seattle \ for a long time

   _____

CHAPTER 1 – TEST 2

Part A *Directions:* Complete the sentences in the paragraph. Use the simple present, simple past, simple future, present perfect, past perfect, or future perfect form of the verbs in parentheses. More than one answer is possible.

Mr. Lim (*be*) _____ 1 _____ currently a photography instructor at the City Art Institute. He (*teach*) _____ 2 _____ there for fifteen years. Since Mr. Lim started teaching, photography (*change*) _____ 3 _____ a lot. Fifteen years ago, all cameras (*use*) _____ 4 _____ film, and photographers (*develop*) _____ 5 _____ and (*print*) _____ 6 _____ their pictures in a darkroom. Nowadays, however, most cameras (*be*) _____ 7 _____ digital, so photographers (*edit*) _____ 8 _____ and (*print*) _____ 9 _____ their photos with a computer. Mr. Lim's classes (*be*) _____ 10 _____ very different from the past, but he still (*enjoy*) _____ 11 _____ teaching. Technology (*continue*) _____ 12 _____ to change in the future, but the basics of photography, such as composition and lighting, probably (*change, not*) _____ 13 _____ much even by the time Mr. Lim retires from teaching.

Part B *Directions:* Correct the errors.

1. What was you do yesterday morning?

2. It will going to rain tomorrow.

3. By the time I go to work, I drank two cups of coffee.

4. She has been studing for final exams all week.

5. He have been watching a movie since 8:00.

Part C *Directions:* Use the given words to make a clear sentence. Pay attention to expressions of time. Add necessary punctuation.

1. by next Friday \ Cathy \ write \ her essay for English class

   _____

2. last night \ a phone call \ wake me up \ at midnight

   _____

3. Jake \ study \ Japanese \ since 2006

   _____

4. Carol \ live \ in Kenya \ from 2005 to 2007

   _____

5. next year \ my parents \ spend \ New Year's Day in London

   _____

6. what \ you \ do \ at this exact time tomorrow

   _____

Present and Past; Simple and Progressive

Simple Present vs. Present Progressive (Charts 2-1 and 2-2)

Directions: Choose the correct completions.

Example: Many people (*(get,)* *are getting*) up early to take the train to work.

1. Every morning passengers (*stand, are standing*) in line to board the trains at Chiswick Station.

2. The train to London (*departs, is departing*) promptly at 7:13 A.M. daily.

3. This morning, there (*is, is being*) a mechanical problem with the train.

4. Right now engineers (*try, are trying*) to figure out what to do.

5. Although it is now 7:30 A.M., the passengers (*still wait, are still waiting*) for the train.

6. Mike Berkley (*takes, is taking*) the train to London every morning.

7. Today Mike (*has, is having*) a business meeting at 9:00 A.M.

8. Mike (*looks, is looking*) at his watch every few minutes.

9. Now he (*taps, is tapping*) his foot impatiently.

10. He (*does not want, is not wanting*) to be late for work in the city.

Simple Present vs. Present Progressive (Charts 2-1 and 2-2)

Directions: Complete the sentences in the paragraphs. Use the simple present or present progressive form of the verbs in parentheses. The first one is done for you.

A. It is a warm, sunny afternoon. Cathy and Joyce (*walk*) _____ are walking _____ in

   Greenlake Park. Some children (*play*) _____ at the playground, and

   a dog (*swim*) _____ in the lake. Everyone (*enjoy*)

   _____ the beautiful day.

B. Josh (*be*) _____ a typical American teenager and (*love*)

   _____ anything with a screen. He (*has*) _____ a

   laptop computer, a digital music player, and a cell phone. Right now Josh (*talk*)

   _____ with his friends on the internet. They (*use, often*)

   _____ email to have conversations. Josh's parents (*understand, not*)

   _____ this. They (*prefer*) _____ to use the phone.

A. **Directions:** Choose the correct completions.

Example: My brother (*is looking,* (*looks*)) like my father.

1. My uncle (*is appearing, appears*) in a TV documentary today. We have to watch it!

2. That fish (*is smelling, smells*) terrible. Are you certain it is fresh?

3. Greg (*is thinking, thinks*) over his career plans. He's trying to decide whether to apply for a new position or not.

4. Right now the chef (*is tasting, tastes*) the meat dish to see if it is ready.

5. You are lucky to have a good sense of humor. People (*are loving, love*) your jokes!

B. **Directions:** Complete the sentences. Use the simple present or present progressive form of the verbs in parentheses.

Example: (*you, understand*) _____*Do you understand*_____ the project we are working on?

1. Right now I (*care, not*) _____ about the election results.

2. Julia and Tim (*see*) _____ a financial advisor now, so they can't come to the phone.

3. What (*you, think*) _____ of our representatives? Are they doing a good job in the government?

4. Mr. Goddard (*feel, not*) _____ well. He has a severe headache.

5. My brother-in-law (*dislike*) _____ his job at the post office.

Directions: Write the simple past tense form of the verbs.

Example: buy _____*bought*_____

1. stop _____
2. make _____
3. catch _____
4. meet _____
5. stand _____
6. occur _____
7. read _____
8. prefer _____
9. write _____
10. sleep _____

11. cost _____
12. study _____
13. find _____
14. ring _____
15. speak _____
16. hear _____
17. wear _____
18. quit _____
19. play _____
20. choose _____

Directions: Answer the questions. Use your ideas to write a complete sentence. Use the simple past tense.

Examples: Did you wear a tuxedo at your wedding?

Yes, I _____*wore a tuxedo at my wedding*_____ .

When did Jane move to Seattle?

Jane _____*moved to Seattle in 2004*_____ .

1. Did Mr. and Mrs. Taylor drive their antique car in the parade?

   Yes, they _____.

2. What time did the political debate start?

   The debate _____.

3. Where did Christopher find his passport?

   He _____.

4. Did the email from your boss come earlier today?

   Yes, the email _____.

5. Did the boys sneak into the movie theater without paying?

   Yes, they _____.

6. Did Victor pay you for the CD that he lost?

   Yes, he _____.

7. Where did you live before you moved here?

   I _____.

8. Did all of the students bring their books?

   Yes, all of the students _____.

9. Did Monika talk to her boyfriend last night?

   Yes, she _____.

10. Where did your teacher leave her keys?

    My teacher _____.

Directions: Choose the correct completions.

Example: The reporter ((asked,) *was asking*) many questions at the press conference yesterday.

1. While Miki (*listened, was listening*) to the lecture in class, her phone rang.
2. Billy was very sad when he (*lost, was losing*) his favorite toy.
3. While Emily (*drove, was driving*) on the freeway, her car ran out of gas.
4. When Stacy (*heard, was hearing*) the joke, she laughed.
5. My ball (*rolled, was rolling*) across the street when the car hit it.
6. The earthquake happened while I (*watched, was watching*) TV last night.
7. The policeman (*cleaned, was cleaning*) his shoes when he got a call about a robbery.
8. The cat (*ran, was running*) up a tree to get away from the dog.
9. Michael (*wanted, was wanting*) to play basketball on Saturday, but he hurt his knee.
10. Lisa (*traveled, was traveling*) on business when she heard the news about her boss' illness.

Directions: Complete the sentences in the paragraphs. Use the simple past or past progressive form of the verbs in parentheses. The first one is done for you.

A. Last year while Giorgio (*work*) _____was working_____ on his house, he
                                1

   (*fall*) _____ off a ladder. He (*break*) _____ his
            2   3

   ankle. Giorgio's neighbor (*take*) _____ him to the hospital. Giorgio
                                 4

   (*be, not*) _____ able to walk for six weeks!
            5

B. Last August my family and I (*take*) _____ a Caribbean vacation. We
                              1

   (*stay*) _____ in a beautiful hotel near the beach. Every day we
            2

   (*spend*) _____ hours on the white sand beaches, and we
            3

   (*eat*) _____ delicious food in colorful restaurants. One evening while
          4

   we (*have*) _____ dinner, a band (*play*) _____
            5   6

   lively music. Many people (*dance*) _____ to the Caribbean rhythms.
                             7

   After dinner we (*walk*) _____ on the beach.
            8

Directions: Check (✓) the correct sentences. Correct the errors in the incorrect sentences.

Examples: ✓ While Ted was writing the email, his computer crashed.

                              crashed
     ___ When his computer ~~was crashing~~, he got angry.

1. ___ Michiko was chopping some vegetables when she was cutting her finger with the knife.

2. ___ While Travis was working on his homework, he was listening to the radio.

3. ___ When Fatima woke up, she was making a cup of tea for herself.

4. ___ When Satoshi stopped smoking, he began eating chocolate all the time.

5. ___ Geoff worked on his report when he was riding the train.

6. ___ While Faruz was shopping for a new computer, he was running into an old friend.

7. ___ When Ana was in Orlando, she went to Disney World every day.

8. ___ James was washing the dishes when he finished reading the newspaper.

9. ___ Toby was painting in his studio when his mother came by for a visit.

10. ___ When Carrie was dropping her laptop computer, she started to cry.

CHAPTER 2 – TEST 1

Part A *Directions:* Circle the correct completions.

1. A: What time _____ you usually work?

   a. are   b. do   c. does

   B: I _____ Monday to Friday from 5:30 A.M. to 2:00 P.M.

   a. worked   b. am working   c. work

2. A: Abdullah _____ a very good play last weekend.

   a. sees   b. was seeing   c. saw

   B: I know. He _____ me about it yesterday.

   a. told   b. did tell   c. was told

3. A: Mr. Smith _____ our office this week.

   a. visit   b. visits   c. is visiting

   B: Really? I _____ that.

   a. don't know   b. didn't know   c. am not knowing

4. A: What _____ at this exact time last year?

   a. did you do   b. did you doing   c. were you doing

   B: I _____ the ruins in Athens. They were fantastic!

   a. toured   b. was touring   c. tour

Part B *Directions:* Complete the sentences. Use the simple present, simple past, present progressive, or past progressive form of the verbs in parentheses.

1. My brother (*have*) _____ a car accident last year, but now he is a good driver.

2. The clock in the living room (*stop*) _____ six hours ago. It shows 3:00, but it's 9:00 now.

3. Mrs. Mitchell (*call*) _____ the police right now. Someone stole her jewelry!

4. Andrew (*go, usually*) _____ skiing in Austria in January.

5. Some friends from South America visited Carl last summer. While they (*visit*) _____, they went to a museum, the zoo, and the beach.

Part C *Directions:* Complete the sentences in the paragraph. Use the simple present, simple past, present progressive, or past progressive form of the verbs in parentheses. More than one answer is possible.

Hani often (*find*) _____ a lot of interesting information on the
                                    1

internet. One unusual Web site (*be*) _____ "Weird News." It
                                        2

(*report*) _____ on strange events from around the world. Yesterday,
            3

Hani (*read*) _____ about a Japanese "air-conditioned shirt." The
              4

shirt (*have*) _____ two tiny fans to keep you cool. Hani
               5

(*decide*) _____ to buy one to try to stay cool in hot weather.
            6

Part D *Directions:* Correct the errors.

1. Every summer Sarah's cousin from England visit her.

2. Ibrahim was very upset when he heared the news.

3. You can't talk to Mr. James right now because he talks to another student.

4. While I was writting my essay, I was also surfing the internet.

5. Karen is very kind and is always helping the teachers with their work.

Part E *Directions:* Answer the questions with complete sentences. Use simple or progressive verbs.

1. Did you watch the evening news on TV last night?

   Yes, I _____.

2. How did Lisa and Ken meet?

   They _____.

3. What are the birds doing?

   They _____.

4. What were you doing when the movie started?

   I _____.

5. Is Leo planning to get the car repaired?

   Yes, Leo _____.

CHAPTER 2 – TEST 2

Part A *Directions:* Circle the correct completions.

1. A: Marissa _____ in working out every day.
    a. believes   b. is believing   c. was believing

   B: I know. She _____ right now.
    a. exercises   b. is exercising   c. was exercising

2. A: Yesterday Phil _____ three cups of coffee before 8:00 A.M.!
    a. drinks   b. was drinking   c. drank

   B: He usually _____ too much coffee!
    a. is drinking   b. was drinking   c. drinks

3. A: Monica _____ an award for outstanding service to the company.
    a. receives   b. received   c. did receive

   B: Wonderful! She _____ it.
    a. earned   b. earns   c. was earning

4. A: Mr. Lin _____ in from China last night.
    a. flew   b. is flying   c. was flying

   B: I'm sure he _____ really tired today.
    a. felt   b. fell   c. is feeling

Part B *Directions:* Complete the sentences. Use the simple present, simple past, present progressive, or past progressive form of the verbs in parentheses.

1. Chris (wake) _____ up at 6:55 A.M. every morning.

2. When I was a child, my parents (work) _____ hard to take care of our family.

3. While I (take) _____ a shower, I got several email messages.

4. This semester I (take) _____ a really fun German class.

5. My best friend was upset about her low grade. She (discuss) _____ her test with the instructor when I left class.

Part C *Directions:* Complete the sentences in the paragraph. Use the simple present or the present progressive form of the verbs in parentheses. More than one answer is possible.

In the Pacific Ocean, various species of whales (swim) _____ thousands

₁

of miles twice a year. In the winter, they (live) _____ in warm tropical seas

₂

near Mexico. In the summer, they (move) _____ to cooler oceans near

₃

Alaska. My dad (be) _____ a scientist and now he (study) _____

₄   ₅

marine mammals. Because of his work, my family (go) _____ whale

₆

watching every spring and fall when the whales (migrate) _____.

₇

Part D *Directions:* Correct the errors.

1. The workers were very tired and forgetted to lock the door when they left for the day.

2. I didn't knew about the party for me.

3. David was very busy yesterday, so today he takes the day off.

4. Steven is in the library reads a book.

5. The little boy buyed another toy because he broke the first one.

Part E *Directions:* Answer the questions. Write a complete sentence. Begin each answer with *Yes, he / she / it.*

Example: Rachael was looking for her phone. Did she find it? _____ *Yes, she found it.* _____

1. It's almost dinner time. Did Jun set the table? _____

_____

2. Did Kathy lay her keys on the hall table? _____

_____

3. It was really cold last night. Did the lake freeze? _____

_____

4. Did Sergei swim in the 1,000-meter race? _____

_____

5. Did Jack sweep the floor this morning? _____

_____

Perfect and Perfect Progressive Tenses

QUIZ 1 **Review of the Past Participle** (Chart 2-4)

Directions: Write the past participle for each verb.

1.	go	*gone*	13.	feed	_____
2.	see	_____	14.	ride	_____
3.	take	_____	15.	lose	_____
4.	buy	_____	16.	give	_____
5.	teach	_____	17.	forget	_____
6.	fly	_____	18.	hold	_____
7.	make	_____	19.	sing	_____
8.	eat	_____	20.	tell	_____
9.	win	_____	21.	shake	_____
10.	steal	_____	22.	study	_____
11.	fall	_____	23.	write	_____
12.	build	_____	24.	drink	_____

QUIZ 2 *Since* and *For* with Present Perfect (Chart 3-1)

Directions: Complete the sentences with *since* or *for*.

Example: The TV has been broken _____*since*_____ Saturday.

1. The Robinsons have lived in Northridge _____ as long as I can remember.

2. Charlie has been in Sri Lanka _____ about three months.

3. The floodwaters have gone down a lot _____ the rain stopped.

4. Selma and Paulo have been married _____ 1984.

5. Going to Europe has gotten more expensive _____ last summer.

6. I have been here _____ a half hour. Why were you late?

7. The clock tower in the train station hasn't been rebuilt _____ the earthquake.

8. There hasn't been a drought in this country _____ fifteen years.

9. Patricia has worked for a Fortune 500 company _____ January.

10. I have thought about you many times _____ you left. I really miss you!

Directions: Choose the correct completions.

Example: George hasn't read any interesting books ((recently,) still).

1. Professor Fetz has taught at the University of Montana (*for, since*) many years.

2. I have lost a lot of weight (*for, since*) I started working out regularly.

3. My sister hasn't graduated from the university (*still, yet*). She hopes to graduate next spring.

4. We have (*already, for*) eaten all of the chocolate. Sorry!

5. Mrs. Josenhans has worked at the post office (*for, since*) 2005.

6. She (*already, still*) hasn't met all of her husband's relatives. He has a large family.

7. I haven't been to the library (*for, since*) months. Have you?

8. My parents have traveled to Germany, Korea, and Canada (*for, so far*) this year. They also plan to travel to Greece.

9. They have lived in Alexandria (*for, since*) January, 2002. They like Egypt very much.

10. We haven't had snow like this (*for, since*) we were children. It's deep!

Directions: Use the given words to complete the sentences. Use the present perfect form of the verbs in parentheses.

Example: The traffic (*be*) _____ *has been* _____ terrible for hours.

1. The team (*win*) _____ all of its games so far this season.

2. My baby (*get, already*) _____ her first tooth!

3. How many times (*you, call*) _____ Trisha?

4. Layla (*promise*) _____ to call us when she arrives in New York.

5. I (*eat, never*) _____ snake meat. Is it good?

6. You (*understand, not*) _____ a word I said!

7. Harry (*try*) _____ to contact his great uncle several times.

8. Mr. Polley (*drive*) _____ a city bus since 1999.

9. Writing a book (*be, not*) _____ as easy as he expected.

10. His education (*give*) _____ him many good opportunities.

Directions: Choose the correct completions.

Example: Joe _____ to check his email last night.
(a.) forgot   b. has forgotten

1. I _____ a cup of coffee since this morning.
   a. didn't have   b. haven't had

2. Norita _____ French in Paris last year.
   a. studied   b. has studied

3. Ms. Field _____ English in Thailand in 2005.
   a. taught   b. has taught

4. We _____ to the art museum several times.
   a. went   b. have gone

5. My son _____ his driving test three times so far.
   a. failed   b. has failed

6. Luka _____ home right after school yesterday.
   a. walked   b. has walked

7. Sam _____ Swiss cheese.
   a. never ate   b. has never eaten

8. Rachael _____ her essay two hours ago.
   a. finished   b. has finished

9. My uncle _____ since last Thursday for his package to arrive.
   a. waited   b. has waited

10. Stephanie _____ a journalist for ten years, from 1997 to 2007.
    a. was   b. has been

Directions: Complete the sentences. Use the present perfect or the simple past form of the verbs in parentheses.

Example: Janice (*talk, not*) _____has not talked_____ to her college roommate for many years.

1. Patrick (*catch*) _____ several big fish so far this weekend.

2. It's too bad we have to cancel the party. I (*call*) _____ some of the guests yesterday. I (*call, not*) _____ everybody yet.

3. Miss Ames (*give*) _____ the students a lot of quizzes so far this term.

4. I just (*meet*) _____ Suzanne three months ago. I really (*know, not*) _____ her long.

5. Beth (*work*) _____ as a teacher for many years. Now she is retired.

6. You (*change*) _____ a lot since we (*see*) _____ you last.

7. My hair (*grow*) _____ six inches in the last year.

Directions: Decide if the sentence is correct (C) or incorrect (I). If incorrect, make the necessary changes.

Example: C   I

    _✓_   _____ She has been reading her book since dinner.

                has seen

   _____   _✓_ Nance ~~has been seeing~~ that movie three times.

C   I

_____   _____ **1.** Rob has been working on his report for two hours.

_____   _____ **2.** Sarah has been going to that museum four times.

_____   _____ **3.** Niko has been taking several computer classes.

_____   _____ **4.** Jordan has not been studying American history this year.

_____   _____ **5.** Ruth has been being sick since Monday.

_____   _____ **6.** Martha has been reading that book several times.

_____   _____ **7.** The Marshalls have been living in Boston for five years.

_____   _____ **8.** Gerhard has been teaching English at Vienna High for nine years.

_____   _____ **9.** Faisal has not been visiting his grandmother yet.

_____   _____ **10.** Teresa has been watching TV since she got home from school.

Directions: Complete the sentences. Use the present progressive or the present perfect progressive form of the verbs in parentheses.

Example: The boys (*swim*) _____are swimming_____ at the beach right now. They

(*swim*) _____have been swimming_____ since this morning.

1. It's almost 3:00 now and the plane is late. I (*wait*) _____ at the airport for about 20 minutes.

2. Right now Rick (*take*) _____ some pictures of his friends. He (*take*) _____ photos of them for 30 minutes.

3. Please be quiet! The movie (*start*) _____ now.

4. I'm really tired this morning. I (*sleep, not*) _____ well recently.

5. Mr. and Mrs. McEnroe (*plan*) _____ their daughter's wedding since last year.

6. The weather is terrible today! It (*rain*) _____. The wind (*blow*) _____ really hard too.

Directions: Complete the sentences with the words in parentheses. Use the past perfect.

Example: When I called my parents, they (*hear, already*) _____had already heard_____ about my car accident.

1. Mr. Holton said that he (*finish, not*) _____ his coffee.

2. The chef (*put*) _____ too much pepper in the soup. It was too spicy!

3. By the time Harriet took the quiz, she (*forget*) _____ most of the vocabulary words.

4. The kids (*break*) _____ the window with a rock, so their mother was angry.

5. I didn't recognize my aunt when she got off the plane yesterday. She (*lose*) _____ about 30 pounds!

6. Ivan couldn't ride his bike. It (*have*) _____ a flat tire for weeks.

7. The bread (*become*) _____ stale, so it didn't taste good.

8. The woman was wearing a beautiful silk dress. She (*buy*) _____ the dress in Hong Kong.

9. The sunset was orange, pink, and gold. I (*see, never*) _____ anything so beautiful.

QUIZ 10 **Simple Past vs. Past Perfect** (Charts 2-6 and 3-5)

Directions: Choose the correct completions.

Example: My brother (*looked,* (had looked)) for his glasses for an hour by the time I arrived.

1. Sarah (*already finished, had already finished*) reading her email when her computer shut down.

2. The students (*didn't finish, hadn't finished*) their tests when the teacher told them to stop working.

3. The old man (*died, had died*) by the time the ambulance (*came, had come*).

4. John woke up at 8:30. Charles woke up at 10:30. In other words, John (*was, had been*) up for two hours by the time Charles woke up.

5. I found the perfect gift for my father. When I (*wanted, had wanted*) to pay for it, I realized that I (*forgot, had forgotten*) my money at home. I (*was, had been*) so embarrassed!

6. Mr. Johnson was worried about his wife. It was 10:00 P.M. and she (*didn't call, hadn't called*) yet.

Directions: Read about Linda's day. Then complete the sentences with the past perfect or the past perfect progressive form of the verbs in parentheses.

Linda had a horrible day yesterday.
    She woke up late.
    She didn't have coffee.
    She missed her bus.
    Her computer at work crashed.
    She lost some important work.
    Her boss was unhappy.
    Linda got a terrible headache.

Example: Linda's (dream) _____*had been dreaming*_____ about a vacation at the beach
         before she woke up.

1. When Linda's alarm clock rang, she (*sleep*) _____ very soundly.

2. She discovered that she (*forget*) _____ to buy coffee.

3. When Linda got to the bus stop, the bus (*leave, already*) _____.

4. By the time the next bus arrived, Linda (*wait*) _____ for 30
   minutes.

5. Before Linda's computer crashed, she (*save, not*) _____ some
   important documents.

6. When her boss came in, Linda (*try*) _____ to recover the
   documents for an hour.

7. When Linda's boss realized that Linda (*lose*) _____ some
   important documents, he was unhappy.

8. Linda (*get*) _____ a headache.

9. Her headache (*stop, not*) _____ by the time she got home from
   work.

10. Linda (*have, never*) _____ such a terrible day!

Directions: Check (✓) the correct sentence in each pair.

Example: __✓__ a. When I had finished my lunch, I went back to the library.

_____ b. When I have finished my lunch, I went back to the library.

1. _____ a. Ray has been seeing a doctor several times about his allergies. I think he is feeling better.

_____ b. Ray has seen a doctor several times about his allergies. I think he is feeling better.

2. _____ a. The concert had just begun when the power went off.

_____ b. The concert just began when the power had gone off.

3. _____ a. I have never been to Asia, but I would like to visit.

_____ b. I had never been to Asia, but I would like to visit.

4. _____ a. By the time we left the café, we have been talking for nearly two hours.

_____ b. By the time we left the café, we had been talking for nearly two hours.

5. _____ a. Megan and Scott have been seeing each other for two months. They are falling in love.

_____ b. Megan and Scott have seen each other for two months. They are falling in love.

6. _____ a. José had been sitting at the computer for two hours. His eyes are tired.

_____ b. José has been sitting at the computer for two hours. His eyes are tired.

CHAPTER 3 - TEST 1

Part A *Directions:* Circle the correct completions.

1. Apple Computers ＿＿＿ many different iPods since 2001.
   - a. produced
   - b. has produced

2. Charlie ＿＿＿ too much chocolate cake at the party last night.
   - a. ate
   - b. has eaten

3. Jason ＿＿＿ on the soccer team, the Switchbacks, for eight years.
   - a. played
   - b. has been playing

4. Mr. and Mrs. Lohman ＿＿＿ in Heidelberg for five years, but now they live in Berlin.
   - a. lived
   - b. have lived

5. The Odens ＿＿＿ in Korea for fifteen years. They live in Seoul, the capital.
   - a. lived
   - b. have been living

6. Tim ＿＿＿ any good movies lately.
   - a. didn't see
   - b. hasn't seen

7. Last week I ＿＿＿ my dog to the veterinarian.
   - a. took
   - b. have taken

8. ＿＿＿ the new book by Stephanie Bond yet? It's really exciting!
   - a. Did you read
   - b. Have you read

9. My parents ＿＿＿ members of the swim club since 1987.
   - a. were
   - b. have been

10. Nathan ＿＿＿me an email two weeks ago.
    - a. sent
    - b. has sent

Part B *Directions:* Complete the sentences in the paragraph. Use the present perfect, past perfect, or perfect progressive form of the verbs in parentheses.

The Museum of Modern Art in New York City is an extraordinary place. It houses more than 150,000 works. My cousin, Tina, *(visit)* ＿＿＿＿＿＿＿＿＿＿ the
   museum several times. The painting she *(enjoy)* ＿＿＿＿＿＿＿＿＿＿ the most is
   The Starry Night by Vincent van Gogh. She *(learn)* ＿＿＿＿＿＿＿＿＿＿ a lot about
   art from her museum visits. Every time she goes to the museum, there is something new.
   The last time she was there, she saw a painting that she *(see, never)* ＿＿＿＿＿＿＿＿＿＿
   before. After Tina *(look)* ＿＿＿＿＿＿＿＿＿＿ at paintings for several hours, the
   museum closed, so she had to leave.

Part C *Directions:* Complete the sentences. Use *since, for, already, yet,* or *still.* Use each word once.

1. Philip has been waiting for the results of the medical tests _____ three weeks.

2. Have you met Anne's new boyfriend? I _____ haven't met him.

3. I don't know which dress I like better. I haven't decided _____ .

4. Maja had _____ forgotten the address and had to look it up again.

5. We haven't gone out to a movie _____ we got our DVD player at home.

Part D *Directions:* Look at the time line of events in soccer star David Beckham's life. Complete the sentences in the paragraph. Use present perfect, past perfect, or a perfect progressive form of the verbs in parentheses.

1975	David Beckham is born in Leytonstone, England.
1980s	Beckham plays on several soccer teams as a child.
1991	Beckham plays for the Manchester United junior team.
1993	Beckham plays in his first professional game with Manchester United.
1996	Beckham becomes one of England's most popular players.
2000–2005	Beckham is captain of the English National Team, and plays in the 2002 World Cup.
2003	Beckham transfers from Manchester United to Real Madrid.
2004	Beckham helps Real Madrid win the Spanish Super Cup.
2007	Beckham signs a 5-year contract with the L.A. Galaxy in Los Angeles, California.

David Beckham was born in England and (*play*) _____ soccer
1

nearly his whole life. Beckham (*play*) _____ on many different teams
2

including several youth teams and three professional teams. By the time he started

playing professionally for Manchester United, he (*play*) _____ soccer
3

for thirteen years. After Beckham (*be*) _____ with Manchester
4

United for ten years, he joined Real Madrid, where he stayed for three years. Since 2007,

Beckham (*play*) _____ for the L.A. Galaxy and (*cause*)
5

_____ great excitement among American soccer fans. Since he first
6

started playing soccer, Beckham (*become*) _____ one of England's
7

most popular soccer players. Over the course of his professional career, Beckham's fans

(*watch*) _____ him develop into a world-class player. He
8

(*score*) _____ many goals with his famous kick. In fact, he
9

(*win*) _____ the hearts of soccer fans around the world.
10

CHAPTER 3 – TEST 2

Part A *Directions:* Circle the correct completions.

1. My wife and I _____ dessert after dinner on Saturday.
   a. have shared   b. shared

2. Eric _____ his homework until 11:30 P.M. last night.
   a. hasn't finished   b. didn't finish

3. My brother repairs cars. He _____ on three different cars so far today.
   a. has worked   b. worked

4. Mai can't find her notebook. _____ it?
   a. Has anyone seen   b. Did anyone see

5. Clara _____ from Stockholm University in 2008.
   a. has graduated   b. graduated

6. The weather _____ especially warm and sunny lately.
   a. has been   b. was

7. Chang _____ for his vocabulary test for two hours yesterday.
   a. has studied   b. studied

8. My mother _____ a cake in years. She always buys one at the bakery.
   a. hasn't baked   b. didn't bake

9. David likes to listen to music. Over the last two years, he _____ many songs on his computer.
   a. has downloaded   b. downloaded

10. Nicola's daughter _____ the violin since 2:00.
    a. has been practicing   b. practiced.

Part B *Directions:* Complete the sentences in the paragraphs. Use the present perfect, past perfect, or perfect progressive form of the verbs in parentheses.

A. Kyoto was Japan's capital from 794 to 1868. Since that time, Kyoto (*become*)

_____ a tourist and cultural center. UNESCO, part of the United
      1

Nations, (*make*) _____ Kyoto a "World Heritage Site" because of the
          2

city's historic buildings such as palaces and temples. Many of the traditional buildings

(*be*) _____ restored, and thousands of tourists visit them every year.
      3

B. Christopher and his wife (*be*) _____ interested in China for a long
            1

time. They went to China last year. Up to that time, Christopher

(*read*) _____ many books about Chinese history and culture,
        2

and he (*study*) _____ the Chinese language for several years.
        3

Part C *Directions:* Complete the sentences. Use *since, for, already, yet,* or *still*. Use each word once.

1. My parents have _____ been so generous. I can't accept more money from them.

2. The taxi driver hasn't had an accident _____ fifteen years. He's a great driver.

3. I _____ haven't found a car I like. I have been looking for two weeks.

4. Mike went to Washington, D.C., last summer. He hadn't been there _____ he was ten years old, and the city had changed a lot.

5. Dana is still waiting for Russ. He hasn't arrived _____.

Part D *Directions:* Look at the time line of events in robotics expert Jennifer Lundquist's life. Complete the sentences in the paragraph. Use present perfect, past perfect, or a perfect progressive form of the verbs in parentheses.

1965	Jennifer Lundquist is born in Portland, Oregon, U.S.
1971	Lundquist gets her first Lego toys and begins building things.
1984	Lundquist studies at the University of Notre Dame and takes her first class in robotics.
1985	Lundquist and her classmate, Charlie Miles, win a robotics competition.
1994 & 1996	Lundquist wins awards for her work.
1998	Lundquist becomes the Director of Robotics at Milton Technology.
2005	Milton Technology invents a robot that can help children with homework.
2007	Lundquist leaves Milton Technology and devotes her time to designing robotic toys.
2008	Lundquist and her business partner Loren Graham form the Robotkids organization.

Jennifer Lundquist is an unusual woman with an amazing career. She

(*build*) _____ things since she was a little girl playing with
        1

blocks. Lundquist (*work*) _____ in robotics since 1984, and
        2

she (*be*) _____ a central figure in the development of
        3

industrial and household robotics since that time. When Lundquist and a classmate,

Charlie Miles, won a robotics competition in college, Lundquist (*learn, already*)

_____ a lot about robots and how to design them. She
        4

continued her work, and by 1996, she (*win*) _____ two awards
        5

in design. Because of her hard work and great ideas, Lundquist was very successful, and

by 1998, she (*become*) _____ the Director of Robotics at Milton
        6

(continued on next page)

Technology. By 2005, Lundquist (*lead*) _____ the company in
7

the development of an amazing HomeworkBot. By 2007, Lundquist

(*work*) _____ at the company for many years, so she quit her
8

job at Milton Technologies. Since then, she (*design*) _____
9

robots for kids. In 2008, Lundquist and her partner started an organization to teach

kids about robots. So far they (*give*) _____ science scholarships
10

to hundreds of young people.

Future Time

Will and Be Going To   (Chart 4-1)

Directions: Complete the predictions. Use **will** and **be going to** with the verbs in parentheses.

Example: Next year, school (be) _____*will be*_____ easier for me than it is now.
Next year, school (be) ____*is going to be*____ easier for me than it is now.

1. a. In 5 years, I (*graduate*) _____ from the university.
   b. In 5 years, I (*graduate*) _____ from the university.

2. a. In 10 years, my mother (*have*) _____ grandchildren.
   b. In 10 years, my mother (*have*) _____ grandchildren.

3. a. In 15 years, children (*take*) _____ a solar-powered bus to school.
   b. In 15 years, children (*take*) _____ a solar-powered bus to school.

4. a. In 20 years, cars (*fly*) _____.
   b. In 20 years, cars (*fly*) _____.

5. a. In 25 years, humans (*live*) _____ on the moon.
   b. In 25 years, humans (*live*) _____ on the moon.

Will vs. Be Going To   (Chart 4-2)

Directions: Decide if each *italicized* verb expresses a prediction, a prior plan, or willingness. Circle your answer.

Example: My mom *is probably going to call* today.   (prediction)   prior plan   willingness

1. Hilary *is going to go* to Texas after the conference.   prediction   prior plan   willingness

2. Barry *will probably be* here soon.   prediction   prior plan   willingness

3. The windows are really dirty. I *will wash* them
   today.   prediction   prior plan   willingness

4. Marcel *is going to start* his new job next week.   prediction   prior plan   willingness

5. Shirley has a beautiful voice. She *is going to be* a
   big success!   prediction   prior plan   willingness

6. I'm so tired. I *am not going to go* out tonight.   prediction   prior plan   willingness

7. A: Calum, your room is a mess!
   B: I'*ll clean* my room later, Mom. I promise!   prediction   prior plan   willingness

8. It'*s going to be* an exciting soccer season.   prediction   prior plan   willingness

9. Pam *will be* late. She's <u>always</u> late!   prediction   prior plan   willingness

10. I *am going to finish* this report by Friday.   prediction   prior plan   willingness

Directions: Complete the sentences. Use *be going to* if the speaker is expressing a prior plan. If you think he/she has no prior plan, use *will*.

Examples: A: What time does the library open?

B: It opens at 8:00 A.M. I (*leave*) _____am going to leave_____ at 7:30.

A: What time does the library open?

B: I don't know. I (*check*) _____will check_____ the schedule on their Web site.

1. A: It's starting to get a little chilly.

   B: I (*get*) _____ your sweater for you.

2. A: With your car in the shop, how are you going to get to work?

   B: I (*take*) _____ the bus.

3. A: Have you made plans for New Year's Eve?

   B: Yes. We (*attend*) _____ a party at the art museum.

4. A: I need to stop at the library before we go to lunch.

   B: Fine. I (*meet*) _____ you on the front steps at noon.

5. A: What are Fareed's plans after graduation?

   B: He (*work*) _____ for a year before he goes to graduate school.

6. A: What are Gary's plans after graduation?

   B: He isn't sure. Perhaps he (*work*) _____ for a year and then begin graduate school.

7. A: What are you going to do this weekend?

   B: I (*clean, probably*) _____ the house and garage. On Saturday night, I (*go*) _____ to the theater.

8. A: Oh, no! We're too late. The copy shop is closed!

   B: Don't worry. I (*get*) _____ up early tomorrow and copy my essay before class.

9. A: How many people do you expect at the party?

   B: I think about 20 to 25 people (*come*) _____.

   A: That's nice.

Directions: Make negative sentences about the future using the given words. Use *will* or *be going to* to express the meaning given in parentheses. More than one answer is possible.

Example: Katarina \ leave \ until Saturday \ not (prior plan)

<u>   Katarina isn't going to leave until Saturday.   </u>

1. my parents \ let \ me \ drive \ on the freeway \ not (refusal)

   _____

2. Teri and George \ come \ to the wedding \ not (prior plan)

   _____

3. that dog \ stop \ barking \ not (refusal)

   _____

4. Luigi \ pass \ his math class \ this semester \ not (prediction)

   _____

5. Nathan and Lucy \ live \ in Bellingham \ after this year \ not (prior plan)

   _____

6. you \ get \ to the airport \ in this traffic jam \ never (prediction)

   _____

7. my neighbor \ turn down \ his music \ at night \ not (refusal)

   _____

QUIZ 5 Expressing the Future in Time Clauses (Chart 4-3)

Directions: Choose the correct completions.

Example: When I (*go,* *will go*) to New York next month, I (*visit,* *am going to visit*) my friend Don.

1. As soon as the timer (*rings, will ring*), I (*take, will take*) the cake out of the oven.

2. When she (*finishes, is going to finish*) sewing the button on, she (*irons, is going to iron*) the shirt.

3. I (*wait, will wait*) here until you (*park, are going to park*) the car.

4. Mark is going to Sweden. After he (*arrives, will arrive*) in Stockholm, he (*rents, is going to rent*) a car.

5. The water is heating now. When it (*boils, is going to boil*), Sally (*makes, will make*) tea.

6. Next year, after I (*get, will get*) my degree, I (*travel, am going to travel*) around the world.

7. Bryan hates his job. When he (*finds, is going to find*) a new job, he (*is, will be*) happier.

8. The students (*go, will go*) home as soon as they (*finish, will finish*) their classes.

9. My dad (*stops, will stop*) smoking after the doctor (*tells, is going to tell*) him to.

10. People (*love, are going to love*) this song as soon as they (*hear, will hear*) it.

Directions: Use the given words to complete the sentences. Use **will** / **be going to** or the simple present tense.

Example: Francis will leave for Vermont on Friday. After he (*spend*) _____spends_____ a week
there, he (*go*) _____will go_____ to New Hampshire.

1. My birthday is next Tuesday. After I (*celebrate*) _____ with my
   family, I (*have*) _____ a party with friends.

2. Rami is going to pick me up at 7:30. I (*wait*) _____ in front of
   the bank until he (*arrive*) _____ .

3. Gary is going to order a book online. Before the book (*come*) _____
   in the mail, Gary (*pay*) _____ for it with his credit card.

4. The movie will begin at 7:15. The audience (*be*) _____ quiet as
   soon as the movie (*start*) _____ .

5. Kevin doesn't have a car yet, but when he (*buy*) _____ his first
   car, he (*give*) _____ his friends a ride.

6. Belinda is going to stay up late tonight. She (*watch*) _____ TV
   until she (*go*) _____ to bed.

Directions: Decide if each sentence expresses *now*, *habitually*, or *in the future*. Circle your
answer.

Example: Nancy goes dancing every weekend.   now   (habitually)   in the future

1. My brother is getting a new computer next week.   now   habitually   in the future
2. Diane usually arrives on time.   now   habitually   in the future
3. I'm waiting for the elevator.   now   habitually   in the future
4. We're going to Morocco in December.   now   habitually   in the future
5. My biology class starts at 8:00 A.M.   now   habitually   in the future
6. In the summer we go to the beach.   now   habitually   in the future
7. The coffee shop closes in ten minutes.   now   habitually   in the future
8. That store charges too much for clothes.   now   habitually   in the future
9. My friends and I are going shopping this weekend.   now   habitually   in the future
10. Look! It's snowing!   now   habitually   in the future

Directions: Complete the sentences. Use the simple present or present progressive form of the verbs in parentheses to express future time. More than one answer may be possible.

Example: Next Thursday the orchestra (*play*) _____is playing_____ a concert.

         The concert (*start*) _____starts_____ at 7:00 P.M.

1. The vegetable market (*open*) _____ at 10:00 tomorrow. Let's go early.

2. My uncle (*come*) _____ for a visit sometime soon.

3. Flight 726 (*leave*) _____ Portland at 7:23 A.M.

4. Next summer we (*visit*) _____ relatives in Calcutta. I'm excited!

5. My boss (*leave*) _____ in a few minutes, so I need to talk to her now.

6. Hurry up! My favorite program (*begin*) _____ at 8:00, and I don't want to miss it.

7. Ruth and David (*go*) _____ on vacation for ten days. I'm jealous!

8. We (*buy*) _____ a new stove next week. Our old one isn't working.

9. The library (*close*) _____ at 5:00 P.M. tomorrow because it's Friday.

10. I (*meet*) _____ my parents for dinner after work.

Directions: Complete the sentences. Use the future progressive form of the verbs in parentheses.

Example: Next Thursday, Pranab (*drive*) _____will be driving_____ from London to Newcastle.

1. The twins (*graduate*) _____ from different universities on the same day in June.

2. At this time next year, Maureen (*live*) _____ in Montreal.

3. Next weekend my wife (*travel*) _____ to a conference in Milan. I (*take*) _____ care of our children at home.

4. Judy (*look*) _____ for a job for several weeks. She will find one soon, I'm sure.

5. Sylvan (*enjoy*) _____ his retirement in a few years.

6. Tomorrow from 10 A.M. to 12 P.M. Tracey (*take*) _____ her driving test.

7. Our family will be busy this Saturday. My husband (*clean*) _____ the garage, my son (*wash*) _____ the car, and I (*relax*) _____ .

A. Directions: Complete the sentences. Use the future perfect form of the verbs in parentheses.

Example: When Martin comes home from work, his children (*finish*) __will have finished__ their homework.

1. I love chocolate cake. By the time I finish this piece of cake, I (*eat*) _____ _____ three pieces.

2. John is going to Canada for a week. By the time he comes back home, the painters (*finish*) _____ painting his house.

3. The baseball team is having a great year. By the end of this season, they (*hit*) _____ _____ over 20 homeruns.

4. Dr. Munsen takes good care of his patients. When he retires next year, he (*be*) _____ _____ a doctor for 25 years.

5. Yasuko is playing in a concert this Saturday. After this concert, she (*play*) _____ _____ in six concerts so far this year.

B. Directions: Complete the sentences. Use the future perfect progressive form of the verbs in parentheses.

Example: When Mark buys his new car next year, he (*save*) __will have been saving__ for it for a while.

1. George is playing a video game. By the time he finishes the game, he (*play*) _____ _____ for several hours.

2. My brother is talking on the phone to his girlfriend. When he finally says good-bye to her, they (*talk*) _____ for over an hour.

3. It rained yesterday, it's raining today, and it will probably rain again tomorrow. It (*rain*) _____ for three days in a row!

4. I moved to Tokyo ten years ago and to Beijing three years before that. In five more years, I (*live*) _____ in Asia for eighteen years.

5. Alexander started learning English when he was in the first grade. By the time he graduates from high school, he (*learn*) _____ English for twelve years.

Directions: Correct the errors.

is going to come

Example: My brother ~~coming~~ to visit us next week.

1. At noon tomorrow, he will have been attending a luncheon at the Hilton Hotel.

2. I willn't be home until 10:00 P.M. tonight.

3. By the time Mr. Wilcox reads my email, I will leave the office.

4. I going to finish my homework after school.

5. After the baby is going to stop crying, she will fall asleep.

6. Is English be an international language in 25 years?

7. The athletes will have been train for several years when the Olympics begin.

8. The TV program will going to start at 8:00.

9. Benjamin plays at a new golf club this weekend.

10. In six months, I will living in a new apartment.

Directions: Change all of the sentences to the future.

Example: By the time Joe arrived, the party had already ended.

    By the time Joe arrives, the party will have already ended.

1. When my brother came home from school, he had two cookies and a glass of milk.

2. The construction workers had been making a lot of noise since early morning.

3. At 10:00 I was teaching my physics class.

4. By 3:00, Junichi had finished his essay on studying in the U.S.

5. After we ate dinner at the Ethiopian restaurant, we went to a movie.

6. Carl was really tired! By the time his favorite TV program ended, he was falling asleep.

7. As soon as I finished my homework, I called my best friend.

   _____

8. After the music stopped, everyone was waiting for the next song.

   _____

9. When the fireworks started, the onlookers clapped excitedly.

   _____

10. Dr. Solack was seeing patients all day. She was very busy.

   _____

CHAPTER 4 – TEST 1

Part A *Directions:* Read each sentence. Decide if the meaning of the verb is *now, habitually,* or *in the future.* Circle your answer.

1. I am going to go to England during winter break. now habitually in the future
2. The plane leaves at 5:30 P.M. today. now habitually in the future
3. I arrive in London at noon the next day. now habitually in the future
4. I am reading a travel book about England right now. now habitually in the future
5. I go to England every winter. now habitually in the future

Part B *Directions:* Complete these short conversations with the future form of the verbs in parentheses. Use **will** or **be going to.**

1. A: Do you want to go to the beach tomorrow?
   B: Oh, I don't think so. According to the weather report, it
       (*rain*) _____ .
2. A: Why did your mom make so much chicken soup?
   B: She (*give*) _____ some to our neighbor. He is sick.
3. A: The kids are really hungry!
   B: OK. I (*make*) _____ some sandwiches for them.
4. A: What are your plans after work today?
   B: I don't know for sure. My friends and I (*go*) _____ out to
       dinner or see a movie.
5. A: My test grade isn't very good. I got a 69%.
   B: That's too bad. Your parents (*not, be*) _____ very happy
       about that.

Part C *Directions:* Circle the correct completions.

1. After Mary _____ her grammar lesson, she _____ on her math homework.
   a. reviews   a. work
   b. will review   b. is going to work
   c. will have reviewed c. will have worked

2. Rob _____ 22 years old before he _____ from college in June.
   a. turns   a. graduates
   b. will turn   b. will graduate
   c. will have turned   c. will be graduating

3. By the time Janice _____ in November, she _____ at the bank for 37 years.
   a. retires   a. works
   b. is going to retire b. will work
   c. will have retired   c. will have been working

(continued on next page)

4. When Margaret _____ to Asia next year, she _____ her sister in Sydney, Australia, too.
   a. travels
   b. will travel
   c. will be traveling

   a. visits
   b. is going to visit
   c. will have visited

5. The boys _____ all afternoon by the time the hole _____ finally deep enough to plant the tree.
   a. dig
   b. will dig
   c. will have been digging

   a. is
   b. will be
   c. will have been

Part D *Directions:* Change all of the sentences to the future.

1. Barbara was working at the computer until she went out with her friends.

   _____

2. By the time Carol went to bed, she had finished correcting all her students' papers.

   _____

3. In the morning we went to the zoo, and then we ate lunch in the park.

   _____

4. When my daughter graduated from the university, I was so proud.

   _____

5. Jason had never met his girlfriends' parents.

   _____

Part E *Directions:* Correct the errors.

1. The movie going to start at 7:45 P.M. and will end around 10:00.

2. As soon as I find my key, I will have opened the door.

3. The book sale will helping the students raise money for their trip.

4. By the time he arrives in Boston, Bert will have spending three weeks cycling across the U.S.

5. I won't going to lend my brother any money. He will never pay it back!

CHAPTER 4 – TEST 2

Part A *Directions:* Read each sentence. Decide if the meaning of the verb is *now, habitually,* or *in the future.* Circle your answer.

1. I am taking three classes this term.   now   habitually   in the future

2. He's reading a really scary book.   now   habitually   in the future

3. The office opens at nine tomorrow.   now   habitually   in the future

4. Mitchell is coming as soon as he can.   now   habitually   in the future

5. Dana starts school at 7:50 A.M.   now   habitually   in the future

Part B *Directions:* Complete these short conversations with the future form of the verbs in parentheses. Use **will** or **be going to**.

1. A: Did you pass the test?

   B: I'm pretty sure I did. I think I (*get*) _____ a high grade.

2. A: Do you have anything special planned this weekend?

   B: Yes! My husband and I (*go*) _____ out to dinner for our anniversary.

3. A: This algebra problem is too difficult for me.

   B: Don't worry. Dennis (*help*) _____ you. He is good at math.

4. A: What are Jamal's plans for his birthday?

   B: His girlfriend (*have*) _____ a party for him.

5. A: Taka had an accident and damaged his new car.

   B: Oh, no! The repairs (*be*) _____ expensive!

Part C *Directions:* Circle the correct completions.

1. Mona ____ on the accounts all day by the time she ____ home.
   - a. works
   - b. will work
   - c. will have been working

   - a. goes
   - b. is going to go
   - c. will have been going

2. After Michael ____ the train to Washington, he ____ writing his report on his laptop.
   - a. catches
   - b. is going to catch
   - c. will have caught

   - a. finishes
   - b. is going to finish
   - c. will have finished

3. As soon as Betty ____ the ripe apples from her tree, she ____ the apples for an apple pie.
   - a. picks
   - b. will pick
   - c. will have picked

   - a. uses
   - b. is going to use
   - c. will have been using

(continued on next page)

4. Robert _____ into his own apartment when he _____ a job.
    a. moves   a. finds
    b. is going to move   b. will find
    c. will have been moving   c. will have found

5. By the time Tracey _____ cutting the last customer's hair, she _____ on her feet for eight hours.
    a. finishes   a. is
    b. will finish   b. will
    c. will have finished   c. will have been

Part D   *Directions:*   Change all of the sentences to the future.

1. Chuck was giving a lecture in his history class.

_____

2. She threw her old shoes away and bought some new ones.

_____

3. By 4:00 we had been sitting on the runway for an hour. Bad weather had delayed our flight.

_____

_____

4. I studied until it was time to go to my appointment with my lawyer.

_____

5. Michelle had never ridden on a motorcycle.

_____

Part E   *Directions:*   Correct the errors.

1. Tommy will have been losing twenty pounds by December.

2. The radio station will be announced the name of the prizewinner at 4:30. We have to listen!

3. My cousins going to send me a postcard from Bali when they get there.

4. When you will explain the situation, your parents will understand your problem.

5. Mr. Ballard will being a very good principal for our school.

Review of Verb Tenses

CHAPTER 5 – TEST 1

Directions: Circle the correct completions.

1. Robert _____ for the International Atomic Energy Agency since 2002.
    a. is working   b. works   c. has worked

2. Mieko broke her leg while she _____ down a mountain.
    a. was skiing   b. skied   c. had been skiing

3. The children _____ into the house when it began to rain.
    a. had run   b. ran   c. are running

4. Every time Nancy _____ some money, she asks her father.
    a. needs   b. needed   c. has needed

5. Kevin _____ very happy at his job until he got a new supervisor.
    a. has been   b. had been   c. is

6. Paloma _____ her family to Disneyland on vacation twelve times.
    a. has taken   b. takes   c. has been taking

7. Nadia will give her report to her boss as soon as she _____ a few figures.
    a. checked   b. will check   c. checks

8. By the time Piet finishes medical school, he _____ over $60,000 to pay for his education.
    a. borrows   b. will borrow   c. will have borrowed

9. It _____ every day since our vacation started.
    a. rained   b. has rained   c. rains

10. Philip _____ most of the peanuts by the time the guests arrived.
    a. is already eating   b. has already eaten   c. had already eaten

11. When I arrived in Vienna, I _____ for 14 hours.
    a. had been traveling   b. was traveling   c. travel

12. While David was washing the dishes, he _____ a glass.
    a. was breaking   b. broke   c. had broken

13. The movie _____ on DVD next Tuesday.
    a. will come out   b. came out   c. has come out

14. This semester I _____ a chemistry class.
    a. take   b. takes   c. am taking

15. When Greg _____ hard, he gets good grades.
    a. studies   b. study   c. studied

16. By this time next week, I _____ my research project.
    a. finish   b. finishes   c. will have finished

17. Watch out! A car _____!
    a. is coming   b. comes   c. will come

18. By the time Fatima retires, she _____ music for 35 years.
    a. is teaching   b. has taught   c. will have been teaching

19. Jin didn't hear the phone because he _____ to music with his earphones on.
    a. was listening   b. listened   c. listens

20. Dad _____ at the airport when I arrive.
    a. was waiting   b. waits   c. will be waiting

21. The Olympic swimmer _____ many races so far this year.
    a. wins   b. has won   c. won

22. As soon as Martina gets over her cold, she _____ to work.
    a. returns   b. returned   c. will return

23. At this exact time next Saturday, we _____ to Hawaii.
    a. will be flying   b. fly   c. flew

24. Last year Tariq _____ a terrible car accident.
    a. has had   b. had had   c. had

25. Judy _____ how to play chess recently.
    a. is learning   b. learns   c. has been learning

Directions: Circle the correct completions.

1. This year the Baldwins _____ skiing in Whistler, British Columbia, over New Year's.
       a. are going   b. go   c. will have gone

2. The computer _____ slowly since we installed the new operating system.
       a. was running   b. has been running   c. will run

3. When I _____ my wrecked car, I cried.
       a. was seeing   b. have seen   c. saw

4. My little brother _____ everywhere. He has a lot of energy.
       a. run   b. runs   c. running

5. People all over the world _____ about the tsunami in 2004.
       a. heard   b. had heard   c. were hearing

6. The new teacher _____ such naughty students. She had to be strict with the class.
       a. has never taught   b. had never taught   c. is never teaching

7. In the past 15 years, the western United States _____ faster than other areas of the country.
       a. is growing   b. has grown   c. had been growing

8. By the time I finish the test, all of the other students _____ the class.
       a. will leave   b. are leaving   c. will have left

9. Maria _____ for the airport at 5:00 A.M. tomorrow.
       a. will be leaving   b. left   c. was leaving

10. In 2020, Collin _____ in politics for 30 years.
        a. worked   b. will work   c. will have been working

11. Right now I _____ my iPod and my cell phone in my pocket.
        a. carried   b. am carrying   c. carry

12. Peter can't budget well. Last month he _____ all of his money by the 15th of the month.
        a. spends   b. was spending   c. had spent

13. Leila _____ two great novels so far.
        a. has written   b. was writing   c. wrote

14. Maurice _____ two soccer teams next season. He loves soccer.
        a. coaches   b. has coached   c. will be coaching

15. Joann and Mark _____ a great view over the ocean from their hotel room. They enjoyed staying there.
        a. had   b. has   c. will have

16. When my father-in-law retired, my mother-in-law also _____ her job.
    a. quitted　　　　　　　b. quit　　　　　　　c. quits

17. Junko _____ in an apartment in Atlanta now.
    a. is living　　　　　　b. living　　　　　　c. has lived

18. While the cat _____ on Monique's lap, it fell asleep.
    a. sat　　　　　　　　b. was sitting　　　　c. has sat

19. The doctor _____ to us when he has finished the surgery.
    a. talks　　　　　　　b. has talked　　　　c. will talk

20. By the time the firefighters _____, the house had burned to the ground.
    a. arrive　　　　　　　b. arrived　　　　　c. will arrive

21. The Chinese _____ moon cakes every year during the Mid-Autumn Festival.
    a. eat　　　　　　　　b. were eating　　　c. are eating

22. Tracey _____ the lesson as soon as she takes attendance.
    a. has begun　　　　　b. began　　　　　　c. will begin

23. I didn't know anything about computer animation until I _____ a class.
    a. took　　　　　　　b. take　　　　　　　c. will take

24. I _____ any good movies recently. Have you?
    a. didn't see　　　　　b. saw　　　　　　　c. haven't seen

25. When the mail carrier came to the door, I _____ a bath.
    a. took　　　　　　　b. was taking　　　　c. have taken

Subject-Verb Agreement

QUIZ 1 Spelling of Final -s / -es (Chart 6-1)

Directions: Write the plurals of the given words. Change the **-y** to an **-i** where necessary.

Examples: ride _____*rides*_____   lash _____*lashes*_____

1. church	_____	**11.** fax	_____
2. boy	_____	**12.** salary	_____
3. chicken	_____	**13.** list	_____
4. box	_____	**14.** edge	_____
5. tack	_____	**15.** friend	_____
6. end	_____	**16.** dish	_____
7. month	_____	**17.** business	_____
8. glass	_____	**18.** minute	_____
9. lady	_____	**19.** valley	_____
10. cough	_____	**20.** family	_____

QUIZ 2 Basic Subject-Verb Agreement (Chart 6-2)

Directions: Choose the correct completions.

Example: Alex and his two brothers (*is,* (*are*)) coming home on Saturday.

1. The chickens on the farm (*lays, lay*) 200 eggs a day.
2. Every student (*needs, need*) to show proof of residency.
3. Each seam and button (*is, are*) carefully checked before the clothing is shipped to stores.
4. The phones available in the U.S. now (*isn't, aren't*) as advanced as the phones sold in Asia.
5. Three representatives from each country (*is, are*) attending the economic meeting.
6. Practicing an instrument several hours a day (*is, are*) necessary if you want to become a professional musician.
7. Plants and animals (*requires, require*) water to survive.
8. The lights that Michael installed along the path (*makes, make*) the steps much safer.
9. Watching TV (*has, have*) fallen in popularity since DVDs became available.
10. Martha, her husband, and their son (*leaves, leave*) for vacation next Monday.

Directions: Complete the sentences. Use the simple present form of the verbs in parentheses.

Example: School (*start*) _____starts_____ promptly at 8:15.

1. Swimming, running, and cycling (*be*) _____ good examples of aerobic exercise.

2. Where (*do*) _____ your sister Jenny and her husband live?

3. Every house in the neighborhood (*have*) _____ holiday decorations in the windows.

4. Most of the kids in my class (*like*) _____ rock music.

5. Mr. and Mrs. Williams and their son (*play*) _____ golf every weekend.

6. Every time the team scores, the crowd in the arena (*scream*) _____.

7. Each of the teams playing in the tournament (*have*) _____ a chance to win.

8. The messages you left on my voicemail (*be*) _____ unclear. I can't understand them.

9. The homework you will be assigned for tomorrow (*require*) _____ a lot of writing.

10. Almost every aunt, uncle, and cousin of mine (*live*) _____ near Seoul.

Directions: Choose the correct completions.

Example: One of my most serious problems with English ((*is*,) *are*) my pronunciation.

1. Three-fourths of the food (*was, were*) cold when the waiter brought it to our table.

2. Most of the lecture (*was, were*) really interesting.

3. A number of the letters (*was, were*) from my friends in Belgium.

4. One of the cartoons in the magazine (*was, were*) really funny.

5. (*Do, Does*) all of the teachers give homework every night?

6. Most of the lectures at our college (*lasts, last*) an hour.

7. None of the books in our school library (*looks, look*) interesting to me.

8. Some of the mail (*was, were*) torn during processing.

9. (*Is, Are*) some of the laundry ready to be ironed?

10. Half of the students in the class (*doesn't, don't*) know the answer to the question.

Directions: Decide if each sentence is correct (C) or incorrect (I). If incorrect, make the necessary changes.

Examples: C   I

        Have
___   ✓ ~~Has~~ any of the students taken this class before?

✓   ___ A number of volunteers are needed to finish this cleaning project.

C   I

___   ___   **1.** Every one of the children need love and affection.

___   ___   **2.** Seventy-five percent of the teachers in our school speaks Spanish.

___   ___   **3.** Some of the stolen jewelry was recovered two weeks later.

___   ___   **4.** A lot of my friends recommends this apartment complex.

___   ___   **5.** None of my friends thinks I should sell my car.

___   ___   **6.** The number of restaurants in San Francisco exceed 2,000.

___   ___   **7.** Each of these bowls are worth more than $150.

___   ___   **8.** All of the money really belongs to that man over there.

___   ___   **9.** One of my pencil needs to be sharpened.

___   ___   **10.** Half of the airplanes leaves on time.

Directions: Choose the correct completions.

Example: How much money ((*was,*) *were*) there in your wallet?

1. There (*is, are*) carrots, beans, and peas in my vegetable garden.

2. There (*has been, have been*) so many accidents here. They really need a stoplight.

3. Why (*isn't, aren't*) there enough seats for all of the students?

4. There (*is, are*) over 10,000 books in the university library.

5. Last night there (*was, were*) a full moon. It was a beautiful night.

6. (*Was, Were*) there a lot of stars in the sky last night?

7. There (*isn't, aren't*) much time. We need to hurry!

8. (*Is, Are*) there anything good to eat in the refrigerator?

9. There (*has been, have been*) a lot of snow in the mountains lately.

10. How many kinds of ice cream (*is, are*) there?

Directions: Choose the correct completions.

Example: How much cash ((*was,*) *were*) there in your wallet?

1. There (*is, are*) too many kinds of bread in the grocery store. I can't decide.

2. Why (*was, were*) there so much noise outside last night?

3. How many rolls of tape (*is, are*) there in the desk drawer?

4. There (*has been, have been*) too many mistakes in the newspaper recently.

5. There (*is, are*) only three ways to get over a cold: drink lots of liquids, eat healthy food, and get plenty of rest.

6. How much time (*is, are*) there before we have to leave for the airport?

7. There (*isn't, aren't*) enough room in the closet for all of our coats.

8. My mother always says there (*is, are*) too much money wasted on fashionable clothes.

9. There (*has been, have been*) a lot of good music on the radio this week.

10. Mr. Wickham thinks there (*is, are*) an old bicycle in his garage. He will give it to me.

QUIZ 8 Some Irregularities in Subject-Verb Agreement (Chart 6-5)

Directions: Correct the errors. Some sentences are correct.

Example: The Japanese ~~lives~~ ^{live} on four major islands and many smaller ones.

1. The news about the earthquakes in Africa are very upsetting.

2. Five dollars is too much for a cup of coffee.

3. The United Nations include representatives from more than 190 countries.

4. Physics and mathematics is really hard for him.

5. The police have come to ask questions about the accident.

6. The United Arab Emirates is a federation of seven states called *emirates*.

7. Fish live in both fresh water and salt water.

8. Rabies are usually spread by infected animals.

9. The disabled have special parking places at most American stores.

10. The *London Times* report daily on the London Stock Exchange.

Directions: Complete the sentences. Use the simple present form of the verbs in parentheses.

Example: The news from my cousins (*be*) ___is___ not good.

1. Two hundred miles (*take*) _____ at least three hours by car.

2. The people in my company (*come*) _____ from many different countries.

3. The Chinese (*be*) _____ the inventors of gunpowder and noodles.

4. The Netherlands (*be*) _____ famous for windmills and tulips.

5. The homeless (*have*) _____ little chance of finding a job.

6. Japanese (*be*) _____ a difficult language to learn because of the different alphabets.

7. The statistics about the economy (*be*) _____ not good this month.

8. Politics (*be*) _____ the major topic of conversation in the nation's capital.

9. Today's newspaper (*have*) _____ an interesting article about the causes of diabetes.

10. The police (*be*) _____ called whenever there is a murder.

Directions: Complete the sentences. Use the simple present form of the verbs in parentheses.

1. Each of the cowboys (*ride*) _____ his horse with skill and grace.

2. Snowboarding (*require*) _____ strong legs, flexibility, and balance.

3. The English (*have*) _____ a long tradition of drinking afternoon tea.

4. Young people today (*remember, not*) _____ life without computers.

5. Diabetes (*be*) _____ a growing health concern around the world.

6. There (*be*) _____ more women with diabetes than men.

7. Only one of the children (*know*) _____ all of the words to the song.

8. Statistics (*use*) _____ a variety of methods to analyze and interpret data.

9. Three-fourths of the factory workers (*take*) _____ the train to work every day.

10. French (*have*) _____ two different words for the verb *to be*.

CHAPTER 6 – TEST 1

Part A **Directions:** Decide if each sentence is correct (C) or incorrect (I). If incorrect, make the necessary changes.

C   I

___ ___ **1.** Every pair of shoes in your closet needs to be cleaned.

___ ___ **2.** I don't know how to correct one of the mistake on my quiz.

___ ___ **3.** Studying all night before quizzes is not a good way to learn.

___ ___ **4.** Every one of my brothers and sisters were at my wedding.

___ ___ **5.** The number of Spanish speakers in the United States increase every year.

___ ___ **6.** My grandmother, mother, and sister has red hair, but my hair is brown.

___ ___ **7.** Each pen and pencil in the little girl's pencil box is new.

___ ___ **8.** The calls she made on her cell phone was expensive.

___ ___ **9.** Some of the speaker in the program look interesting.

___ ___ **10.** A number of the students were unhappy with their test results.

Part B **Directions:** Complete the sentences with *is* or *are*.

1. How many chairs _____ there in this classroom?

2. There _____ a lot of expensive clothing in that store.

3. There _____ excellent computer labs at my college.

4. Why _____ there homework in every class?

5. There _____ an umbrella in the closet for you to use.

Part C **Directions:** Complete the sentences. Use the simple present form of the verbs in parentheses.

1. Japanese (*be*) _____ the most popular foreign language at my school.

2. Thirty minutes (*be*) _____ not enough time to finish this test.

3. The United States (*have*) _____ 12,383 miles of coastline.

4. Mathematics (*help*) _____ people in many different kinds of jobs.

5. The elderly often (*tell*) _____ interesting stories about their lives.

6. The news about the robbery (*be*) _____ shocking.

7. Measles (*affect*) _____ few people in the United States nowadays.

Part D *Directions:* Circle the correct completions.

My favorite place for vacation (*is, are*) a beautiful island called Tranquila. The weather

1

on the island (*is, are*) very warm all year. There (*is, are*) beautiful white sand beaches all

2   3

around the island. The people on Tranquila (*is, are*) very friendly to visitors. They

4

(*helps, help*) you find the beaches or the shopping district. Many stores (*has, have*)

5   6

handcrafted jewelry. The jewelry (*is, are*) beautiful and cheap, and twenty dollars

7

(*buys, buy*) a necklace that can cost over a hundred dollars at home. Some tourists on

8

Tranquila (*spends, spend*) a lot of time shopping. Tranquila is a quiet and friendly island.

9

Every visitor (*comes, come*) back from Tranquila happy and well rested.

10

CHAPTER 6 – TEST 2

Part A *Directions:* Decide if each sentence is correct (C) or incorrect (I). If incorrect, make the necessary changes.

C   I

___ ___ **1.** My lawyer and his assistants research their cases carefully.

___ ___ **2.** Each carry-on bag and purse were checked carefully at the security gate.

___ ___ **3.** The number of crimes in the city are decreasing.

___ ___ **4.** Growing roses are my neighbor's specialty.

___ ___ **5.** The chocolates from the shop on Grant Avenue are sweet and creamy.

___ ___ **6.** Some of the story was funny.

___ ___ **7.** Every one of the students attend class regularly.

___ ___ **8.** Half of the money is my father's.

___ ___ **9.** Running marathons take discipline, endurance, and strength.

___ ___ **10.** The flowers in my garden needs a lot of water every day.

Part B *Directions:* Complete the sentences with *is* or *are*.

1. _____ there any good sales at the market this weekend?

2. The weather forecast says there _____ a huge windstorm coming from the northwest.

3. I think there _____ only two ways to solve that problem.

4. Why _____ there so many cars parked in front of our house?

5. How much time _____ there until the bus comes?

Part C *Directions:* Complete the sentences. Use the simple present form of the verbs in parentheses.

1. Diabetes (*be*) _____ more common in women than in men.

2. The Swiss (*like*) _____ things to run on time and to run well.

3. Economics (*be*) _____ a social science.

4. Italian (*sound*) _____ similar to Spanish and Portuguese.

5. Two thousand five hundred miles (*be*) _____ the distance between Seattle and New York City.

6. Cattle (*be*) _____ expensive to breed and raise.

7. The United Kingdom (*consist*) _____ of England, Scotland, Northern Ireland, and Wales.

Part D *Directions:* Circle the correct completions.

The Seattle to Portland Bike Ride (*happens, happen*) every year in July. Thousands of
1
cyclists (*takes, take*) over the roads in a 200-mile ride between Seattle, Washington, and
2
Portland, Oregon. Riders from all over the United States (*leaves, leave*) Seattle early in the
3
morning. Men, women, and children (*rides, ride*) through the beautiful farmlands and
4
forests of western Washington and Oregon. Along the way there (*is, are*) several rest stops
5
for riders. Volunteers at the rest stops (*serves, serve*) the cyclists food and drinks.
6
Two-thirds of the cyclists (*rides, ride*) for two days. Others (*makes, make*) the trip in just
7   8
one day! The number of riders (*increases, increase*) every year. The Seattle to Portland
9
Bike Ride (*is, are*) one of the best cycling events in the U.S.
10

Directions: Write the plural form of each word in the correct column. The first one is done for you.

✓belief	deer	hero	memo	shelf	species
bush	echo	life	piano	shrimp	tomato
cliff	fox	loaf	sheep	solo	wolf

-s	-es	-ves	no change
beliefs			

Directions: Complete the sentences with the plural form of the given nouns. Use each noun only one time.

child	man	phenomenon
hypothesis	✓medium	ticket
lady	mouse	tooth

Example: The internet is a news source that is replacing traditional _____*media*_____ such as newspapers, TV, and radio.

1. The _____ in the photo wore long black skirts and white blouses. The

   _____ wore suits and ties.

2. You must brush your _____ every day to keep your mouth healthy.

3. The scientists at the conference discussed several untested _____.

4. Mark, John, and Anthony bought their movie _____ over the internet.

5. Rats and _____ look similar, but rats are bigger.

6. From my office window I watched some _____ playing on the playground

   across the street.

7. Halley's Comet is one of many amazing _____ in space.

Directions: Complete the sentences. Use the possessive form of the nouns in parentheses.

Example: (Nancy) _____*Nancy's*_____ baby was born on December 9th.

1. (*Mr. Jones*) _____ brother is a banker in downtown Chicago.

2. The baseball hit (*Marissa and George*) _____ window and broke it.

3. The (*group*) _____ decisions affected many people in our company.

4. Parents usually enjoy their (*children*) _____ musical performances.

5. My (*boss*) _____ daughter attends the University of Toronto.

6. (*Andrea*) _____ job as a reporter is always interesting.

7. The (*baby*) _____ bottle fell off the table and rolled across the kitchen floor.

8. I don't know my (*cousins*) _____ new address. They moved to Rome.

9. Last year the (*building*) _____ owner increased the rent.

10. One (*month*) _____ rent in Manhattan is very expensive.

Directions: Choose the correct completions.

Example: An (*elephants*, (*elephant's*)) tusks can lift up to 2,000 pounds.

1. The lost (*woman's, women's*) clothing was torn and dirty when the police found her.

2. My (*wife's, wive's*) cooking is better than mine.

3. (*Rhonda, Rhonda's*) and (*Mick, Mick's*) wedding was an especially happy occasion for their families.

4. I was really unhappy with the (*movie's, movies'*) ending.

5. Next year I will visit my mom's (*friends, friend's*) in Italy.

6. Mark's (*parents, parents'*) house is on the top of a hill.

7. Kirsten had problems with her (*brother's, brothers'*) car. She called him for help.

8. The weather (*forecasters, forecaster's*) predictions are often all wrong.

9. I want to read all of (*Shakespeares, Shakespeare's*) works.

10. The (*magazines, magazine's*) in the bus station were cheap. I bought one to read on my trip.

Directions: Correct the errors.

Example: I have a ~~three years old~~ cat.
               three-year-old

1. Simone works at a shoes store.

2. The three-weeks vacation was enough for us to really relax.

3. The movie was two-hour-long.

4. There are several seventeen year olds students in our class.

5. My grandmother makes the best tomatoes sauce.

6. In many countries eighteen year old is the legal age for voting.

7. I needed a steaks knife to cut the thick piece of meat.

8. The storms clouds were gathering in the western sky.

9. The flower-shop has a special on roses this week.

10. The Plaza Hotel is a well known hotel in New York City.

QUIZ 6 Count and Noncount Nouns (Charts 7-4 and 7-5)

Directions: Add final *-s/-es* to the nouns in *italics* if necessary. Do not add or change any other words.

Example: There was a lot of *garbage* in the street after the parade. Many *citizen*ˢ of the town helped clean up the mess.

1. Our teacher gave us *suggestion* on how to be successful students. We appreciated her *advice*.

2. My dad bought new *luggage* for his trip. He got three large *suitcase* and a small duffle bag.

3. I just got today's *mail*. There are *bill* and a magazine.

4. Everyone admired the old man's *knowledge*.

5. Pat always puts *pepper* on his food. He likes spicy *dish*.

6. David bought *coffee*, *butter*, and *apple* at the grocery store yesterday.

7. The queen's necklace was made of *gold* and *diamond*.

8. Many Chinese meals include *rice*, *meat*, and *vegetable*.

9. Lee received twenty *dollar* for his birthday. Now he has enough *money* to buy a new game.

10. Marcos enjoys reading *poetry* in his free time.

Directions: Complete the sentences with the given nouns. Add final *-s/-es* if necessary. Use each noun only one time.

beef	coffee	✓ jewelry	orange
chess	hair	light	trip
chicken	homework	luck	

Example: John gave his wife beautiful gold _____*jewelry*_____ for their anniversary.

1. Min prepared some delicious spicy _____ for her guests.

2. Paul's grandpa plays _____ in the park every Sunday afternoon.

3. Carrie turned off all the _____ before she went to bed.

4. My best friend gave me a four-leaf clover for good _____ .

5. Jorge ate some juicy _____ for a snack after school.

6. Ron has some _____ in his yard. He gets fresh eggs almost every day.

7. Cathy drinks _____ for breakfast on weekends.

8. Our dog loses a lot of _____ in the spring.

9. Steven finished all of his _____ before he watched TV.

10. They enjoy _____ to the mountains in the summer.

Directions: Add *a/an* if necessary. Write Ø in the blank if the noun is noncount. Capitalize as necessary.

Example: __Ø__ G̶iraffes are the tallest animals on earth today.

1. _____ international airport is a busy place at any hour.

2. _____ leather furniture is difficult to clean.

3. _____ teacher is responsible for many students.

4. _____ flag is a national symbol.

5. _____ computers have changed the way people communicate.

6. _____ baseball is very popular in Japan.

7. _____ piano is very heavy and difficult to move.

8. _____ oranges contain a lot of vitamin C.

9. _____ effective speaker prepares well before giving a presentation.

10. _____ children need eight to ten hours of sleep a night.

Directions: Choose the correct completions.

Example: Mr. Seymour is reading _____ magazine.

      a. some   (b.) a   c. an

1. Joan's husband gave her _____ flowers on their anniversary.
    a. some   b. a   c. an

2. Edward bought _____ kilo of potatoes.
    a. some   b. a   c. an

3. Judy put _____ salt in the stew.
    a. some   b. a   c. an

4. We saw _____ amazing animals on the safari.
    a. some   b. a   c. an

5. I need to make _____ appointment with the dentist.
    a. some   b. a   c. an

6. Teresa got _____ fresh lettuce for a good price.
    a. some   b. a   c. an

7. Do you have _____ package for me?
    a. some   b. a   c. an

8. Tina and Jack haven't been to _____ concert in several months.
    a. some   b. a   c. an

9. Frederick found _____ helpful information on a Web site.
    a. some   b. a   c. an

10. My son didn't have _____ answer to my question.
    a. some   b. a   c. an

Directions: Complete the sentences with *the* or Ø. Capitalize as necessary.

Example: I hate ___Ø___ homework! ___The___ homework from biology class is really difficult.

1. I can't find _____ key to my car.

2. Kevin asked his older brother for _____ advice about college.

3. Jared doesn't like _____ tomatoes. He never eats them.

4. Did you get _____ book about French cooking?

5. Sylvia lives in _____ house at the end of the street.

6. Donald works hard to earn _____ money.

7. _____ wind is blowing hard today!

8. I haven't finished _____ laundry yet.

9. _____ strawberries are my favorite fruit.

10. What's wrong with _____ TV? It's making a strange sound.

Directions: Complete the sentences with *a, an, the,* or Ø.

Example: Susan heard ___the___ telephone ringing when she walked into her apartment.

1. I'm looking for _____ article about giant pandas.

2. Do you know where _____ post office is? I need to mail _____ letter.

3. I saw _____ news report on TV about _____ tornado in Oklahoma. _____ wind was blowing 100 miles an hour. _____ storm destroyed several homes.

4. These days _____ video games are becoming more active. The game called *Dance Dance Revolution* has _____ electronic pad that you tap with your feet. Another game, *Guitar Hero,* has _____ guitar that gamers use to play electronic music.

5. Students are often tired of _____ studying by the time they graduate from high school. Many students choose to take _____ year off from _____ school. They work for _____ year before they start college.

Directions: Complete the conversations with *a, an, the*, or Ø.

Example: I need ___*a*___ new notebook, ___*Ø*___ scissors, and ___*an*___ eraser.

1. A: Emily's parents gave her _____ laptop computer for graduation.

   B: Great! She will use _____ laptop a lot in college next year.

2. A: Tomás listens to _____ music a lot.

   B: I know. He really likes rock and pop.

3. A: What's _____ answer to question number 7? I don't understand it.

   B: I don't know. I don't understand it either.

4. A: Mr. Warren, may I ask you _____ question?

   B: I'm sorry. I don't have _____ time right now. Let's make _____ appointment to talk tomorrow.

5. A: Do you want _____ eggs or _____ pancakes for breakfast?

   B: I'm not really hungry, thanks.

6. A: Have you heard _____ news about Ben?

   B: Yes. He was in _____ accident on the freeway. He's in _____ hospital.

   A: I hope he's going to be OK.

7. A: Can you help me with _____ dishes?

   B: Sure. I will wash and you can dry.

8. A: My daughter needs _____ information about City College.

   B: She should write to _____ college admissions office.

   A: Thanks for _____ advice.

Directions: Complete the sentences with ***much*** or ***many*** and the correct form of the nouns in parentheses. Use the plural as necessary.

Example: When Eddie goes out for Chinese food, he always shares it with (*friend*)

_____many friends_____.

1. Machiko has been teaching Japanese for (*year*) _____.

2. I was in a hurry. I didn't have (*time*) _____ for breakfast this morning.

3. The students asked (*question*) _____ in class yesterday.

4. Hank's apartment was full of newspapers, books, and magazines. He had too

   (*stuff*) _____!

5. Scientists have (*theory*) _____ about how the universe was formed, but no one knows for sure.

6. Young children don't have (*patience*) _____ and have limited attention spans.

7. There are (*reason*) _____ for obesity in children, including diets high in fat and sugar, and low levels of physical activity.

8. Washington state grows (*variety*) _____ of apples that are exported around the world.

9. Australia is a country with (*sheep*) _____. In fact, there are about ten times more sheep than people.

10. The internet is an amazing resource. There is (*information*) _____ on almost any topic you're interested in.

A. Directions: Complete the sentences with *a few*, *few*, *a little*, or *little*.

Example: I have ____*a little*____ money left. Let's go get coffee.

1. Our history teacher has _____ patience with students who talk during his lectures.

2. The bus should be here in _____ minutes.

3. Matthew knows _____ about photography. You can ask him for help with the photo project.

4. Jack has _____ relatives in the area. He usually spends holidays with his friends.

5. This stew is not very flavorful. I think it needs _____ salt.

B. Directions: Without changing the meaning of the sentences, replace the *italicized* words with *a few*, *(very) few*, *a little*, or *(very) little*.

Example: I have lived in this apartment for five years, but I know ~~hardly any~~ people in the building.

^(*(very) few*)

1. Liam has never been to Berlin, but he has been to Munich *two or three* times.

2. Last Saturday Julia went for a walk in the park. There were *almost no* other people. It was very peaceful.

3. The apartment was plain. There was *not much* furniture and only one window.

4. It's a good idea to ask *some* questions before you purchase any electronic equipment.

5. We have *some* time before our plane leaves. Do you want to get something to eat?

Directions: Choose the correct completions.

Example: We spent _____ days at the beach last summer.

      a. a great deal of   ⓑ many

1. The candidate shook hands with _____ people at the meeting.
    a. each of the   b. each

2. Jennifer invited _____ friends to her birthday party.
    a. a great deal of   b. a number of

3. The boys were late, so they had _____ time to eat dinner.
    a. few   b. hardly any

4. One of the _____ fainted on stage during the concert.
    a. musicians   b. musician

5. Every _____ in the class has a grammar book and a workbook.
    a. student   b. students

6. The art dealer bought _____ paintings at the auction.
    a. several of   b. several

7. Barbara has _____ laundry to do on Saturday.
    a. too much   b. too many

8. _____ the students in my class passed the final exam.
    a. Three-fourths   b. Almost all of

9. After their trip to France and Spain, Shelley and John kept _____ euros to give to their children as souvenirs.
    a. a few   b. few

10. There were _____ messages in my in-box when I got back from vacation.
    a. hundreds   b. hundreds of

Directions: Correct the errors.

Example: My best friend from college is married and has three <u>childs</u>. ^(children)

1. I found several of new movies at the video store.

2. Mr. McDonnell is unhappy about his daughters wedding plans. She is too young to get married.

3. When Greg was a college student, he didn't have many money for going out.

4. My mom set the table with knives, forks, salads forks, and spoons.

5. The flower-shop across the street has the most beautiful roses I've ever seen.

6. Mary has few good friends. She enjoys spending time with them.

7. My teacher gave me some good advices.

8. Fifty percent of my classmates is from Asia.

9. Maurice doesn't like the fruit, but he loves vegetables.

10. I have a sixteen-years-old sister.

11. Two deers were standing near the lake in the early morning.

12. The English is an international language.

13. Joan needs more bookshelfs in her room. She has lots of books.

14. One of the student asked the teacher for help after class.

15. Steve loves sports. A basketball is his favorite game.

CHAPTER 7 – TEST 1

Part A *Directions:* Complete each sentence with the plural form of the nouns in parentheses.

1. On Friday night, John rented two (*video*) _____ to watch during the weekend.

2. Michael is only ten years old, but he is already five (*foot*) _____ tall.

3. Catherine played the same piece on several different (*piano*) _____ before she chose which piano to buy.

4. We need to put out steak (*knife*) _____ because we are having roast beef for dinner.

5. When our house caught on fire, the firefighters sprayed water on our neighbors' (*roof*) _____ to stop the fire from spreading.

Part B *Directions:* Complete each sentence with the possessive form of the nouns in parentheses.

1. The teacher collected the (*students*) _____ papers at the end of the test.

2. I am going with Linda to a party at a (*friend*) _____ house this Saturday.

3. (*Doris*) _____ dog has been missing for two weeks.

4. You can find (*men*) _____ sportswear on the third floor of the store.

5. The nurse was reviewing the (*patients*) _____ charts when the doctor asked for her assistance.

Part C *Directions:* Add final *-s/-es* to the nouns in *italics* if necessary. Do not add or change any other words.

1. I love *snow* in the winter, especially when it falls in big *flake*.

2. The *information* on the internet is much more current than in printed *article*.

3. Grace has had some good *job*. She really enjoys her *work* as a customer service representative.

4. *Life* is an adventure full of interesting *experience*.

5. Baxter bought a lot of *stamp*. He was unsure about how much *postage* he needed.

Part D *Directions:* Circle the correct completions.

1. Last Saturday, Scott had to clean his office. His desk was covered with (*a, an, the, Ø*) mail, scraps of paper, coins, and (*a, an, the, some*) old newspapers. He took (*a, an, the, some, Ø*) mail and threw it away, and he recycled (*a, an, the, some, Ø*) newspapers.

2. Maria did her laundry last night. She sorted (*a, an, the, Ø*) clothes and put them in (*a, an, the, Ø*) washing machine. Then she read (*a, an, the, some, Ø*) book while she waited.

3. While I was waiting for (*a, an, the, some, Ø*) doctor, I had to write (*a, an, the, some*) information on (*a, an, the, Ø*) insurance form.

Part E *Directions:* Correct the errors.

1. When Gloria went to the zoo yesterday, she took a few pictures because it was raining.

2. My nephew is going to be eighteen year old on his next birthday.

3. One of the problem facing big cities is homelessness.

4. Brian was late for work because there were so many traffics on the road.

5. Outside the train station there is a bicycles rack where Ron can lock up his bike.

Part F *Directions:* Circle the correct completions.

On Saturday, I needed to clean (*some thing, some of thing, some things, some of things*)

in the kitchen. First, I cleaned out (*a, an, the, some, Ø*) refrigerator. I had

(*a lot, lots of, a lots of, lot of*) leftover food, and some of it was very old. I threw away

(*a, an, some, some of*) rotten tomatoes, (*a, an, some, some of*) old bread, a piece of dried-up

chicken, and an open can of soda. I also found (*few, little, a few, a little*) grapes in the back

of the refrigerator. I didn't know how long they had been there. I wiped off (*a, an, the, Ø*)

inside of the (*vegetable, vegetables, vegetables'*) drawer and the (*meat, meats, meat's*) drawer.

Then, I swept and mopped (*a, an, the, some, Ø*) floor. I also scrubbed (*a, an, the, some, Ø*)

kitchen sink.

CHAPTER 7 – TEST 2

Part A *Directions:* Complete each sentence with the plural form of the noun in parentheses.

1. My uncle's ranch has more than 200 cattle and 150 (*sheep*) _____ .

2. Mr. Lee's alarm system has protected his jewelry store from (*thief*) _____ .

3. You can see many (*mouse*) _____ around the tracks in the subway station.

4. The prime minister had to deal with several political (*crisis*) _____ as soon as he took office.

5. The dentist is going to clean Mary's (*tooth*) _____ when she visits him next Tuesday.

Part B *Directions:* Complete each sentence with the possessive form of the nouns in parentheses.

1. Did you read about the earthquake in (*this morning*) _____ newspaper?

2. There is a great sale going on in (*ladies*) _____ shoes this week.

3. (*Louis*) _____ car broke down on the freeway last night.

4. What is wrong with the (*city*) _____ cell phone service? They are always having problems.

5. (*Patty and Mike*) _____ apartment is only three blocks from the grocery store.

Part C *Directions:* Add final *-s/-es* to the nouns in *italics* if necessary. Do not add or change any other words.

1. Tim spent a lot of time on his *homework*. He had to finish *assignment* in chemistry and math.

2. Nina has fun trying on *dress* and *shoe*. She loves to shop for *clothing*.

3. The *garbage* didn't fit in the trash can.

4. The police found several *hair* at the crime scene while they were gathering *evidence*.

5. It was difficult to lose *weight,* but I lost twenty *pound*.

Part D *Directions:* Circle the correct completions.

1. People collect (*a, an, the, some,* Ø) things for different reasons. I have (*a, an, the, some,* Ø) friend who collects (*a, an, the, some,* Ø) rocks. He has (*a, an, the, some,* Ø) different story to tell about each rock.

2. My aunt has (*a, an, the,* Ø) unusual painting that she bought for ten dollars. (*A, An, The, Some,* Ø) painting is now worth over two hundred dollars. My aunt is (*a, an, the,* Ø) lucky woman!

3. I am not feeling well today. I have (*a, an, the, some*) awful headache and (*a, an, the, some,* Ø) fever. I think I need (*a, an, the, some*) medicine.

Part E *Directions:* Correct the errors.

1. Mr. Johnson sent his lawyer a six pages letter about his estate.

2. When I asked him for advice, he didn't have much suggestions.

3. I have only a little minutes to finish my homework.

4. Most of parking spaces in the parking lot are full.

5. This store accepts both of credit cards and traveler's checks.

Part F *Directions:* Choose the correct completion.

Last Monday was (*a, an, the,* Ø) holiday, so I didn't have to go to work. I had
                                        1
(*much thing, many thing, much things, many things*) to do, and I was happy to have
                                        2
(*few, a few, little, a little*) time to finish all my chores. In the morning, I cleaned my house.
        3
After lunch, I did (*a, the, some,* Ø) work in my backyard. I mowed the lawn and pulled
                            4
(*a lot, a lots, a lot of, a lots of*) weeds. I trimmed the branches on (*few, a few, little, a little*) of
        5   6
my trees. I also needed to prune (*a, an, some,* Ø) rose bush by the back gate. Finally, I
                                        7
planted (*a, an, the, some*) flowers around (*a, an, the, some,* Ø) front door. It was 3:00 P.M. I
        8   9
was exhausted but very happy. I had finished (*all, all of, all my*) chores.
                                                        10

QUIZ 1 **Personal Pronouns: Subjects and Objects**   (Chart 8-1)

Directions: Identify the antecedent for each personal pronoun in *italics*. Write the antecedent on the line.

Example: Rosa gave her boyfriend a CD for his birthday. He liked *it* very much. *it* = ___CD___

1. Maria is a good student. *She* always studies hard and tries her best. *She* = _____

2. Sean and Adam's mom wants *them* to do well in school. *them* = _____

3. Most cats are quite independent. *They* have very distinct personalities. *They* = _____

4. Our school team won the championship game. *It* was very exciting! *It* = _____

5. My parents and I visited my grandma last Sunday. She baked *us* a delicious cake.

   us = _____

6. Coffee, tea, and cola all have caffeine. Too much of *it* can keep you awake. *it* = _____

7. Coffee, tea, and cola all have caffeine, but I drink *them* anyway. *them* = _____

8. What was the point of the lecture? I didn't understand *it* at all. *it* = _____

9. James is the tallest boy in our class. *He* is 6'2" tall. *He* = _____

10. My sister lives in Michigan. I visit *her* every summer. *her* = _____

QUIZ 2 **Personal Pronouns: Subjects and Objects**   (Chart 8-1)

Directions: Complete the sentences with subject or object pronouns: ***she, her, he, him, it, we, us, they,*** or ***them***.

Example: Ted and his wife are expecting a baby in August. ____They____ are very excited.

1. Michelle is very clever. _____ always gets good grades, and at the end of last year, the school gave _____ an award for excellence.

2. Suzanne met her parents at the museum and _____ looked at the art exhibit together. Afterwards, Suzanne took _____ out for dinner.

3. Something was wrong with the door to our apartment. When I tried to open _____ , I broke my key. I asked our landlord Joe for help. _____ opened the door, fixed the lock, and gave _____ new keys.

4. Ryan was in a car accident last week. Fortunately _____ wasn't hurt. However, the police asked _____ many questions and gave _____ a ticket.

5. Email has changed the way people communicate. Now _____ can contact friends and relatives all over the world quickly and easily.

Directions: Choose the correct completions.

Example: (Me, (My)) brother is the mayor of Newton, Illinois.

1. This book is (*my, mine*) and that one on the table is (*your, yours*).

2. (*Their, Theirs*) soccer team plays more games every year than (*our, ours*) does.

3. Maggie is wearing a pink sweater. Pink is (*she's, her*) favorite color.

4. Tyler needs a haircut. (*His, He's*) hair is too long.

5. (*Your, Yours*) desktop computer is much more powerful than (*my, mine*) laptop.

6. (*Their, They*) house is at 5488 Greenough Place. (*Its, It's*) about a mile from here.

7. Tammy is a tax accountant. (*Her, Hers*) busiest time is in February and March when people have to pay (*their, they're*) income taxes.

8. (*Our, Ours*) best friends just got a new puppy. It is full of energy and likes to chase (*its, it's*) tail.

Directions: Complete the sentences with possessives.

Example: Laura teaches science in a middle school. _____Her_____ students are all between twelve and fourteen years old.

1. Last night, a cat was stuck in our tree. _____ loud meowing woke us up.

2. A: Whose book is that? It looks interesting.

   B: It's _____. I bought it at the college book sale yesterday.

3. Dr. Richard Wells will be the keynote speaker at the medical convention. _____ lecture will be about vision problems in young adults.

4. I just got a new cell phone. It is cool! Now I can watch videos on _____ phone.

5. Marie talks on the phone at least an hour a day. This upsets _____ parents.

6. I can't find an eraser. Can I borrow _____, Mickey?

7. Caitlin and Terry moved to Florida last summer. _____ house is on the beach.

8. _____ family is huge! We have eight aunts, eight uncles, and eighteen cousins.

9. Ms. Paulos cooks wonderful Greek food. She is very proud of _____ moussaka.

10. I'll bring a calculator to the meeting. Albert can't find _____.

(Charts 8-2 and 8-3)

Directions: Complete the sentences with pronouns. More than one answer is possible. Choose the correct singular or plural form of the verbs in parentheses as necessary.

Example: A parent is responsible for taking care of _____*his or her*_____ children.

1. A doctor has to communicate well with _____ patients.

2. I have a lot of respect for the faculty at Edmonds Community College. _____ (*is, are*) very caring instructors.

3. Somebody forgot _____ calculator in math class today.

4. A firefighter risks _____ life to help other people.

5. Anyone can learn to speak a foreign language if _____ (*practices, practice*).

6. Everybody in the class had _____ own opinion on the subject of dating and marriage.

7. Frank is on the city planning committee. _____ (*has, have*) seven members.

8. Nobody (*forgets, forget*) _____ computer password as often as I do!

9. The team is looking forward to the tournament. _____ practiced very hard every day last week.

10. A teacher needs to return _____ students' papers promptly.

Directions: Choose the correct completions.

Example: Maria baked this soufflé (*myself, himself,* (*herself*)).

1. Don't copy your work from Junichi. Do it (*myself, yourself, himself*).

2. The girls took pictures of (*herself, yourselves, themselves*) and sent them to pen pals in Europe and Asia.

3. My uncle told me that he (*myself, himself, herself*) had built the small greenhouse.

4. No one helped us with this project. We did it (*ourself, ourselves, yourselves*).

5. The cruise ship personnel were extremely helpful. They prided (*itself, theirself, themselves*) on good service.

6. The Miller's dog is a smart animal. The dog uses its paws to open doors by (*itself, ourself, yourself*).

7. Karen was shopping for a new purse yesterday. Her mom offered to buy it, but she wanted to pay for it (*yourself, himself, herself*).

8. Last month Mike moved to a new apartment. He moved all the furniture (*yourself, himself, herself*).

9. My parents always told me to take good care of (*myself, himself, themselves*).

Directions: Complete the sentences with reflexive pronouns.

Example: Mark is a funny guy. He sings to _____*himself*_____ when he is happy.

1. My friends have a new picnic table. They built it _____.

2. Roberta sews all her own clothes. She taught _____ to sew.

3. Rick is really proud of _____ because he has learned so much about photography.

4. I _____ do not believe in ghosts.

5. I'm sorry. I can't help you with your test. You have to do it _____.

6. We are planning our summer vacation, but we're not using a travel agent. We are making all of the reservations _____.

7. My grandpa lives by _____ on a small farm in Montana.

8. The children entertained _____ with a game while they were waiting for their parents.

9. The president's wife _____ will speak at the next meeting of our parents club.

10. I scared _____ this morning when I nearly had an accident while I was driving.

QUIZ 8 Forms of *Other* (Chart 8-6)

Directions: Choose the correct completions.

Example: One of my brothers has brown hair and (*another*, (*the other*)) has blonde hair.

1. These shoes don't fit me. Are there (*other, others*) in a larger size?
2. Chris dropped his cell phone and broke it. He had to buy (*another, the other*) one.
3. There are two pieces of chocolate cake left. You can eat one, and I will eat (*another, the other*).
4. Books for art classes are usually expensive. Some cost around $50, and (*the others, others*) cost as much as $80.
5. I already ate one sandwich, but I'm still hungry. May I please have (*other, another*)?
6. Georgia has seven cousins. One lives in Chicago, (*another, the other*) lives in Dallas, and (*another, the others*) live in San Francisco.
7. Do you like this sweater? It's quite different from (*another, the others*) I tried on.
8. A: Did you know that Ken has a new girlfriend?
   B: Really? (*Another, The other*) one?
   C: Yes, but I don't really like her. I've liked his (*other, others*) girlfriends better.

QUIZ 9 Common Expressions with *Other* (Charts 8-6 and 8-7)

Directions: Complete each sentence with a word or expression from the list. The first one is done for you.

> another
> ✓each other
> every other
> in other words
> one after another
> one another
> other than
> the other

1. Miguel and Selma are getting married next month. They love _____*each other*_____ very much.

2. The children took turns playing the game. They threw the ball _____.

3. My friends from Italy come home to the U.S. about _____ year. I wish they could come more often!

4. The scientists wanted to spend _____ three years doing research, but they couldn't afford it.

5. Julie and Kathy are best friends. They tell _____ all their secrets.

6. A: Have you talked to Kevin lately?
   B: Yes. He called me just _____ day, and we had a long conversation.

7. I am not fond of anchovies. _____, I don't like them.

8. No one _____ members is allowed into the private club.

Directions: Correct the errors.

His

Example: Javier is sixteen. ~~He's~~ brothers are thirteen and eleven.

1. A good employee does their job well.

2. Anna and me will fly to Toronto on Sunday.

3. Everybody on the bus was talking on their cell phone.

4. I was happy when I saw me in the picture. I looked good!

5. Ted worked there for two years. The first year was in accounting and another was in marketing.

6. In my grammar class, some students are from Korea, the others are from China, and the others are from Vietnam.

7. Maria wanted to use my phone, so I lent it to she.

8. Mr. Carlson forgot him jacket on the bus yesterday.

9. My family travels to Japan every others year.

10. Susan's family are large. She has five brothers and three sisters.

11. The businessmen introduced himself at the meeting.

12. The support staff in our company consist of 50 people.

13. Us and our parents have dinner together every week.

14. Where did you park yours car?

15. Willy repaired the computer by hisself and saved a lot of money.

CHAPTER 8 – TEST 1

Part A *Directions:* Choose the correct completions. Circle your answer.

1. (*I, me, my*) gave Sergei (*I, my, mine*) piece of pie because (*he, him, his*) asked (*me, my, mine*).

2. Yesterday, Susan left (*she, her, hers*) purse on the bus when (*she, her, hers*) went downtown.

3. Amelie got a bad grade on (*she, her, hers*) test in Mr. Thomas' class. (*She, Her, Hers*) is going to talk to (*he, him, his*) during (*he, him, his*) office hours tomorrow.

4. Grace and Karl took (*they, their, theirs*) baby to the doctor for a checkup. (*They, Them, Their*) need to take (*he, him, his*) in every four months.

5. John doesn't want anybody to touch (*he, him, his*) things, and Julie doesn't want anyone to touch (*she, her, hers*).

Part B *Directions:* Identify the antecedent for each personal pronoun in *italics*. Write the antecedent on the line.

1. The class is too big. The school needs to move it into a larger room. *it* = _____

2. My family is quite tall. All of *them*, including the women, are over 5'10".
   them = _____

3. A bus driver has a very stressful job. *He or she* often needs to deal with heavy traffic and angry customers. *He or she* = _____

4. The young couple won a trip to Hawaii. *They* also received a color TV.
   They = _____

5. The committee consists of representatives from different parts of the city. *It* even includes members from the financial district and the industrial area. *It* = _____

6. Somebody parked *his or her* car in my driveway. I can't drive into my garage!
   his or her = _____

Part C *Directions:* Complete the sentences with reflexive pronouns.

1. When Nathan fell down the stairs, he hurt _____ very badly.

2. I didn't think that I would, but I really enjoyed _____ at Jane's party last night.

3. Sayako promised _____ that she would do better next time.

4. The members of the team are very proud of _____ after winning the city championship.

5. If you don't take care of _____, no one will.

6. We forgot to leave a tip for the waiter. We were so ashamed of _____.

7. It wasn't true that we had forgotten something. The list _____ was incomplete.

Directions: Complete the conversations with *another, the other, other, the others,* or *others*.

1. CUSTOMER: Do you have anything for people on special diets?

    WAITRESS: Yes, we do. Some dishes are low-fat, and _____ are

    1

    vegetarian.

    WAITRESS: And what would the children like to drink?

    CUSTOMER: She'll have a root beer, and _____ will have milk.

    2

    WAITRESS: For dessert, we have a wonderful apple pie.

    CUSTOMER: I really don't like pie. What _____ desserts do you have?

    3

2. WAITRESS 1: What a horrible day!

    WAITRESS 2: What happened?

    WAITRESS 1: Well, at one table, a child kicked me when I was walking by, and I

    dropped a tray of drinks. Later, _____ child wouldn't stop

    4

    screaming, and all _____ customers were very annoyed.

    5

Directions: Complete each sentence with a word or expression from the list.

another	in other words	one another	the other
every other	one after the other	other than	

1. I swim on Sundays, Tuesdays, and Thursdays. I go to the swimming pool
    _____ day.

2. My mother told me that, in a good relationship, the two people communicate with each
    other, help _____, and forgive each other.

3. Did I tell you about running into Louis _____ day? I was at the bank,
    and he walked in to make a deposit. We had a nice chat.

4. _____ fish, no pets are allowed in this apartment building.

5. Jenny cheered as her team members ran across the finish line, _____.

6. I'm almost done using the computer. It will only take _____ ten
    minutes. Then you can use it.

7. Before I can help you with the budget report, I have to finish this project summary, check
    the data for the Web page, and meet with my boss. _____, I can't
    help you until tomorrow.

Directions: Complete the sentences with personal pronouns that refer to the antecedents in *italics*.

1. *Robert* is taking classes at Clearwater College this semester. Last year, _____ was working at a car factory in Milpitas. _____ didn't enjoy _____ job.

2. Many *people* find a great job after _____ go back to school and finish _____ degree.

3. *My family* used to live in Kansas, where the land is very flat and rich. _____ had a wonderful vegetable garden behind _____ house.

4. *Someone* left _____ dictionary in the classroom last Friday. _____ can go to the department office to claim it.

5. *Personal computers* have changed education. When _____ were invented in the early 1980s, _____ cost more than $2,000 each. Today, people can buy _____ much cheaper in discount stores and on the internet.

CHAPTER 8 – TEST 2

Part A   *Directions:*   Circle the correct completions.

1. (*We, Us, Our*) are worried that no one will come to (*we, us, our*) party because no one has called (*we, us, our*) yet.

2. Barbara went to (*she, her, hers*) nephew's birthday party yesterday. (*She, Her, Hers*) gave (*he, him, his*) a book that a friend of (*she, her, hers*) had recommended.

3. Teresa bought a sweater as a gift. She is going to give it to (*he's, his, her*) brother. She also bought some towels. She is going to give (*it, they, them*) to a friend as a wedding present.

4. If (*you, your, yours*) don't finish (*you, your, yours*) homework on time, the teacher will ask (*you, your, yours*) to correct it by yourself.

5. My brother and (*I, my, mine*) are planning an anniversary party for (*we, our, ours*) parents. (*They, Their, Them*) will celebrate their 25th year together.

Part B   *Directions:*   Identify the antecedent for each personal pronoun in *italics*. Write the antecedent on the line.

1. The public should be aware of the dangers that this new power plant can cause. The government needs to inform *them* of the risks that this project carries.

   them = _____

2. A dentist not only cleans patients' teeth, but *he or she* also checks for diseases and infections that can cause tooth decay.

   he or she = _____

3. The audience clapped loudly for the actors. *They* appreciated the wonderful performance.

   They = _____

4. Everyone who paints knows how to take care of *his or her* paintbrushes.

   his or her = _____

5. The team won a gold medal in volleyball. *It* was honored to represent its country.

   It = _____

6. Most of the faculty is going to come to the president's meeting. *They* want to find out about the new internet use policy.

   They = _____

Directions: Complete the sentences with reflexive pronouns.

1. I always talk to _____ about important things that I am thinking about.

2. Because we were in a hurry, we carried our bags up to our hotel room

   _____ .

3. While Alex was working on his car, he cut _____ on a sharp edge.

4. After rehearsing for two hours, the musicians allowed _____ a ten-minute break.

5. Rita was very angry at _____ for missing the important meeting.

6. The dog scratched _____ happily as it lay in the sun.

7. If you want a job done right, you have to do it _____ .

Part D *Directions:* Complete the sentences with *another, the other, other, the others,* or *others*.

1. WAITRESS: There are two specials on the menu tonight. The first is a delicious broiled sea bass. _____ is an oven-roasted chicken with rosemary.

   CUSTOMER: I'll have the bass, please.

2. WAITRESS: Are you ready to order?

   CUSTOMER: There will be five of us, but only three of us are here. We'll wait until _____ arrive before we order.

3. MARY: Where should we go for dinner?

   JOHN: How about Ray's Boathouse on the waterfront?

   MARY: Have you ever eaten there? Is it any good?

   JOHN: I've never eaten there, but many _____ have and recommend it highly.

Directions: Complete each sentence with a word or expression from the list.

another	every other	one after the other	the other
each other	in other words	other than	

1. John can't go with us to the museum on Thursday, so he will have to see the exhibition of Impressionist paintings on _____ day.

2. During the war, my mother and father wrote to _____ every day. In fact, they still have all their letters.

3. My job working on an assembly line is very boring. All day long I put together electric circuits. They come down the line, _____, and I put them together.

4. I don't need another haircut yet. I just got one _____ morning.

5. Firenz doesn't have any plans this weekend _____ studying. He is a serious student!

6. Online education uses the internet to connect teachers and students. _____, you need a computer to take an online class.

7. My bridge club meets on the first and third Saturdays of the month. I usually play bridge _____ Saturday.

Part F *Directions:* Complete the sentences with personal pronouns that refer to the antecedents in *italics*.

1. If *people* drive above the speed limit, _____ should expect to get a speeding ticket. When the police officer gives _____ a ticket, _____ should just accept it quietly.

2. Have you seen my *purse?* I left _____ on this desk. _____ is brown with a gold clasp.

3. I want *everyone* at my party to have a good time. _____ should relax and have fun. If _____ want to take off _____ shoes, that's OK with me.

4. The *government* announced last night that _____ was going to help the earthquake victims in the south. _____ voted to approve $100 million in assistance and supplies.

5. A *professor* has many responsibilities. First and foremost, _____ has an obligation to help students learn. Second, _____ should do research that will improve the prestige of _____ college.

QUIZ 1 **Polite Requests**   (Charts 9-2 → 9-4)

Directions: Read each sentence. Decide if it expresses a *request* or *permission*.

Example: Will you please help me open this door?   (request)   permission

1.	Could you bring my suitcases up to my room, please?	request	permission
2.	May I have another cookie?	request	permission
3.	Would you mind if we sat here?	request	permission
4.	Would you please put away your clothes?	request	permission
5.	Will you come to my party on Friday?	request	permission
6.	Would you mind stepping a few feet to the left?	request	permission
7.	May we come in?	request	permission
8.	Would you mind calling me back in ten minutes?	request	permission
9.	Could I go to Europe next summer?	request	permission
10.	Would you mind if I didn't eat dinner tonight? I'm not hungry.	request	permission

QUIZ 2 **Polite Requests**   (Charts 9-2 → 9-4)

Directions: Complete the polite requests with **I** or **you**.

Example: Could ____I____ borrow five dollars?

1. Could _____ answer the phone for me, please?

2. May _____ use the car tonight, Dad?

3. Could _____ go to the movies with Jason, please? He invited me.

4. Would _____ make me a sandwich?

5. Can _____ help me wash the dishes?

6. Can _____ have another piece of cake?

7. Will _____ call me tomorrow?

8. Would _____ mind closing the window?

9. Could _____ please give me a ride to the airport?

10. Could _____ please borrow your car?

A. *Directions:* Complete the sentences with *if I* + *past tense* or the *-ing* form of the verbs in parentheses.

Examples: My car is almost out of gas. Would you mind (*get*) _____*if I got*_____ gas?

I don't understand this math. Would you mind (*help*) _____*helping*_____ me with my homework?

1. I didn't eat breakfast, so I'm really hungry. Would you mind (*eat*) _____ my lunch?

2. I can't find my phone. Would you mind (*lend*) _____ me your phone?

3. My umbrella is broken. Would you mind (*borrow*) _____ yours?

4. I'm not wearing a watch. Would you mind (*tell*) _____ me the time?

5. I want to take John home. Would you mind (*give*) _____ him a ride?

B. *Directions:* Change each sentence into a polite request.

Examples: I want to cook dinner tonight. _____*Would you mind if I cooked dinner tonight?*_____

I want you to cook dinner tonight. _____*Would you mind cooking dinner tonight?*_____

1. I want you to help me with my homework.

Would you mind _____?

2. I want to go to a café.

Would you mind _____?

3. I'm tired. I want to take a nap.

Would you mind _____?

4. This box is too heavy. I want you to carry it.

Would you mind _____?

5. I want you to wait for me.

Would you mind _____?

Directions: Circle the correct completions.

Example: At the Stover's house, the children _____ do their homework immediately after dinner.

    (a.) must / have to   b. must not   c. doesn't have to

1. If Americans want to travel abroad, they _____ have a passport.
    a. must / have to   b. must not   c. don't have to

2. Students _____ cheat on tests or exams!
    a. must / have to   b. must not   c. don't have to

3. You _____ have any special equipment to go jogging, but a good pair of shoes helps.
    a. must / have to   b. must not   c. don't have to

4. The store opens at 10:00 A.M., so I _____ be there to work by 9:30.
    a. must / have to   b. must not   c. don't have to

5. Children _____ be impolite to adults. They should be respectful.
    a. must / have to   b. must not   c. doesn't have to

6. To make a contract valid, both people agreeing to the contract _____ sign it.
    a. must / have to   b. must not   c. don't have to

7. Tomorrow is Saturday. It's my day off, so I _____ go to work!
    a. must / have to   b. must not   c. don't have to

8. Good photographers _____ take pictures carefully to make sure there is nothing strange in the background.
    a. must / have to   b. must not   c. don't have to

9. On most freeways in Washington state, drivers _____ drive over 60 miles per hour or they will get a speeding ticket.
    a. must / have to   b. must not   c. don't have to

10. Our plane leaves at 8:30 A.M. The airport shuttle is picking us up at 6:00 so we _____ take our car.
    a. must / have to   b. must not   c. don't have to

Directions: Complete the sentences with **must** (**not**) or (**do not**) **have to** and the verbs in parentheses.

Example: Kumi's visa is good until July. After that she (*return*) _____must / has to return_____ to Japan.

1. Jason's mom says he (*go*) _____ to bed at 10:00 P.M.

2. If you want to get a good grade, you (*study*) _____ hard.

3. We (*go, not*) _____ shopping today if you don't want to. You decide.

4. Leslie failed her Spanish class. She (*take*) _____ it again next year.

5. Visitors (*smoke, not*) _____ in the hospital. It is not allowed.

6. Mr. Lehmann just had a major heart attack. The doctors (*do*) _____ emergency surgery right away.

7. Marcia (*worry, not*) _____ about her grade in my class. Her work is very good!

8. I am so stressed! I (*finish*) _____ this marketing proposal before the meeting on Friday.

9. Carlos borrowed $500 from his brother. He (*pay*) _____ it back in a month.

10. You (*cross, not*) _____ the street in the middle of the block. Please use the crosswalk.

Directions: Read each sentence. Decide if it expresses *advice, an important duty,* or *a strong warning.*

Example: I should study tonight, but I don't feel like it.   (advice)   duty   warning

1. Children shouldn't watch more than an hour of television daily.   advice   duty   warning
2. Police officers should protect the public in dangerous situations.   advice   duty   warning
3. You'd better not park in the loading zone. You'll get a ticket.   advice   duty   warning
4. Sharon should take some time off. She needs a vacation.   advice   duty   warning
5. Liz shouldn't talk so much. She is extremely talkative.   advice   duty   warning
6. Visitors to any country should follow that country's rules.   advice   duty   warning
7. Bob is driving too fast! He'd better slow down.   advice   duty   warning
8. Steve should eat less and exercise more.   advice   duty   warning
9. Parents should teach their children how to handle money.   advice   duty   warning
10. My kids had better be home on time tonight.   advice   duty   warning

Directions: Complete the conversations with **should, had better, must** or **have / had to.** More than one answer is possible.

Example: A: What time does the concert start?

      B: Seven-thirty. We _____*had better*_____ hurry if we want to get good seats.

1. A: James, can I borrow your camera tomorrow for school?

    B: Yes, but you _____ not lose it or damage it. It was

       expensive.

    A: OK. I'll be very careful.

2. A: If you want this apartment, you _____ sign the rental

       agreement by Friday or we'll rent it to someone else.

    B: Thank you for letting me know.

3. A: I _____ work last weekend, so I missed Gretchen's party.

    B: That's too bad.

4. A: Hello. This is Sam. Is Erica home?

    B: No, she's not here right now, but you _____ try her cell

       phone. Do you have the number?

    A: Yes, I'll try that. Bye.

5. A: Michael stayed up late watching a movie last night and fell asleep on the train to work.

    B: Oh, no! He _____ go to bed earlier tonight.

6. A: I am going to San Francisco during spring break. Do you want to come?

   B: Oh, I'd love to, but I can't. I _____ stay here and study for my medical school exams.

7. A: Look at that little boy who fell off the swing!

   B: Oh, here comes his mom. She _____ watch him more carefully or he's going to get hurt.

8. A: We _____ leave on time or we'll miss our connecting flight in Houston.

   B. Yes, I hope we leave at 9:45 like we're supposed to.

9. A: What _____ we do while we're waiting for Dan?

   B: I _____ get something to drink. I'm really thirsty.

   A: OK. Let's find a cafeteria.

QUIZ 8 The Past of *Should: Should Have / Shouldn't Have* (Chart 9-8)

Directions: Read each story. Then complete the statements about it with ***should have*** or ***shouldn't have***.

Example: You are in a restaurant in the non-smoking section. A man at the next table lights a cigarette. You speak to the waiter, who then asks the man to move to a different table.

The man _____ *shouldn't have* _____ sat in the non-smoking section.

A. Kate recently started surfing the internet, and she discovered all the different stores that offer online shopping. Many of them offered really good bargains. Kate bought books, CDs, clothes, toys for her nephews, computer equipment, and even a TV. Yesterday Kate got her credit card bill. She found she had spent more than $2,500 last month. She was shocked.

   1. Kate _____ been more careful with her online shopping.

   2. Kate _____ spent so much money.

   3. Kate _____ been shocked by her bill.

   4. Kate's credit card company _____ limited her credit.

B. Mr. and Mrs. Taylor read about a new play at the City Theater. Mr. Taylor promised to buy tickets. Unfortunately, he always had to do something else first. When he finally went to the box office two weeks later, the show was sold out. His wife was very disappointed.

   5. Mr. Taylor _____ disappointed his wife.

   6. Mr. Taylor _____ gone to the box office sooner.

   7. Mr. Taylor _____ put off buying the tickets.

   8. Mrs. Taylor _____ bought the tickets herself.

C. Marcia went shopping for a new suitcase with her mother. Marcia's mother recommended that she buy the TravelPro suitcase for $250. Marcia's mother had one, and she said it was very good quality. A similar suitcase was on sale for $100, so Marcia bought the cheaper suitcase. Within a year, the suitcase lost a wheel and a zipper broke. Marcia's mother's TravelPro suitcase is still in good condition and works well.

9. Marcia _____ ignored her mother's advice.

10. Marcia _____ spent more money on her suitcase.

11. Marcia's mother _____ given Marcia money for a TravelPro suitcase.

12. The suitcase _____ started falling apart so soon.

QUIZ 9 Unfulfilled Intentions: *Was / Were Going To* (Chart 9-10)

Directions: Circle *yes* if the speaker is expressing an intention or plan; circle *no* if not.

Example: I was going to call you, but I lost your number. (Yes) No

1. We were going to the grocery store when our car broke down.   Yes   No
2. I was going to give the book to my sister, but she didn't want it.   Yes   No
3. Jack had planned to retire this year but decided not to.   Yes   No
4. Joyce was thinking about her upcoming vacation.   Yes   No
5. We were going to cancel the newspaper, but we forgot.   Yes   No
6. I was going to the gym when I ran into a former classmate.   Yes   No
7. Charlotte was thinking about renting a movie last night.   Yes   No
8. Mr. Marshall had intended to visit his wife in the hospital.   Yes   No

---

QUIZ 10 Making Suggestions with *Let's, Why Don't, Shall I / We, Could* (Charts 9-11 and 9-12)

Directions: Complete the conversations with appropriate pronouns. If no pronoun is needed, write Ø.

Example: A: Good afternoon, Madame. Shall ___I___ take your coat for you?
          B: Yes, thank you.

1. A: What do you want to do tonight, Georgia?
   B: I'm tired. Let's _____ just stay home.
   A: OK. Why don't _____ go and rent a movie?
   B: That would be nice, thanks.

2. A: Miss Jones? Do you have the number for the district attorney's office?
   B: Yes, Ms. Babcock. Shall _____ get him on the line for you?
   A: Yes, please. I need to discuss a case with him.

3. A: Mom, I'm bored.
   B: _____ could read a good book, or _____
      could go outside and play for a while.
   A: I think I'll go outside.

4. A: Let's _____ go to the zoo this weekend, Daddy!
   B: I'm sorry, but I think it's going to rain. Why don't _____ go to a
      movie instead?

5. A: Jim, did you get a new car?
   B: Yes. Why don't _____ get in and I'll take you for a ride?

6. A: Mrs. Dann, what are we going to practice?
   B: Students, we'll be playing "Für Elise" today. Shall _____ begin?

7. A: I've been studying for three hours. My brain is numb.
   B: Why don't _____ take a break?

QUIZ 11 Making Suggestions: *Could* vs. *Should* (Chart 9-12)

Directions: Choose the correct completions.

Example: Martha ((should,) could) not eat such sugary foods. It's unhealthy.

1. Theo isn't sure about his plans for the weekend. He (should, could) go hiking, but he's not
   sure if he wants to.

2. A: I have a problem and I don't know what to do. My roommate is driving me crazy!
   B: Well, you (should, could) find a new roommate, but that takes time. I think you
      (should, could) talk with your roommate about whatever is bothering you.

3. My English teacher says students (should, could) speak English every day if they really
   want to improve their communication skills.

4. A: How are we going to get from the airport to our hotel?
   B: We (should, could) take a taxi, but that's a little expensive. There's also an airport bus.

5. I need a new camera, but I can't decide what to buy. I (should, could) do more research
   before I go shopping. Then I'll have more information to make my decision.

6. A: Alice has a terrible headache.
   B: That's too bad. She (should, could) take two aspirin and lie down.

7. I'm excited about going to New York next month! There are so many things to do there.
   For example, we (should, could) see a Broadway show or go to the Museum of Modern
   Art. We (should, could) also visit the Statue of Liberty. Whatever we do, we (should, could)
   try to purchase tickets online before we go.

Directions: Read the paragraph. Then complete the sentences with *could, could have, should,* or *should have.* Use the information in parentheses to help you. The first one is done for you.

Jane's ten-year-old son, Kevin, really wanted a dog. Jane wasn't sure about getting a pet, but finally, when Kevin promised to take care of the dog himself, Jane agreed. They got a puppy last year. They named him Lucky. Kevin really loves Lucky, but it has become Jane's job to take care of him and walk him. Kevin is always too busy with school and sports, or he forgets. Jane isn't happy about this, but she isn't sure what to do.

1. Jane and Kevin _____*should*_____ solve this problem. (advice)

2. Jane _____ said no when Kevin asked for a puppy. (advice)

3. They _____ gotten a cat instead. (suggestion)

4. Jane _____ teach Kevin to be responsible for his pet. (advice)

5. Kevin _____ thought more carefully about getting a dog. (advice)

6. Kevin _____ ask a friend to help him with the dog. (suggestion)

7. Kevin _____ kept his promise. (advice)

8. Jane and Kevin _____ take turns walking the dog so Jane doesn't always have to. (suggestion)

9. Jane _____ waited until Kevin was older to get him a dog. (suggestion)

10. Kevin _____ take care of his dog. (advice)

11. Jane _____ named the dog Unlucky. (advice)

Directions: Correct the errors.

go
Example: Let's ~~going~~ to the market on Saturday.

1. May I borrowed your grammar book?

2. Could you please to turn the air-conditioning off? I'm cold.

3. Mr. Sutherland is rich. He had better not work for a living.

4. I should have studying for the quiz, but I didn't.

5. Why don't you will call me tomorrow?

6. Olivia and Robert should gotten married.

7. If you lose your credit card, you should to cancel the card immediately.

8. John must goes to bed at 8:30 tonight.

9. When Mark was sick, he should stay home.

10. Let's we go to the grocery store. I need some milk.

CHAPTER 9 – TEST 1

Part A *Directions:* Complete the polite questions. Add the subject where necessary and use the verbs in parentheses.

1. I want to open the window. Would you mind (*open*) _____

   _____

2. I want you to help me wash the dishes. Could (*help*) _____

   _____

3. I want you to take me to the airport. Would you mind (*take*) _____

   _____

4. I want to go to a movie tonight. May (*go*) _____

   _____

5. I want you to vacuum the carpet. Would (*vacuum*) _____

   _____

Part B *Directions:* Complete the sentences. Use ***must, have / had to, must not,*** or ***don't / didn't have to***.

1. A: Did you go to the movies last night?

   B: No, I _____ study for a test in math today.

2. A: When _____ we _____ turn in our quarterly reports?

   B: I think they're due on the 15th.

3. Here is the last point in my safety lecture. You _____ operate these machines if your hands are wet. You could get a serious shock.

4. A: I'm surprised to see you on the bus. Is your car still having problems?

   B: Yeah. I _____ take it to the garage, but I never seem to find time.

5. A: I'm so relieved!

   B: Why?

   A: Originally, our essays were due on Friday, but the teacher has put off the due date. Now we _____ hand them in until next Wednesday.

Part C *Directions:* Read the paragraph. Then complete the sentences with *could, could have, should,* or *should have.* Use the information in parentheses to help you.

You and your friend Jimmy are walking to class. You have a test today, but Jimmy doesn't feel well. He was up all night coughing, and he slept very little. Now he has a slight fever and a headache. Jimmy is clearly not well enough to take a test.

1. Jimmy _____ not _____ come to school today. (advice)

2. Jimmy _____ talk to the teacher about the test and take it later. (suggestion)

3. Jimmy _____ stayed home in bed. (advice)

4. Jimmy _____ sent the teacher an email. (suggestion)

5. You _____ not get too close to Jimmy. You might get sick, too. (advice)

Part D *Directions:* Circle the correct completions.

1. A: Everyone's using a computer these days. I (*must, could*) catch up if I want to stay competitive in the job market. What can I do?

   B: You (*could, should have*) take classes at a business school or use those video lessons. However, I think the best idea is to take a class at the community college first. You (*could, should*) make sure you like computers before you spend a lot of money.

2. A: I'm so tired! I'm really happy that tomorrow is a holiday and I (*must not, don't have to*) go to work. I can sleep late. (*Let's, Why don't*) we do something fun?

   B: Not me. We took last Friday off, so I still (*have to, had to*) go to work tomorrow.

   A: I'm planning to go downtown and do a little shopping. I also have some errands to run.

   B: Speaking of errands, (*could, should*) you pick up some stamps for me at the post office?

   A: No problem. I (*had better, have to*) mail a package, so I can do both things at the same time. I (*had better, should have*) pay my bills tonight, too, so that I can mail them at the post office tomorrow. I (*ought to, should have*) mailed them last week, but I was too busy.

Part E *Directions:* Correct the errors.

1. Silvia must sent out her thank-you notes soon.

2. In the United States, children are suppose to go to school until age sixteen.

3. Should you please help me move this table?

4. Tony shouldn't have came to school with the flu.

5. Would you mind to call me tomorrow?

Part A **Directions:** Complete the polite questions. Add the subject where necessary and use the verbs in parentheses.

1. I want you to put the laundry away. Could (*put*) _____

   _____

2. I want to get a drink of water. Would you mind (*get*) _____

   _____

3. I want you to tell me what time it is. Would (*tell*) _____

   _____

4. I want to go shopping. May (*go*) _____

5. I want you to empty the garbage. Would you mind (*empty*) _____

   _____

Part B **Directions:** Complete the conversations. Use ***must, have / had to, must not,*** or ***don't / didn't have to***.

1. A: You aren't leaving the party already, are you?

   B: I'm really sorry, but I _____ go. I've had a wonderful time.

2. A: This presentation is very important if we want to attract new business. There
      _____ be any problems.

   B: Don't worry, sir. I'm sure everything is ready.

3. A: I'm going to leave work early today. I _____ see my doctor.

   B: Are you sick?

   A: Last night, I _____ wake up every hour to blow my nose or take
      some more cough medicine. I barely slept.

4. A: I think we can finish this by ourselves now. You _____ stay. You
      can go home.

   B: I can stay longer. I _____ do anything else tonight.

   A: Thanks, but you've worked long enough. Go home and put your feet up.

Part C *Directions:* Read the paragraph. Then complete the sentences with *could, could have, should,* or *should have.* Use the information in parentheses to help you.

You went out for the evening with your spouse. A babysitter looked after your children. Before you left, you gave the children some rules of behavior. When you came home, the babysitter reported that the children had been very naughty. They didn't obey the babysitter. They watched TV, played video games, and refused to go to bed.

1. The children _____ obeyed the rules. (advice)

2. The babysitter _____ turned off the TV. (suggestion)

3. You _____ take away the video games the next time you go out. (suggestion)

4. The children _____ apologize to the babysitter. (advice)

5. The children _____ not _____ misbehaved. (advice)

Part D *Directions:* Read the conversations. Circle the correct completions.

1. A: Hi! What are you doing tomorrow evening?
   B: I don't have any plans. Why?
   A: I was thinking that we (*could, have to*) do something together.
   B: (*Must, Should*) we go out to dinner and then to a movie?
   A: That would be really fun. What do you want to see?
   B: (*Let's, Why don't*) see *Secrets of the Dark Woods.* I hear that it's good and scary.
   A: Sounds great. If I meet you at the theater, (*should, would*) you drive me home? I'll probably go directly to the theater from work.
   B: No problem. Well, I (*had better, could*) go and finish my work. See you tomorrow.

2. A: Wow! This box is heavy. What's in it?
   B: My old records. I don't have a record player anymore, and I (*could, have to*) make room for my CDs and DVDs, so I'm putting these in the garage.
   A: You (*should, should have*) sell them. There's a used music store on 24th Street. (*Why don't, Let's*) we take your records there and see if they'll buy them?
   B: They're awfully heavy. (*May, Would*) you drive me down there in your car?
   A: No problem, but I need to be at my parents' house for dinner in an hour, so if you want to go, we (*have to, ought to*) go now.

Part E *Directions:* Correct the errors.

1. Matthew should not had fallen asleep at work yesterday.

2. I must to help my parents in their store after school, so I can't play basketball.

3. Lindsay had better to call me tonight.

4. Would you mind if I leaving work early today?

5. When does Ben had to be at the airport?

CHAPTER 10 Modals, Part 2

Degrees of Certainty: Present Time (Charts 10-1 and 10-2)

Directions: Choose the correct completions.

Example: My sister ((*might,*) *must*) come to visit next weekend. I'm not sure yet.

1. The boys have been playing video games all afternoon. They (*may, must*) love those games.

2. I wonder how many people will come to our party this weekend. We (*may, must*) have twenty or thirty guests.

3. My dog is standing by its food dish, but it (*couldn't, mustn't*) be hungry. I just fed it 30 minutes ago.

4. I don't know what my husband is getting me for my birthday. It (*may, must*) be jewelry or perfume.

5. The weather (*might not, must not*) be very good for a picnic this weekend. The forecast is predicting rain.

6. Movies about the American West (*might, must*) be popular in other countries. I'm not sure.

7. Natasha is in really good shape and has muscular arms. She (*might, must*) exercise regularly.

8. Mick (*might not, must not*) like potato salad. He didn't eat any potato salad at the picnic.

9. I'm not sure where Julia went. She (*could, must*) be doing her laundry, or she (*might, must*) be studying at the library.

Directions: Complete the sentences. Use ***must, may, might,*** or ***could***.

Examples: Tanya's boyfriend wrecked her new car. She _____*must*_____ be angry.

I don't know what the weather forecast is. It ____*may / might / could*____ rain today.

1. Helen's son just got a big promotion at work. She _____ be very proud of him.

2. I'm not sure what our homework assignment for tomorrow is. It _____ be pages 250 to 255, but I can't remember for sure.

3. Debra eats dinner out in a restaurant almost every night. She _____ not like to cook!

4. We're trying to make plans for a trip this summer. We'd like to go to Scotland, but we _____ visit the Virgin Islands instead.

5. Mr. and Mrs. Jackson just became grandparents. They _____ be excited about their new granddaughter.

6. I found a Web site for an online dating agency called "Marry an Ugly Millionaire." This _____ not be a real dating agency! It's too weird!

7. The problem with online shopping is that you _____ spend more money than you realize because you usually have to pay taxes and shipping charges.

8. Jessica just tried to call Anita's cell phone, but she didn't answer. Her phone _____ be off, or she _____ not have it with her.

9. Andy is carrying five books, his laptop, and a calculator in his backpack. That _____ be heavy!

Directions: Complete the sentences. Use the past forms of *must,* or *may, might,* or *could* and the correct form of the verbs in parentheses.

Example: We (*get*) _____*could have gotten*_____ tickets to the hit show, but they were too expensive, so we decided not to go.

1. I'm not sure what Chuck did last weekend. He (*go*) _____ camping.

2. A: What did you get on the quiz?

   B: I got 100%!

   A: That's impossible! You (*get, not*) _____ 100%! You didn't even study!

3. I wonder where Sharon is. She's not usually late. She (*have*) _____ _____ a late appointment today.

4. Last week someone stole Mitch's wallet with $200 in it. He (*be*) _____ _____ angry.

5. Jasmine looked really tired this morning. She said there was a lot of noise outside her apartment last night. She (*sleep, not*) _____ well.

6. I'm not sure what happened, but Uncle Seth's car has a big scratch on the hood and one headlight is broken. He (*hit*) _____ a tree or something.

7. My mom offered to cook my breakfast this morning, but I wasn't hungry. I just had a cup of coffee. I (*miss*) _____ out on a delicious breakfast.

8. Mia told me that she and her boyfriend had broken up. She (*be, not*) _____ _____ very upset about it though because she was smiling and wanted to go out dancing.

9. The airline pilots went on strike last week. It (*be*) _____ because of vacation pay or salaries. I don't really know.

10. When the earth was formed, there (*be*) _____ incredible forces that shaped it.

Directions: Read each situation. Use past modals to restate the sentences in parentheses. More than one modal may be possible.

Example: (Maybe Brian went to the grocery store.) Brian _____*may / might have gone*_____ to the grocery store.

SITUATION 1: I am supposed to meet my friend Joyce at a local coffee shop. I've been waiting for 30 minutes and she hasn't come yet. I tried to call her, but she didn't answer her cell phone.

1. (Maybe Joyce forgot her cell phone at home.)

_____

2. (It's not possible that Joyce forgot our meeting. I talked with her this morning.)

_____

3. (I'm 95% sure that Joyce left her office late. She told me she had a lot to do today.)

_____

SITUATION 2: George can't find his car. He parked it on the street across from the post office, but now it isn't there. He is really worried.

4. (It's possible that George parked his car on a different street.)

_____

5. (A post office worker is 95% sure the police towed the car. He saw a tow truck in front of the post office.)

_____

6. (George is guessing that he probably didn't park the car legally.)

_____

7. (Maybe George had many unpaid parking tickets before this.)

_____

Directions: Using the information about each situation, complete the sentences.

Example: SITUATION: The students are taking a two-page quiz. There are five minutes left for the quiz.
Who will finish the quiz?

INFORMATION: The last two questions on **Ron's** paper are still blank.
Sheila is working on the last question.
Wendy is still working on the first page of the quiz.

a. _____Wendy_____ won't finish the quiz.

b. _____Ron_____ might finish the quiz.

c. _____Sheila_____ should finish the quiz.

SITUATION 1: People are running in a 26-mile marathon. Who will finish the marathon?
INFORMATION: **Mark** is in very good shape and has already run in two marathons this year.
Jane has never run a marathon before, and she trained for only two weeks.
Martha has never run a marathon before, but she has been training for three months.

a. _____ might not finish the marathon.

b. _____ could finish the marathon.

c. _____ ought to finish the marathon.

SITUATION 2: We are at the airport in Chicago. Whose flight will arrive on time?
INFORMATION: **Alice's** plane left on time and has had no problems in the air.
Kay's plane had a mechanical problem and left an hour late.
Jack's plane left fifteen minutes late, but a strong tail wind helped the plane go faster.

a. _____ should arrive on time.

b. _____ won't arrive on time.

c. _____ might arrive on time.

SITUATION 3: Several people were interviewed for a job. Who will get the job?
INFORMATION: **Mr. Anton** answered all the questions well, and he is well qualified for the position.
Mrs. Chu answered the questions well, but she lacks some job qualifications.
Ms. Callahan was extremely nervous and did not make a good impression.

a. _____ won't get the job.

b. _____ should get the job.

c. _____ may get the job.

SITUATION 4: Three friends are talking about weddings. Who will get married this year?

INFORMATION: **Esther** is engaged to Michael and they are planning their wedding.

Megan has a serious boyfriend. They have been dating for over a year.

Holly was planning a wedding, but she just broke up with her fiancé.

a. _____ may get married this year.

b. _____ won't get married this year.

c. _____ should get married this year.

QUIZ 6 **Progressive Forms of Modals** (Chart 10-5)

Directions: Complete the sentences. Use the appropriate progressive forms of ***must, should,*** or ***may / might / could*** and the verbs in parentheses.

Example: Laura had a lot of homework and came home late from the library. She
(*study*) _____must have been studying_____ .

1. Nora has been on the phone for an hour! I wonder who she is talking to. She
   (*talk*) _____ to her daughter.

2. A: Do we turn right or left at the corner?
   B: I'm not sure. I (*listen*) _____ more carefully when
      Lawrence gave us directions to his house.

3. Johann looked really sleepy when he came to the door. I'm not sure, but he
   (*take*) _____ a nap when I arrived.

4. A: Where's Cassie?
   B: She (*eat*) _____ lunch in the cafeteria. She said
      she was really hungry and wanted a hamburger.

5. My house is a mess and I have guests coming tomorrow. I (*clean*) _____
   _____ now, but I don't feel like it. I'll
   clean later.

6. Max's car was badly damaged in the accident. He (*drive*) _____
   too fast.

7. I (*sleep*) _____ at 3:00 A.M., but a police siren woke
   me up. Then I couldn't go back to sleep.

8. A: Where is Khaled?
   B: I don't know. He (*wash*) _____ his car or maybe
      he's gone shopping.

9. Margaret looks upset and her eyes are red. She (*cry*) _____ .

10. A: What are you doing?
    B: I'm reading a novel, but I (*pay*) _____ bills instead.

Directions: Read each sentence. Decide if it expresses *a physical ability, an acquired skill, permission,* or *possibility.*

Example: James *can* speak three languages fluently.

     a physical ability   ⟨an acquired skill⟩   permission   possibility

1. Both the University of Wisconsin and Rutgers University have offered Sam scholarships for next year. He *can* attend either one.
    a physical ability   an acquired skill   permission   possibility

2. Galen is a sound technician. He *can* work with all of the newest electronic recording equipment.
    a physical ability   an acquired skill   permission   possibility

3. Mom, *can* I go out with my friends to a movie tonight?
    a physical ability   an acquired skill   permission   possibility

4. Bald eagles have amazing eyesight. They *can* see fish in water from several hundred feet in the air.
    a physical ability   an acquired skill   permission   possibility

5. I *couldn't* do my algebra homework because I didn't understand it.
    a physical ability   an acquired skill   permission   possibility

6. Did you know that kittens *can* make a hissing sound even before they open their eyes?
    a physical ability   an acquired skill   permission   possibility

7. I *can* drive you to the doctor's office tomorrow if you need me to.
    a physical ability   an acquired skill   permission   possibility

8. Students, you *can* begin the exam now.
    a physical ability   an acquired skill   permission   possibility

9. Beth broke her foot and now she *can't* walk.
    a physical ability   an acquired skill   permission   possibility

10. You *can* buy delicious fresh bread at the Great Harvest Bakery.
    a physical ability   an acquired skill   permission   possibility

Directions: Complete the sentences with **can, can't, could,** or **couldn't.** Use the hint in parentheses. More than one answer is possible.

Example: Bob had to get glasses because he _____*couldn't*_____ see well. (ability)

1. My dad is the best cook in our family. He _____ cook *anything,* and it'll taste great! (skill)

2. After Juan went to the dentist, he _____ feel his tongue. It was numb. (ability)

3. Jessica _____ stay out too late. She has to be home by 10:00 P.M. or her parents will be upset. (permission)

4. Because of the terrible weather, we _____ go on a picnic today. (possibility)

5. Humpback whales _____ "sing" to each other to communicate. It's an interesting phenomenon. (ability)

6. My parents said I _____ study abroad during my third year of university. I am so excited! (permission)

7. Learning French is really difficult for Pat. He just _____ pronounce the words. (skill)

8. When I walked by the flower stand, I _____ smell the lilies and roses. (ability)

9. When I was a teenager, I _____ skateboard really well. I even won a skateboard competition. (skill)

10. I really enjoy having coffee at the Hotwire Café. You _____ try different types of coffee from Ecuador, Mexico, Ethiopia, or Cameroon. (possibility)

Directions: Decide if each sentence is correct (C) or incorrect (I). If incorrect, change *would* to **used to** to make a correct sentence.

Examples: C   I   *used to*
____   __✓__ Alan ~~would~~ be a veterinarian, but now he is retired.

__✓__   ____ I would ride my bike to work when I lived in Taylorville.

C   I

____ ____ **1.** Last semester Jake would be late for class every morning because he had a job on the night shift.

____ ____ **2.** Lisa would be able to speak Chinese when she was younger, but she can't anymore.

____ ____ **3.** When my Uncle Stanley was alive, he would take us children for rides in his sports car.

____ ____ **4.** Before Dennis took the spelling improvement class, he would always lose points on his assignments because of poor spelling.

____ ____ **5.** My grandmother would work in her garden every day until she developed arthritis in her knees.

____ ____ **6.** Before Tom got his own cell phone, he would use his brother's old phone.

____ ____ **7.** Alex would work for Microsoft last year, but now he is working for Apple Computer.

____ ____ **8.** I would study at the University of Florida before I transferred to the University of Georgia.

____ ____ **9.** Every night when my dad got home from work, he would sit down in his armchair, read the newspaper for five minutes, and fall asleep.

____ ____ **10.** In 2007 Mary would live in a chic apartment in midtown Manhattan. She loved it!

Directions: Complete the sentences. Use *would rather* and the appropriate form of the verbs in parentheses.

Example: I (*stay*) _____ would rather have stayed _____ home last night.

1. Paul (*take*) _____ his driving test next week.

2. Ruth (*have*) _____ fish than chicken for dinner. She's going to stop by the fish market.

3. I (*cook, not*) _____ dinner tonight. Let's go out.

4. I'm so tired! I (*sleep*) _____ right now.

5. My kids really wanted to go to Disneyland, so we did. I (*go*)

   _____ on a vacation to the beach. Maybe next year!

6. Ann (*visit*) _____ Seattle than San Francisco anytime. She likes Seattle's green environment.

7. My grandfather likes the fruit trees in their garden, but my grandmother

   (*plant*) _____ roses.

8. Yumi got 90% on her grammar test. She (*get*) _____ a higher grade on it.

9. It's 8:00 A.M. on Saturday, and Tomás is taking a college entrance exam. He

   (*take, not*) _____ the exam. He

   (*play*) _____ basketball with his friends this morning.

Directions: Correct the errors.

have to
Example: Joe is going to ~~must~~ finish his homework tonight.

1. Alice must have forget her phone at home. She doesn't have it with her.

2. Children had got to go to bed early on school nights.

3. The meeting with our attorney is suppose to start at 9:30 A.M.

4. Dan had better not to use bad language around his parents.

5. I might can meet you at the airport.

6. Jason should had spent less money on my birthday present.

7. Maxine would rather drinking coffee than tea.

8. May I borrowed your dictionary?

9. Students may have left the examination room when they finish the test. It's allowed.

10. That couldn't been true! I don't believe it!

11. Charles must to be at work by 5:30 A.M. every morning.

12. My uncle Willy will not can come for a visit this summer.

13. Emily, may you lend me twenty dollars until Saturday?

14. We haven't seen John since summer. We maybe get together with him this weekend.

15. When I was growing up, we could riding our bicycles all over my hometown.

CHAPTER 10 – TEST 1

Part A *Directions:* Complete the sentences, using an appropriate modal with the verb in parentheses.

1. Those two people look so similar that they (*be*) _____ closely related. I think Julie told me they are first cousins.

2. A: Wow! You are an hour late. The traffic (*be*) _____ awful!

   B: It is. A terrible accident is blocking three lanes. The traffic is barely moving.

3. A: If I (*change*) _____ my reservation, I would like to leave on an earlier flight. Right now I'm booked on the 6:00 P.M. flight.

   B: There (*be*) _____ plenty of room on the 4:30 flight. Saturday afternoons are usually pretty light. Let me check for you.

4. I'm sorry, but I (*need*) _____ to leave in a few minutes.

5. A: This speaker is so boring. Can we go now?

   B: No, that would be rude. He (*finish*) _____ soon.

Part B *Directions* Using the information about each situation, complete the sentences.

SITUATION 1: The students took a difficult quiz. This is how far they had gotten five minutes before the end of the quiz. Who finished the quiz?

INFORMATION: The last two questions on **Sam's** paper were still blank.

Linda was working on the last question.

Liz had not finished one of the questions on page one, but I think she had finished the other page.

a. _____ must have finished the quiz.

b. _____ might have finished the quiz.

c. _____ might not have finished the quiz.

SITUATION 2: Mr. Anton loves to read, and his friends often give him recommendations. Which book did Mr. Anton read?

INFORMATION: **Ms. Adams** recommended *Trials by Night*. Mr. Anton has enjoyed all of the books Ms. Adams has recommended.

Mr. French recommended *The Terrible War*. Mr. Anton has enjoyed one or two of the books Mr. French has recommended.

Mrs. White recommended *The Thinking Mystery*. Mr. Anton has never enjoyed any of her recommendations, but she is a very close friend.

a. Mr. Anton may have read the book _____ recommended.

b. Mr. Anton might not have read the book _____ recommended.

c. Mr. Anton must have read the book _____ recommended.

Directions: Complete the sentences, using the progressive forms of ***must, should,*** or ***may / might / could*** with the verbs in parentheses.

1. A: Excuse me, Miss, are we going to take off soon?

   B: Yes, Sir. There was a small problem, but it has been fixed. We

   (*leave*) _____ momentarily.

2. A: Should I pack my umbrella?

   B: I checked the weather report, and it wasn't good. When we get there, it

   (*rain*) _____ .

3. A: Oh, my! This month's water bill is over $100! Last month it was less than $40.

   B: Water (*leak*) _____ somewhere. We'd better call a

   plumber.

4. A: Johnny, why are you watching TV? Your room is a mess, and you

   (*clean*) _____ your room right now.

   B: All right, Mom. I'm going!

5. A: Excuse me. I'm looking for the Investment Seminar. It's supposed to be in Room

   4301.

   B: If it's not in 4301, they (*meet*) _____ in Room 2301.

   Let me check for you.

Part D *Directions:* Circle the correct completions to express *ability*.

1. The library was already closed when we arrived. We (*can, can't, could, couldn't*) get any
   books.

2. Brenda has a new wireless computer. She (*can, can't, could, couldn't*) search the internet
   without actually being connected to a modem.

3. Research has shown that children (*can, can't, could, couldn't*) learn foreign languages more
   easily before they reach age thirteen.

4. I'm really sorry, but I (*can, can't, could, couldn't*) help you this weekend. I'm going to be
   out of town.

5. When I was younger, I (*can, can't, could, couldn't*) eat a lot more than I
   (*can, can't, could, couldn't*) now.

Directions: Complete the sentences with ***would*** or ***would rather*** and the appropriate form of the verbs in parentheses.

1. In the past, Mrs. Mitchell (*call*) _____ her sister in Illinois every week. Now she doesn't call so often.

2. I am taking a test right now, but I (*eat*) _____ lunch now instead.

3. Last year our teacher (*give*) _____ us "pop" quizzes. We never knew when we were going to have one.

4. Before 2008, the professional basketball team (*play*) _____ at least twice a week in Key Arena. Now the team plays in Fischer Pavilion.

5. Barbara lives in Miami, but she's thinking about moving to Phoenix next year. She (*live*) _____ there.

Part A *Directions:* Complete the sentences, using an appropriate modal with the verb in parentheses.

1. I have a math test tomorrow, but I (*go*) _____ to a movie with you instead of studying. I studied a little yesterday, so I (*do*) _____ OK on the test.

2. Jen said she doesn't want to go skiing this weekend, but she (*change*) _____ her mind. I'll call her on Friday to check.

3. I don't know why I told Mrs. Ramirez that I would babysit her naughty children tomorrow night. I (*be*) _____ crazy!

4. If I (*leave*) _____ work early, I (*be able to*) _____ meet you for dinner.

5. Ten years ago, it took me ten minutes to drive to work. Now the traffic is so bad that I (*get, not*) _____ to work in less than forty minutes.

Part B *Directions:* Using the information about each situation, complete the sentences.

SITUATION 1: Jean made some phone calls to her friends at 7:30 P.M., but no one answered. What were her friends doing?

INFORMATION: **Jeff** is usually at the library every evening from 7:00 P.M. to 9:00 P.M.
Eva usually eats dinner at 7:30 P.M., and sometimes she doesn't answer the telephone.
When **Ken** is at home, he always answers the telephone.

a. _____ could have been at home.

b. _____ must not have been at home.

c. _____ may not have been at home.

SITUATION 2: **Mrs. Chang** is in the kitchen. Her husband and three children are at home. She hears water running. Who is taking a shower?

INFORMATION: **Mr. Chang** often takes a shower after work, but he's out working in the garage.
Her son **Tom** had a basketball game that afternoon, and when he got home, he was very sweaty.
Her daughter, **Julie**, only takes a shower in the morning.
Her other son **Kevin** was working in the garden earlier, and she thinks he is still outside.

a. _____ may be taking a shower.

b. _____ must not be taking a shower.

c. _____ couldn't be taking a shower.

d. _____ must be taking a shower.

Part C   *Directions:*   Complete the sentences, using the progressive forms of ***must***, ***should***, or ***may / might / could*** with the verbs in parentheses.

1. A: That's the third time this week that I've seen you looking in the job section of the newspaper. You (*look*) _____ for a new job.

    B: You're right. My new boss and I aren't getting along, so it looks like it's time for me to go elsewhere.

2. A: Peter has been awfully quiet for more than an hour. What's he doing?

    B: I'm not sure. He (*play*) _____ a computer game, or he (*read*) _____ a comic book.

3. A: I haven't seen Kelly all night. What's she doing?

    B: She (*study*) _____. She has two exams tomorrow.

4. A: I can't believe it's really 11:30 P.M. It's been so nice visiting with you, but we (*go*)

    _____.

    B: And I (*get*) _____ to bed. I have to get up at 6:30 A.M.

Part D   *Directions:*   Circle the correct completions to express *ability*.

1. (*Can, Can't, Could, Couldn't*) you lift this box of books? It's too heavy for me.

2. Mr. Rodriguez (*can, can't, could, couldn't*) speak both Spanish and English when he was a little boy. Now he speaks mostly English, though.

3. My uncle Joe never learned to swim. He still (*can, can't, could, couldn't*) swim, and he's afraid to go in water.

4. Last summer I wanted to take a long road trip, but I broke my arm and (*can, can't, could, couldn't*) drive.

5. Harriet (*can, can't, could, couldn't*) sing really well. She's in the school choir.

Part E   *Directions:*   Complete the sentences with ***would*** or ***would rather*** and the appropriate form of the verbs in parentheses.

1. Olivia and Robert used to work for a tour boat company. They (*take*) _____ _____ tours to Ellis Island several times a day.

2. Nick hates flying. He (*take*) _____ a bus or a train than fly.

3. We watched a movie at home last night, but I (*see*) _____ the movie on a big screen in a theater.

4. Last semester David failed his science class. This semester he (*pass*) _____ _____.

5. My nephew graduated from physical therapy school last year. It was really difficult and he (*study*) _____ for hours when he had exams.

Active vs. Passive (Chart 11-1)

Directions: Decide if the sentences are active (**A**) or passive (**P**).

Examples: _A_ A speeding truck hit my car.

_P_ My car was hit by a speeding truck.

1. _____ Thousands of computers are recycled in the U.S. every year.

2. _____ All of Jimmy's money was spent by the end of his vacation.

3. _____ The waitress is going to bring your drink very soon.

4. _____ The gift was wrapped beautifully with colorful paper and ribbon.

5. _____ Mary is taking care of Alex's son.

6. _____ Final exams are given at the end of every semester.

7. _____ The students asked the teacher many questions after the lecture.

8. _____ The children have cleaned the house.

9. _____ My mom's expensive vase was knocked off the hall table by my little sister.

10. _____ The dog is given medicine three times a day.

Active vs. Passive Meaning (Charts 11-1 and 11-2)

Directions: Circle the letter of the sentence that has the same meaning as the given sentence.

Example: The hospital patients were cared for by wonderful nurses.
    a. The patients took care of wonderful nurses.
    (b.) Wonderful nurses took care of the patients.

1. John will be introduced to Tammy's parents next weekend.
    a. Someone will introduce John to Tammy's parents.
    b. John will introduce someone to Tammy's parents.

2. The teacher congratulated the students on their success.
    a. The teacher was congratulated by the students.
    b. The students were congratulated by the teacher.

3. Miriam often misunderstands her older sister, Paula.
    a. Paula is misunderstood by Miriam.
    b. Miriam is misunderstood by Paula.

4. Joel scratched his dog, Butch, behind the ears.
    a. Butch was scratched by Joel.
    b. Butch scratched Joel.

5. All of Satoshi's questions were answered by his teacher.
   a. Satoshi answered his teacher's questions.
   b. Satoshi's teacher answered his questions.

6. Margot's photograph is taken every year.
   a. Margot takes her own photograph every year.
   b. Someone else takes Margot's photograph every year.

QUIZ 3 Forms of the Passive (Chart 11-2)

Directions: Change the verbs in *italics* to the passive. Do not change the tense.

Example: Many people *read* the newspaper on Sunday mornings.

The newspaper ____is read____ by many people on Sunday mornings.

1. Thieves *stole* two priceless paintings from the art museum.

   Two priceless paintings _____ from the art museum.

2. The board members *are going to discuss* the vacation policy at their next meeting.

   The vacation policy _____ at the next board meeting.

3. A woman in our neighborhood *has found* a rare book in an antique store. She *will give* it to her husband for his birthday.

   A rare book _____ by a woman in our neighborhood. It

   _____ to her husband as a birthday gift.

4. Everyone in my family *enjoys* drinking tea after dinner.

   Drinking tea after dinner _____ by everyone in my family.

5. When the police arrived at the accident scene, the paramedics *had already helped* the injured man. They *took* him to the hospital a short time later.

   When the police arrived at the accident scene, the injured man _____

   _____ by the paramedics. He _____ to the

   hospital a short time later.

6. The teacher *will have given* the students their homework assignment by the end of class.

   The students _____ their homework assignment by the

   end of class.

7. Someone *is analyzing* the results of the survey.

   The results of the survey _____.

8. A loud noise outside *woke up* the baby, and she started to cry.

   The baby _____ by a loud noise outside, and she started to

   cry.

Directions: Change the active sentences to passive if possible. Use the *by*-phrase if necessary. Some verbs are intransitive and cannot be changed.

Examples: The director chose an unknown actress for the leading role in his movie.

    An unknown actress was chosen for the leading role by the director.

An accident happened on the corner of First and Main Streets.

    no change

1. A speeding truck hit my car.

2. Nearly 200 people died in the train wreck.

3. An earthquake has damaged several of the downtown office buildings.

4. The rock band recorded their first CD last year.

5. Kathy and Jane live next door to each other.

6. The travel agent is going to make the reservations very soon.

7. Mr. Miron was the funniest man in our neighborhood.

8. Someone washed all of the windows last weekend.

9. The artist completed her masterpiece when she was only 25 years old.

10. Many scientists believe that humans have caused global warming.

Directions: Complete the sentences with the passive form of the verbs in parentheses. Use any appropriate tense.

Example: My wallet (*steal*) _____ was stolen _____ out of my pocket while I was in a busy train station.

1. Every year on the Fourth of July, hundreds of thousands of hamburgers and hot dogs

   (*eat*) _____ at picnics all across the U.S.

2. The game of basketball (*invent*) _____ by Dr. James Naismith

   around 1891.

3. Josh's school project (*finish*) _____ by next Friday.

4. A new president (*elect, not*) _____ yet. The election will be in

   November.

5. A pedestrian (*hit*) _____ by a car in front of my house. He

   (*give*) _____ medical treatment but is going to be OK.

6. An award-winning movie (*show*) _____ at the new theater

   downtown until next weekend. Let's go see it!

7. My parents (*give*) _____ some land in the mountains when my

   grandfather died.

8. Algebra (*teach*) _____ formally in middle and high school, but

   the basics of algebraic thinking (*introduce*) _____ much earlier.

Directions: Complete the sentences about William Shakespeare with the passive forms of the verbs in parentheses. Use any appropriate tense. The first one is done for you as an example.

William Shakespeare (*know*) _____*is known*_____ as one of the greatest writers
1

of the English language. Shakespeare lived in the 16th and 17th centuries, but even

today, his many plays and sonnets (*read*) _____ and (*study*)
2

_____ by people everywhere. Many of Shakespeare's most
3

famous plays (*write*) _____ between 1594 and 1599.
4

During that time, *A Midsummer Night's Dream, Romeo and Juliet, Richard II,* and *The*

Merchant of Venice (*perform*) _____ for the first time.
5

However, Shakespeare's plays (*publish, not*) _____ by the
6

time he died in 1616. Since that time, they (*translate*) _____
7

into over 80 languages and (*print*) _____ in languages
8

from Arabic to Zulu. Today, Shakespeare's plays (*see*) _____
9

on stages around the world. The works of William Shakespeare

(*keep*) _____ alive for future generations. They
10

(*enjoy*) _____ by young and old for many years to come.
11

Directions: Make complete sentences using the given words. Some are active and some are passive. Use the simple past tense.

Examples: The movie \ end \ before 9:00

_____*The movie ended before 9:00.*_____

The movie \ see \ by thousands on opening night

_____*The movie was seen by thousands on opening night.*_____

1. The east coast of Florida \ hit \ by Hurricane Betty two days ago

_____

2. The storm winds \ reach \ speeds of 150 miles per hour

_____

3. Many houses \ damage \ in the storm

_____

4. Many people \ go \ to stay with friends and relatives

_____

5. Injured people \ take care of \ by aid workers

_____

6. Many coastal towns \ lose \ electricity during the storm

_____

7. The damage \ assess \ in the morning after the storm

_____

8. Some people \ not allow \ to go back to their homes

_____

QUIZ 8   **The Passive Form of Modals and Phrasal Modals**   (Chart 11-4)

Directions: Complete the sentences with the words in parentheses. Use the appropriate form, active or passive.

Example: James (_should + tell_) _____should be told_____ the truth about the company's financial situation.

1. Your teeth (_must + check_) _____ regularly in order to avoid cavities.

2. People (_ought to + not + fire_) _____ from their jobs because of their age.

3. Your homework (_have to + finish_) _____ before 11:00.

4. This species of fish (_can't + identify_) _____ by scientists.

5. We (_should + sit_) _____ down because the interview is about to begin.

6. According to the fire chief, the fire (_must + start_) _____ by a cigarette.

7. This conversation group is too large. It (_should + split_) _____ into two groups.

8. My plumbing (_had better + fix_) _____ soon, or I will complain to the building manager.

9. More than 30 people (_may + injure_) _____ in the bus accident.

10. Roberto (_may + give_) _____ more difficult exercises by his teacher because he already understands these ideas completely.

Directions: Use passive modals to restate the recycling guidelines. Make two sentences for each rule. Use a variety of modals.

Example: Recycle clean paper, plastic, cans, and glass.

        Clean paper, plastic, cans, and glass can be recycled.

        Clean paper, plastic, cans, and glass should be recycled.

RECYCLING GUIDELINES

1. Rinse all food from plastics, glass, and cans.

    _____

    _____

2. Press clean boxes and paper items flat.

    _____

    _____

3. Do not recycle any paper with food on it. Put it in the trash.

    _____

    _____

4. All clean recyclable items go into your recycling bin.

    _____

    _____

5. Put recycling bins out for pick up by 7:00 A.M. on collection day.

    _____

    _____

Directions: Complete the sentences with the correct prepositions. Use *about, for, from, in, of, to,* or *with*.

Example: My mother is interested __*in*__ art, but my dad prefers music.

1. Trish was really disappointed _____ her grade in biology last semester. Her average was 85%.

2. Parents are always concerned _____ their children, no matter how old the children are.

3. Bill has been married _____ his wife for 40 years.

4. The new computer lab is equipped _____ the latest technology.

5. The applicants were all well qualified _____ the position. It was a difficult choice.

6. My computer is not connected _____ the internet at the moment.

7. I'm tired _____ seeing so many advertisements every time I open a Web page on my computer.

8. Hannah is accustomed _____ the humid Florida weather, but she doesn't like it.

9. Many citizens are opposed _____ the new policies of the government.

10. John was bored _____ his job, so he quit. Now he's looking for a new job.

QUIZ 11 **Non-progressive Passive** (Charts 11-5 and 11-6)

Directions: Complete each sentence with an appropriate form of the words in the list. Add the correct preposition. Use the present tense. Use each word only once. The first one is done for you.

annoy	excite	remember
compose	limit	terrify
crowd	locate	✓worry
do	prepare	

1. I _____*am worried about*_____ the next test. It's going to be really difficult.

2. One of my friends _____ spiders. She is really afraid of them.

3. Anton's ability to communicate in English _____ his lack of vocabulary.

4. During the holidays, the stores _____ shoppers.

5. The state of Maine _____ the northeast corner of the U.S.

6. I'm ready to go. _____ you _____ your homework?

7. A complete sentence _____ a subject and a verb.

8. I _____ the neighbor's dog. It is always barking!

9. Abraham Lincoln _____ ending slavery in the U.S.

10. My sister and her fiancé _____ their wedding next weekend.

11. Tracy _____ the rain. She brought her umbrella and wore rubber boots.

Directions: Choose all possible completions for each sentence.

Example: I am getting _____, so I had better go to bed.

      a. sleep   ⓑ tired   ⓒ sleepy   d. late

1. When Mr. Mitchell heard that Dennis had picked all of his flowers, he got _____.
    a. annoy   b. annoyed   c. angry   d. anger

2. Jennifer got _____ during the exam and made some careless mistakes.
    a. confused   b. confuse   c. worry   d. nervous

3. Now that he has lived here for six months, Chang has gotten _____ American food.
    a. use to   b. accustomed to   c. comfortable to   d. comfortable with

4. I'm going to get _____ after I finish this chapter of the book I'm reading.
    a. readied   b. ready   c. to dress   d. dressed

5. If we don't go home soon, we are going to get _____.
    a. chilly   b. sunburned   c. sunburn   d. easy

6. You can take the children to the park if they get _____.
    a. bored   b. are bored   c. bore   d. lost

7. I don't like to go out at night. I get _____ in the dark.
    a. nervous   b. late   c. anxious   d. scared

8. Yesterday Steve waited for 30 minutes for the bus. It was raining, and he got really _____ .
    a. wet   b. chilly   c. lost   d. annoyed

Directions: Complete the conversation with an appropriate form of ***get*** and the given words. Use the correct tense. The first one is done for you.

MARY: John! It's good to see you again. How have you been lately?

JOHN: Not too well. Unfortunately, I (*hurt*) _____*got hurt*_____ in a car accident last
                                                         1

month, and I missed two weeks of work.

MARY: Oh! That's too bad. How do you feel now?

JOHN: Better, but I still have headaches. I'm lucky, though. The other driver

(*arrest*) _____ for reckless driving. I could
                        2

(*kill*) _____ .
                  3

MARY: Are you behind on your work?

JOHN: I was lucky. I was able to take a lot of work home with me, so all my work

(*do*) _____ . Now I (*worry*) _____
                4   5

about my car. It (*damage*) _____ .
                                          6

MARY: Can you (*fix*) _____ it _____?
                            7   7

JOHN: I'm not sure if it's worth it. The insurance company just

(*finish*) _____ with the repair estimates.
                      8

MARY: Well, I hope all of that (*take*) _____ care of soon.
                                                    9

JOHN: Thanks, Mary. In the meantime, I'm taking the bus. I

(*accustom*) _____ to it.
                        10

MARY: That's great, John. Bus drivers rarely (*arrest*) _____ for
                                                                            11

reckless driving, and you can relax on your way to work!

Directions: Choose the correct completions.

Example: I was watching TV last night, but the program was so (*bored,* (*boring*)) that I fell asleep.

1. Yesterday, a group of friends and I went to a (*depressed, depressing*) soccer game.

2. We were very (*surprised, surprising*) because not many people were there.

3. At first, the teams played well, and it was (*thrilled, thrilling*) to watch them.

4. Jim got so (*excited, exciting*) that he jumped out of his seat.

5. It was (*embarrassed, embarrassing*) because he spilled his soda on the lady in front of him.

6. She was quite (*annoyed, annoying*) and got mad at Jim.

7. We were (*shocked, shocking*) when our favorite player got hurt and had to leave the game.

8. Without him, it was very (*frustrated, frustrating*) because our team couldn't score.

9. It was very (*disappointed, disappointing*) for us to watch our team lose.

10. We were sad about our (*injured, injuring*) player.

Directions: Complete the sentences with present or past participle of the verbs in parentheses.

Example: The (*exhaust*) _____exhausted_____ hikers took off their boots and relaxed at the end of the day.

1. The (*entertain*) _____ shows in Las Vegas are famous for their music, dancing, and costumes.

2. Some women feel (*embarrass*) _____ if they are asked their age.

3. The (*frighten*) _____ movie gave Sarah nightmares.

4. There's nothing worse than a (*bore*) _____ lecture.

5. That math problem was too (*confuse*) _____. I couldn't figure it out.

6. The teacher patiently answered the (*frustrate*) _____ students' questions.

7. I'm reading a (*fascinate*) _____ book about the life of Dr. Martin Luther King Jr.

8. The (*surprise*) _____ student gratefully accepted her Outstanding Achievement Award.

9. Jane enjoyed the movie. It had a (*satisfy*) _____ conclusion.

10. The renters on the third floor played loud music all night. The building manager responded to several complaints by (*annoy*) _____ neighbors.

Directions: Circle the correct completions.

Example: Ms. Haugen _____ at the Ajax Company.
      a. is employing   b. employed   c. employing   (d.) is employed

1. I still can't believe it! My bicycle _____ last night.
    a. was stolen   b. was stealing   c. stolen   d. stole

2. The current constitutional problem is _____ by the top legal minds in the country.
    a. studying   b. being studying   c. being studied   d. been studied

3. The child's arm was swollen because he _____ by a bee.
    a. stung   b. had stung   c. had been stung   d. had being stung

4. Today, many serious childhood diseases _____ by early immunization.
    a. are preventing   b. can prevent   c. prevent   d. can be prevented

5. Many U.S. automobiles _____ in Detroit, Michigan.
    a. manufacture   b. have manufactured   c. are manufactured   d. are manufacturing

6. The rescuers _____ for their bravery and fortitude in locating the lost mountain climbers.
    a. were praised   b. praised   c. were praising   d. praising

7. A: When _____?
   B: In 1928.
    a. penicillin was discovered   b. did penicillin discovered   c. was penicillin discovered   d. did penicillin discover

8. In recent years, the government has imposed pollution controls on automobile manufacturers. All automobiles must _____ anti-pollution devices.
    a. equip with   b. be equipped with   c. equip by   d. be equipped by

9. A shortage of water is a problem in many parts of the world. In some areas, water _____ from the ground faster than nature can replenish the supply.
    a. is being taken   b. has been taking   c. is taking   d. has taken

10. Vitamin C _____ by the human body. It gets into the blood stream quickly.
    a. absorbs easily   b. is easily absorbing   c. is easily absorbed   d. absorbed easily

11. A: When can I have my car back?
   B: I think it'll _____ late this afternoon.
    a. finish   b. be finished   c. have finished   d. be finish

12. I didn't think my interview went very well, but I guess it must have. Despite all my anxiety, I _____ for the job I wanted.
    a. was hiring   b. hired   c. got hiring   d. got hired

13. Ed was new on the job, but he quickly fit himself into the _____ routine of the office.

    a. established   b. establishing   c. establishes   d. establish

14. George is _____ Lisa.

    a. marry with   b. marry to   c. married with   d. married to

15. Let's go ahead and do it now. Nothing _____ by waiting.

    a. accomplishes   b. accomplished   c. has accomplished   d. will be accomplished

CHAPTER 11 – TEST 1

Part A **Directions:** Complete the sentences with the passive form of the verbs in parentheses. Use any appropriate tense. More than one answer is possible.

1. The robber's photo (*take*) _____ by the store's security camera, and the robber (*arrest*) _____ by the police a few hours later.

2. An announcement about the government's plans for economic reform (*make*) _____ at a press conference this afternoon.

3. Young people in many countries (*encourage*) _____ to get a college degree.

4. Claire (*give*) _____ a $5,000 college scholarship.

5. I think the movie is starting. The theme music (*play*) _____. Let's hurry!

Part B **Directions:** Change the following sentences from active to passive. Use the **by**-phrase where necessary.

1. Nearly everyone is using cell phones these days.

   _____

2. Rick and Dennis will clear the snow from the roof later today.

   _____

3. The museum lent the old book to the university.

   _____

4. People close government offices, schools, and many businesses on holidays.

   _____

5. The mechanic at Maher's Auto Repair is fixing our car.

   _____

Part C *Directions:* Complete the sentences with the verbs in parentheses. Use the appropriate form, active or passive.

1. All signs and posted notices (*should + obey*) _____.

2. It's too bad you threw those steak bones away. They (*could + give*)
   _____ to my dog.

3. The birthday card I sent to my brother (*should + arrive*) _____
   by tomorrow.

4. This report (*must + finish*) _____ by the end of the week.

5. The smoke from the forest fire (*can + see*) _____ from miles
   away.

Part D *Directions:* Complete the sentences with the correct prepositions.

1. The expensive dress is made _____ silk.

2. Marianne is interested _____ movies from the 1950s.

3. Owen is really devoted _____ his wife and child. He always puts them first in his life.

4. Many people are involved _____ the effort to raise money for our class trip.

5. My parents are acquainted _____ several of my teachers.

6. The director is quite pleased _____ the final cut of the movie. It will open in theaters
   next weekend.

7. Seattle is known _____ such companies as Microsoft, Boeing, and Starbucks.

Part E *Directions:* Circle the correct completions.

1. My sister lives in a very (*interested, interesting*) part of London.

2. The mystery story was so (*excited, exciting*) that I stayed up until 2:00 A.M. finishing it.

3. The (*fascinated, fascinating*) little boy stared as the magician performed (*amazed, amazing*)
   tricks.

4. The (*frightened, frightening*) storm tore the roof off of the house across the street.

5. My (*embarrassed, embarrassing*) mother blushed when she forgot my fiancée's name.

1. When I woke up and looked outside, the landscape had changed. The ground had been lightly _____ with a dusting of snow during the night.
   - a. covering
   - b. cover
   - c. covers
   - d. covered

2. We can't even walk in this storm. Let's wait in the hallway where we'll be _____ the strong winds until things quiet down.
   - a. protected from
   - b. protected by
   - c. protecting from
   - d. protecting by

3. A: _____ about the eight o'clock flight to Chicago?
   B: Not yet.
   - a. Has been an announcement made
   - b. Has an announcement made
   - c. Has an announcement been made
   - d. Has been made an announcement

4. Last night a tornado swept through Rockville. It _____ everything in its path.
   - a. destroyed
   - b. was destroyed
   - c. was being destroyed
   - d. had been destroyed

5. Be sure to wash these vegetables thoroughly. A lot of pesticide residue _____ on unwashed produce.
   - a. can find
   - b. can found
   - c. can be found
   - d. can be finding

6. The building of the bridge had been delayed for three years because of political problems on both sides of the river. Finally, it _____ because the public demanded action, and now many hours of driving have been saved for daily commuters.
   - a. was constructed
   - b. gets constructed
   - c. constructed
   - d. has constructed

7. On Friday afternoon before a three-day holiday weekend, the highways _____ people on their way out of the city.
   - a. are crowding by
   - b. are being crowd with
   - c. are crowded with
   - d. crowd by

8. Fortunately, the hospital's new air-conditioning system _____ when the first heat wave of the summer arrived.
   - a. had installed
   - b. installed
   - c. had been installed
   - d. had been installing

9. It's hard to believe that my application for a scholarship _____. I was sure I'd get it. I don't know now if I'll go to school next year.
   - a. was denied
   - b. denied
   - c. was denying
   - d. has denied

10. The man died because medical help was not summoned. A doctor should _____ immediately.
    - a. have called
    - b. been called
    - c. called
    - d. have been called

CHAPTER 11 – TEST 2

Part A **Directions:** Complete the sentences with the passive form of the verbs in parentheses. Use any appropriate tense.

1. Courtney (*ask*) _____ to give a karate demonstration for the elementary school children.

2. Next year the university entrance exams (*give*) _____ in January and February.

3. Madeline's flight (*schedule*) _____ to leave at 6:50 A.M. We'll have to leave for the airport by 4:00.

4. The contract provisions (*agree*) _____ on by both the union and administration teams. The negotiations were successful.

5. The new software (*load*) _____ onto your laptop right now. The technician (*finish*) _____ in a few minutes.

Part B **Directions:** Change the following sentences from active to passive. Use the **by**-phrase where necessary.

1. The school is giving scholarships to many students from low-income families.

   _____

2. A falling pine cone hit Michael on the head.

   _____

3. People check each computer five times before they put it in a box for shipping.

   _____

4. Someone is going to cut down the weeds on the hill.

   _____

5. An anonymous donor gave the Cancer Foundation $2 million.

   _____

Part C *Directions:* Complete the sentences with the verbs in parentheses. Use the appropriate form, active or passive.

1. We have to throw this old salad out. It (*should + eat*) _____ by now.

2. I can't find my keys. I (*must + leave*) _____ them in my coat pocket.

3. My uncle Philip (*can + always + count*) _____ on for help.

4. The cake (*should + bake*) _____ at 350 degrees for about 30 minutes.

5. Tom (*may + invite*) _____ to the party. I'm not sure.

Part D *Directions:* Complete the sentences with the correct prepositions.

1. I am very concerned _____ my husband's health. Although he quit smoking, he still coughs a lot.

2. Duncan's parents were satisfied _____ his grades last semester.

3. Most people are opposed _____ any tax increases.

4. Carolina is well qualified _____ a job as a publicist. She has a lot of experience.

5. After exams, the students are exhausted _____ so much studying and not enough sleep.

6. I am really bored _____ this novel. I need to go to the library and get another book.

7. Many people were exposed _____ the flu, but only a few got sick.

Part E *Directions:* Circle the correct completions.

1. My first date was such an (*embarrassed, embarrassing*) experience that I'll never forget it.

2. The chemistry experiment did not have the (*expected, expecting*) result. That was (*surprised, surprising*).

3. My teacher tries to provide (*balanced, balancing*) instruction; she usually has some group discussion in addition to her lecture.

4. (*Experienced, Experiencing*) musicians practice almost every day to keep their technique strong.

5. I love roller coasters! The roller coaster in Santa Cruz gives you a (*thrilled, thrilling*) ride.

Directions: Circle the correct completions.

1. A: Can't we do something about the situation?
   B: Something _____ right now.
      a. is doing   b. is done   c. is being done   d. has been doing

2. A: Are you interested in scuba diving?
   B: Very. Undersea life is _____.
      a. fascinated   b. fascinating   c. being fascinating   d. being fascinated

3. The university _____ by private funds as well as by tuition income and grants.
      a. is supported   b. supports   c. is supporting   d. has supported

4. My car made strange noises, sputtered to a stop, and then wouldn't start again. Fortunately, the mechanic at my garage _____ the source of the problem.
      a. was discover   b. discovered   c. was discovered   d. has been discovered

5. A: Alex, please type those letters before noon.
   B: They've already _____. They're on your desk.
      a. typed   b. been typed   c. being typed   d. been being typed

6. A: Has the committee made its decision yet?
   B: Not yet. They are still _____ the proposal.
      a. considering   b. been considered   c. being considered   d. considered

7. In some rural areas of the United States, health care _____ by only a small number of doctors, nurses, and other health professionals. It's often more than they can handle.
      a. is providing   b. is being provided   c. provides   d. provided

8. A: How did that window _____?
   B: I don't know.
      a. get broken   b. broke   c. got broken   d. broken

9. Renoir is one of the most popular French impressionist painters. His paintings _____ masterpieces all over the world.
      a. had considered   b. are considering   c. are considered   d. consider

10. As the fairy tale goes, the prince _____ into a frog by an evil magician, and only a kiss from a beautiful princess could restore him to his original state.
      a. turned   b. was turning   c. was turned   d. had been turning

Noun Clauses

QUIZ 1 Identifying Noun Clauses (Chart 12-1)

Directions: <u>Underline</u> the noun clauses in each sentence.

Example: James wants to know <u>where the meeting is going to be</u>.

1. Mr. Murphy doesn't know how much the tickets are.
2. The students will ask their teacher when the final exam is.
3. Patricia wanted to know if her dad would give her a ride to school.
4. The police are trying to find out what happened.
5. That we start on time is really important to our boss.
6. Can you tell me what time it is?
7. Mike didn't know who the man was or why he had come to the meeting.
8. It was unbelievable that we had to pay $90 to take the exam.
9. I don't know what the weather forecast for tomorrow is.
10. Nan agreed that carpooling to work was a good idea.

QUIZ 2 Noun Clauses Beginning with a Question Word (Chart 12-2)

Directions: Complete the sentences. Change the questions into noun clauses.

Example: (*How long has Hank lived in Memphis?*)

Do you know ___*how long Hank has lived in Memphis*___ ?

1. (*What is the purpose of your visit?*)

Please tell me _____.

2. (*Who is the mayor of Shoreline?*)

Do you know _____?

3. (*How much did Sue's car cost?*)

_____ is none of your business.

4. (*How much time do we have left?*)

I don't know _____.

5. (*Who left the door unlocked?*)

I wonder _____.

6. (*Which pages are we supposed to study?*)

Let's ask the teacher _____.

7. (*Where is the nearest post office?*)

Could you tell me _____?

8. (*Why is there so much traffic today?*)

I don't understand _____.

9. (*How will they solve their financial problems?*)

_____ is still under discussion.

10. (*Whose dictionary is that?*)

I'm not sure _____.

QUIZ 3 **Noun Clauses Beginning with a Question Word** (Chart 12-2)

Directions: Complete the sentences with the words in parentheses. Use any appropriate verb tense. Some contain noun clauses and some contain questions.

Example: A: What (*Marion, want*) _____*does Marion want*_____ for her birthday?

B: Gosh, I don't know what (*she, want*) _____*she wants*_____. Let's ask her.

1. A: How much (*your digital camera, cost*) _____?

B: I don't remember exactly how much (*I, pay*) _____ for it. I

got it last year.

2. A: Yesterday Sam couldn't remember where (*he, park*) _____ his

car. He walked around the parking lot for ten minutes until he found it.

B: That has happened to me before too. I feel so silly when (*I, can find, not*) _____

_____ my car.

3. A: How many tickets to the art show (*you, sell*) _____?

B: I think about ten. Do you know how many (*Ted, sell*) _____?

He said nearly everyone he knew had bought one from him.

4. A: Hey look! This old bottle has a note in it!

B: Really? What (*it, say*) _____?

A: I can't read it. The ink is too faded.

5. A: Do you have a key to the supply room?

B: No, but I know where (*the key, be*) _____.

A: Where (*it, be*) _____?

B: I can't tell you. Where (*it, be*) _____ is a secret.

Directions: Complete the sentences. Change the questions into noun clauses.

Example: (*Is the bookstore open today?*)

Do you know _____if/whether the bookstore is open today or not? OR_____

Do you know _____whether or not the bookstore is open today?_____

1. (*Is Mandy going to pass her chemistry class?*)

    I don't know _____.

2. (*Did an overnight mail package arrive today?*)

    We can ask the mail clerk _____.

3. (*Does Andy like the new basketball coach?*)

    _____ is unknown.

4. (*Has anyone seen the new show at the Paramount Theater?*)

    Let's find out _____.

5. (*Was Jim at the party last night?*)

    I meant to ask you _____.

6. (*Do you prefer coffee or tea for breakfast?*)

    Please let me know _____.

7. (*Had Ken ever been to an opera before last night?*)

    I wonder _____.

8. (*Does Tom mind when his brother practices the drums?*)

    _____ is unimportant.

9. (*Are the Smiths coming over for dinner on Saturday?*)

    I need to know _____.

10. (*Will Liz be going to Orlando with us?*)

    Liz isn't sure _____ or not.

A. Directions: Make sentences with the same meaning by using infinitives.

Example: Tom didn't tell me where I should meet him.

　　　Tom didn't tell me where to meet him.

1. Mick showed me how I could solve a Sudoku puzzle.

_____

2. I can't decide whether or not I should travel over the holidays.

_____

3. Julie wanted to know when she should start the barbecue.

_____

4. I had several huge flowerpots that I didn't want. I wondered what I should do with them.

_____

5. Sandy and Jack discussed where they should go on vacation.

_____

B. Directions: Complete the sentences with your own words. Use infinitives in your completions.

Example: A: What are you going to fix for dinner?

　　　B: I don't know. I can't decide ____*whether to have*____ fish or pasta tonight.

1. A: Mom, can you help me with this math homework?

　　B: Hmmm . . . . Sorry. I don't know _____ that type of math problem anymore.

2. A: I bought a new computer, but I'm having trouble setting it up. Can you come over and help me with it?

　　B: Sure, but you'll have to explain _____ to your house.

3. A: I need a book on gardening. Can you tell me _____ one?

　　B: Of course. All of our gardening books are in the back of the store on the right side.

4. A: I don't know _____ about my failing grade in English class.

　　B: Try doing some homework now and then!

5. A: What's the problem? Why haven't you started painting yet?

　　B: I don't know _____ the walls white or pale yellow. What do you think?

A. *Directions:* Add the word ***that*** to the sentences to mark the beginning of a noun clause.

Example: I didn't know ∧ Alice had a broken leg.
                   that

1. Are you sure you didn't leave your cell phone in the car?

2. It's a fact pirates captured a boat off the coast of Africa recently.

3. Steve failed his driving test is unfortunate.

4. Did I remind you we are going shopping after work?

5. Ginger is excited she will go to Costa Rica in March.

B. *Directions:* Write each sentence in another way, but keep the same meaning. Include a noun clause.

Example: That Don isn't feeling well is obvious.

      It's obvious that Don isn't feeling well.

1. It is unfortunate that Sarah won't be able to attend the ceremony.

   _____

2. That the doctor gave you the wrong prescription is unlikely.

   _____

3. That the little boy survived the plane crash is a miracle.

   _____

4. It surprises me that Rosa didn't finish the project on time.

   _____

5. It is clear that no one will pass this class without additional help from the teacher.

   _____

Directions: Match each sentence from Column A to a sentence in Column B. Then combine the sentences into one that contains a noun clause. Use *it* or *that* where necessary to make the noun clause. More than one answer is possible. The first one is done for you.

Column A	Column B
1. The rain isn't going to stop anytime soon.	That is surprising.
2. Martha and Jim will arrive tomorrow.	I promise.
3. Mary got an award for Teacher of the Year.	I'm lucky.
4. I have a very loving and supportive family.	I'm pleased.
5. Our soccer team is going to do well this season.	It's wonderful.
6. A meteorite hit the earth 65 million years ago.	Martin is confident.
7. A number of the tests were graded incorrectly.	Scientists believe.
8. My daughter got a job as a flight attendant with Amazon Airlines.	✓That's unfortunate.
9. I will pay back the money I borrowed by the end of the month.	That is possible.

1. _____It is unfortunate that the rain isn't going to stop anytime soon._____

2. _____

_____

3. _____

_____

4. _____

_____

5. _____

_____

6. _____

_____

7. _____

_____

8. _____

_____

9. _____

_____

Directions: Add punctuation and capitalization.

Example: I am looking forward to summer said Anne

      "I am looking forward to summer," said Anne.

1. where are you going on your vacation   Ruth asked

2. we are going on a road trip to Alaska   replied Anne

3. wow   said Ruth   that sounds like fun   how long will you be gone

4. around three weeks   answered Anne   we are going to tour the southeast coast and visit a glacier   we also hope to go to one of the national parks

5. I hear Alaska is beautiful   commented Ruth   so you're sure to have a wonderful vacation

6. yes   added Anne   and we're sure to put lots of miles on our car

QUIZ 9 Reported Speech (Chart 12-7)

Directions: Complete the sentences by rewriting the speaker's words. Use noun clauses. Use past verb forms in the noun clauses where appropriate.

Example: "Those jeans are too expensive," said Laura.

      Laura said _____*(that) those jeans were too expensive.*_____

1. "What time does the meeting start?" asked Cynthia.

   Cynthia wanted to know _____.

2. "The earth has seven continents and five oceans," said the geography teacher.

   The teacher told the children _____.

3. Scott asked, "Do you play golf?"

   Scott asked me _____.

4. Emma said, "We forgot to pick up our dry cleaning."

   Emma told her husband _____.

5. "I've got a lot of work to do today," stated Kate.

   Kate told me _____.

6. "Have you ever been to Mexico?" asked Felipe.

   Felipe asked us _____.

7. "I will be there in fifteen minutes," promised Kevin.

   Kevin just texted me _____.

8. Helena asked, "Are there any new magazines available?"

Helena asked the clerk _____.

9. "I think that is an excellent book," said Matthew.

Matthew commented _____.

10. Children always ask, "Why is the sky blue?"

Children always want to know _____.

QUIZ 10 **Reported Speech** (Chart 12-7)

Directions: Write reports for these conversations. Your reports should include an accurate idea of the speaker's words, but they don't have to use the exact words. Use the formal sequence of tenses as appropriate. Answers will vary.

Example: Lynne said, "I had a wonderful vacation."
Neil said, "That's good. What did you do?"
Lynne answered, "I went skiing in Montana. The snow was perfect."

Possible answer: *Lynne told Neil that she had had a great vacation. Neil wanted to know what she had done, and she told him she had gone skiing in Montana. She added that the snow had been perfect.*

1. "How was your English test?" David's mom asked.
"It wasn't too hard," David replied.

_____

_____

2. Harry said, "I'm so tired today."
Max said, "You should get more sleep."

_____

_____

3. Doug asked, "Where can I find the shoe department?"
The clerk answered, "It's on the second floor."
Doug said, "Thank you for your help."

_____

_____

_____

4. "I have my first accounting class today," Susan said.
"Who's your instructor?" Carol asked.
"Professor Nelson," Susan replied.
"She's great. I was in her class last year," Carol said.

_____

_____

_____

_____

5. "Do you have any plans for the weekend?" my brother Jim asked.

"Nothing special," I answered. "Why do you want to know?"

"I've got some tickets to the baseball game on Saturday. Do you want to go?" he said.

"That sounds like fun," I said. "What time is the game?"

"Well, the game starts at two," said Jim, "but we should probably leave here by one or so."

"OK. I'd love to go with you," I said, "and I'll buy the hot dogs."

_____

_____

_____

_____

_____

_____

QUIZ 11 **Noun Clauses with -*ever* Words** (Chart 12-8)

Directions: Change the words in *italics* to an -*ever* word.

Example: Anyone who drives too fast on Route 66 should get a speeding ticket.

_____*Whoever*_____ drives too fast on Route 66 should get a speeding ticket.

1. You can hang the picture *anyplace that* you want.

   You can hang the picture _____ you want.

2. I can't stand talking to Andrea on the phone. *Any time that* she calls me, I don't answer.

   _____ she calls me, I don't answer.

3. Will isn't very independent. He does *anything that* his friends tell him to do.

   He does _____ his friends tell him to do.

4. *The person that* sent Michelle those flowers must love her very much!

   _____ sent Michelle those flowers must love her very much!

5. My history teacher said he had three books about Genghis Khan and that I could borrow *any of the books that* I wanted.

   My history teacher said he had three books about Genghis Khan and that I could borrow

   _____ book I wanted.

6. My hair stylist is amazing. She can fix my hair *in any way that* I ask, and it always looks great.

   She can fix my hair _____ I ask, and it always looks great.

7. *Anytime that* Mr. Lee takes an overseas flight, he prefers to fly first class because it is more comfortable.

   _____ Mr. Lee takes an overseas flight, he prefers to fly first class

   because it is more comfortable.

8. Jacob is a very kind man. He will help *anyone who* asks him.

   He will help _____ asks him.

9. There are several flavors of ice cream to choose from. Jason probably won't like *any flavor that* I choose.

   Jason probably won't like _____ flavor I choose.

10. When kids are hungry, they will eat *anything that* is served for dinner without complaining.

    When kids are hungry, they will eat _____ is served for dinner without complaining.

Directions: Correct the errors.

                                       I wanted

Example: My brother asked me what ~~did I want~~.

1. The student asked her counselor which class she should to take.

2. I'm not sure if or not we will buy a new car this year.

3. Can you tell me what time does the concert start?

4. I know Nellie will be accepted to whomever college she chooses.

5. Marcos knows if that I am going to ride to Vancouver with him.

6. Marcy asked the clerk how much the bag does cost?

7. How many times a month you visit your grandparents?

8. That Jordan was angry it was obvious.

9. I wonder is it supposed to rain tomorrow.

10. Whenever time you want to go is fine with me.

Part A *Directions:* Complete the sentences. Change the questions into noun clauses.

1. (*When does Flight 2803 arrive?*)

   The timetable can tell you _____.

2. (*Has the mail already been picked up?*)

   Debbie wants to know _____.

3. (*How did the fire start?*)

   Investigators are trying to find out _____.

4. (*What grade did I get on the last quiz?*)

   I wonder _____.

5. (*Would Jim prefer a sweater or a shirt?*)

   I'm not sure _____.

Part B *Directions:* Make sentences with the same meaning by using infinitives.

1. I've told you everything I know about the crime. I don't know what else I should say.

   I've told you everything I know about the crime. I _____.

2. I was completely lost. I didn't know which way I should go or whom I should ask for help.

   I was completely lost. I _____.

3. The supervisor gave Maria terrible directions. She wasn't sure what she should do or how she should begin.

   The supervisor gave Maria terrible directions. She _____

   _____.

4. Mr. Lee can't decide whether he should go on a trip or visit his family during the holidays.

   Mr. Lee _____.

Part C *Directions:* Combine the sentences into one that contains a noun clause. Use **it** or **that** where necessary to make the noun clause.

1. James is lying. It is a shame.

   _____.

2. I am amazed. Sophie got 100% on the vocabulary quiz.

   _____.

3. Women live longer than men. That is a fact.

   _____.

4. The coffee at the Campus Café is terrible. I agree with that.

_____.

5. It is unusual. Max's father has six names.

_____.

Part D *Directions:* Add punctuation and capitalization.

1. I don't want to waste time   said Mary   so let's hurry

2. why did the mother bird fly away from the nest   asked Jimmy

3. Valerie told the tour group   please stay close together so no one gets lost

4. Mr. Donovan is our attorney   Margaret said   he is very good

5. when he saw the car coming towards them   James shouted   look out

Part E *Directions:* Write a report of the conversation. Use the formal sequence of tenses.

ANITA: Do you sell computer accessories?

CLERK: Yes, we do. What are you looking for?

ANITA: I need a wireless mouse for my laptop.

CLERK: What kind of a computer do you have?

ANITA: It's a Sony Notebook.

CLERK: All of these should work with your computer.

ANITA: Thanks very much.

_____

_____

_____

_____

_____

_____

Part F *Directions:* Complete the sentences with *-ever* words.

1. A cell phone is very convenient. I can call my friends _____ I want.

2. A: Mmmm! There are so many good things on the menu. It's hard to decide.

   B: Please order _____ you want.

3. There are several good movies playing now. We can go to _____ movie you prefer.

4. I don't know who wrote that book, but _____ it was had a great sense of humor. It's really funny.

5. Students can decorate their dormitory rooms _____ they want. Some students do a lot of decorating, but others keep their rooms simple.

CHAPTER 12–TEST 2

Part A *Directions:* Complete the sentences. Change the questions into noun clauses.

1. (*How often do you go to the gym?*)

    I would like to know _____.

2. (*Did Teresa stay after school for the meeting?*)

    Do you know _____?

3. (*What time does the movie start?*)

    Let's ask him _____.

4. (*Where did she go after the lecture?*)

    I don't know _____.

5. (*Do her meetings usually end on time?*)

    Please tell me _____.

Part B *Directions:* Make sentences with the same meaning by using infinitives.

1. Alan has two girlfriends. He can't decide which one he should invite to the school dance.

    Alan has two girlfriends. He _____.

2. The patient asked the doctor how often she could take the medicine.

    The patient _____.

3. The teacher gave us very clear directions for our essay. He told us how many words we should write, what type size we should use, and when we should turn it in.

    The teacher gave us very clear directions for our essay. He _____

    _____.

4. The director told the actors that they should rehearse their lines more before the performance.

    The director _____.

Part C *Directions:* Combine the sentences into one that contains a noun clause. Use *it* or *that* where necessary to make the noun clause.

1. Mischa needs to study harder. That is the truth.

    _____.

2. It is too bad. Emma had to take her driving test three times before she passed.

    _____.

3. The Chinese have used traditional medicines for thousands of years. Many Chinese are proud of that.

    _____.

4. Too much sun can cause skin cancer. That is a well-known fact.

   _____.

5. The library is a quiet place to study. Jason is glad.

   _____.

Part D *Directions:* Add punctuation and capitalization.

   1. are you ready to order   asked the waiter

   2. please help me   Doug begged   this box is too heavy for me to carry

   3. I don't want to go home   cried the angry child

   4. it is an unusual problem   said the scientist   but I think we can find a solution

   5. Ms. Bell said to the students   please talk quietly in the library

Part E *Directions:* Write a report of the dialogue. Use the formal sequence of tenses.

   MR. THOMAS: You didn't do well on the quiz. What happened?

   MARY: I really didn't have enough time to study.

   MR. THOMAS: Why not?

   MARY: My mother has been sick, so I've been taking care of her.

   MR. THOMAS: You should have told me! You could have taken the quiz on a different day.

   _____

   _____

   _____

   _____

   _____

   _____

   _____

Part F *Directions:* Complete the sentences with *-ever* words.

   1. I have the whole day free, so _____ long you want to spend working
   in the garden is fine with me.

   2. I will follow you _____ you go because I have no idea where we are,
   and I don't want to get lost.

   3. You should buy _____ jacket you like because you're going to wear it,
   not me.

   4. At the end of the semester, the art students can bring home _____
   they made in class.

   5. _____ correctly answers the most questions in 30 seconds will get a
   chance to win the $25,000 prize.

Directions: Choose all the possible completions for each sentence. Do not add any commas or capital letters.

Example: The soccer team _____ won the city championship practiced three times a week.
     a. who   b. whom   (c.) that   (d.) which   e. they

1. The woman _____ Jim remembered meeting several years earlier had completely changed her appearance.
     a. who   b. whom   c. that   d. which   e. she

2. The movie _____ we watched last night was so exciting that I couldn't sleep for hours afterwards.
     a. who   b. whom   c. that   d. which   e. she

3. I met a very interesting man _____ works as a museum curator.
     a. who   b. whom   c. that   d. which   e. he

4. My daughter had on a dress _____ was too short. I made her change her clothes before she went out.
     a. who   b. whom   c. that   d. which   e. it

5. Mr. Scott, to _____ I sent the email yesterday, hasn't responded yet.
     a. who   b. whom   c. that   d. which   e. him

6. Yesterday's game, _____ was canceled due to the weather, will be rescheduled.
     a. who   b. whom   c. that   d. which   e. they

7. I don't know the man _____ Teri is engaged to.
     a. who   b. whom   c. that   d. which   e. he

8. The era of history _____ Gordon is most interested in is the Middle Ages.
     a. who   b. whom   c. that   d. which   e. it

9. The students _____ I study with are smart, hard-working, and helpful.
     a. who   b. whom   c. that   d. which   e. they

10. Larry Miller won first prize for a science project on radiation _____ he had been working on for several months.
     a. who   b. whom   c. that   d. which   e. it

QUIZ 2 **Basic Patterns of Adjective Clauses** (Charts 13-1 → 13-3)

Directions: Combine the two sentences. Use the second sentence as the adjective clause.

Example: Midori served tasty Japanese snacks. We enjoyed them very much.
        Midori served tasty Japanese snacks which / that we enjoyed very much.

1. Robin told the children a story. The story made them laugh.

2. Jason met a famous baseball player. The baseball player had hit many homeruns during his career.

3. The pianist played a Mozart concerto. It was one of Mark's favorite pieces of music.

4. My roommate invited her brother to our party. I had never met him before.

5. The new computer makes my work easier. I just bought it last week.

6. Angela is the oldest child in her family. She has three younger sisters and a younger brother.

7. The elderly woman was grateful. Anne helped her with yard work.

8. Julia's husband gave her a beautiful bouquet of roses. He bought it at the flower market.

QUIZ 3 **Using *Whose* in Adjective Clauses** (Chart 13-4)

Directions: Complete the sentences with *who* or *whose*.

Examples: The boy ____*whose*____ bike was stolen was really angry.
        The boy ____*who*____ lives next door is very friendly.

1. I forgot the name of the teacher _____ teaches French.

2. The little girl _____ hair is in ringlets is so cute!

3. The neighbors _____ live upstairs are very noisy.

4. Juanita works for a company _____ employees get good salaries and benefits.

5. Rob knows a Ukrainian man _____ family immigrated here in 1965.

6. Mark and Leroy have a building manager _____ collects the rent every month.

7. This coat belongs to the man _____ came to the meeting with Jonathan.

8. Mrs. Manzinalli is looking for the student _____ notebook was left in class.

9. There are two students in my class _____ knowledge of American history is impressive.

10. Rose's uncle, _____ full name is Stanislaus, uses the nickname "Stash."

QUIZ 4 Using *Whose* in Adjective Clauses (Chart 13-4)

Directions: Combine the sentences with ***whose.*** Use the second sentence as the adjective clause.

Example: The woman lives in Los Angeles. Her daughter is an actress.
        _____*The woman whose daughter is an actress lives in Los Angeles.*_____

1. The boy has beautiful teeth. His father is a dentist.

   _____

2. We want to do business with that company. Its products are top quality.

   _____

3. Sarah feels sorry for her neighbors. Their car was stolen last night.

   _____

4. The student came to class late every day. Her homework was never done.

   _____

5. I have never met Meg's brother. His wife is the conductor of the symphony orchestra.

   _____

6. The dog always begs for food. Its back leg is injured.

   _____

7. Ellen met a kind man. His parents died when he was very young.

   _____

8. The Johnsons live in the apartment upstairs. Their son goes to Stanford University.

   _____

Directions: Complete the sentences with ***where*** or ***when***.

Example: Please tell me a story about the time _____*when*_____ you were a child.

1. I remember the small town in Montana _____ I grew up.

2. In the 1960s, _____ I was a kid, life was simple.

3. We lived in a wonderful neighborhood _____ there were many families.

4. The kids of all ages played games outdoors _____ there was room enough for everyone.

5. In the summertime, we played outside until 10:00 P.M. _____ our parents called us home.

6. One of our favorite summertime activities was to sell lemonade on hot days _____ everyone was thirsty.

7. We put up a table in front of our house _____ many people passed by.

8. On good days, _____ we sold all of our lemonade, we made several dollars.

9. After we had sold all of our lemonade, we happily walked to the neighborhood store _____ we spent our hard-earned money on ice cream, penny candy, and soda pop.

10. Next year _____ I go on vacation, I would like to visit my old neighborhood again.

Directions: Combine the sentences with *where* or *when*. Use the second sentence as the adjective clause.

Example: My mother enjoys going to the library. She can check out many books and materials there.

> *My mother enjoys going to the library where she can check out many books and materials.*

1. My favorite season is spring. The daffodils and tulips bloom then.

   _____

2. That is the furniture store. We bought our couch and coffee table there.

   _____

3. The store is near our house. They sell many Scandinavian products there.

   _____

4. Jim remembers a time. Gasoline cost $1.25 per gallon then.

   _____

5. The Chinese restaurant served delicious seafood. We ate dinner there.

   _____

6. Do you know the name of the city? The Olympic games will be held there.

   _____

7. Every student looks forward to the day. School gets out then.

   _____

8. I last saw Jerry on that day. Jerry got his new car then.

   _____

Directions: Use an adjective clause from the list to complete each sentence. Write the letter on the line. The first one is done for you.

a. who has met the prime minister
b. who knows the answer to number 12
c. she says
d. who get too much help from others
e. I can do to help you
f. who can repair it for him

g. that are the ripest
h. who went to the concert
i. ✓who can perform like they do
j. my husband said
k. who knew how to unlock the safe

1. My favorite rock group is The Skinks. There's nobody ____*i*____.

2. Carl's bicycle has a flat tire. He has to find somebody _____.

3. Everyone _____ really enjoyed the music.

4. I know many interesting people, but I don't know anybody _____.

5. Mary is so funny! Everything _____ makes me laugh.

6. Students must be honest and do their own work. Those _____ don't learn as much.

7. Jerry was the only one _____. We had to wait for him to open it.

8. I'm sorry, but there's nothing _____.

9. My cell phone was low on power. I couldn't hear anything _____.

10. I need three tomatoes. Please give me the ones _____.

11. I'm stuck on this problem. Is there anybody _____?

Directions: Choose the correct explanation of the meaning of each sentence.

Example: My brother, who lives in Phoenix, works at an engineering firm.
      (a.) I have only one brother.
      b. I have more than one brother.

1. The students who were accepted into the university were very excited.
   a. All of the students were accepted into the university.
   b. Only some of the students were accepted into the university.

2. The visiting executives, who were from Okinawa and were used to a warm climate, arrived in Chicago during a snowstorm.
   a. All of the executives were from Okinawa.
   b. Only some of the executives were from Okinawa.

3. John watched a movie on the DVD player that is in the den.
   a. John has more than one DVD player.
   b. John has only one DVD player.

4. Our wood-burning stove, which is in the corner of our living room, keeps the first floor of the house warm.
   a. There is only one wood-burning stove in the house.
   b. There is more than one wood-burning stove in the house.

5. Conifers, which have needles instead of leaves, are plentiful in the forests of the western United States.
   a. All conifers have needles instead of leaves.
   b. Only some conifers have needles instead of leaves.

Directions: Add commas where necessary.

Example: Dr. Janice Miller who is an expert in children's health spoke at the Parents' Club meeting.

    Dr. Janice Miller, who is an expert in children's health, spoke at the Parents' Club meeting.

1. The city of Dubrovnik which is on the Adriatic coast is surrounded by an ancient stone wall.

2. The instructor who teaches grammar class gives very clear explanations.

3. On our last family vacation we went to Disneyland where we shook hands with Mickey Mouse.

4. I saw Alex and Alice who are twins at the shopping center.

5. The Mississippi River which is one of the most important rivers in the United States has an interesting history.

6. Mr. Mitchell with whom we shared our back fence was a fantastic gardener.

7. People who travel and live in other countries learn to appreciate other cultures and customs.

8. *The Marriage of Figaro* which is one of Mozart's comedic operas is performed regularly on stages around the world.

9. Jason has two brothers. His older brother who lives in New York is a financial advisor, and his younger brother is a police officer.

10. The book that I'm reading is from the Everett Public Library where you can borrow books for up to three weeks.

QUIZ 10 **Expressions of Quantity in Adjective Clauses** (Chart 13-9)

Directions: Combine the two sentences. Use the second sentence as the adjective clause.

Example: Michael has two cars. Both of them are low on gasoline.

_____*Michael has two cars, both of which are low on gasoline.*_____

1. This story has three main characters. All of them are interesting and funny.

   _____

2. My school employs 60 teachers. More than half of them have master's degrees.

   _____

3. I bought a pound of strawberries. A few of them are still green.

   _____

4. The building caretaker found two jackets. Neither of them was Josh's.

   _____

5. Peter advises many students. Most of their questions are easy to answer.

   _____

6. The students listened to the boring professor talk. Several of them were half asleep.

   _____

7. Mr. Carter talked to the large group of college students. Some of them did not know that he used to be the president.

   _____

   _____

8. The workers attended the meeting about the merger of the two companies. Many of their jobs were in danger because of consolidation and cost-cutting.

   _____

   _____

A. Directions: Decide if the adjective clause modifies a noun or the whole sentence.

Examples: Sally missed the bus, which made her late for work.   a noun   (the sentence)

        Sally missed the 98 bus, which she usually takes to work.   (a noun)   the sentence

1. The teacher gave the students a careful explanation of the
   homework assignment, which had totally confused them.   a noun   the sentence

2. The teacher assigned 20 pages of homework, which made
   all of the students groan.   a noun   the sentence

3. Max lived for several years in Istanbul, which was one of the
   most interesting times in his life.   a noun   the sentence

4. Mrs. Anderson used to live in Dalian, which is a city in
   northeastern China.   a noun   the sentence

5. The people who were sitting behind us talked loudly during
   the movie, which was really annoying.   a noun   the sentence

6. Dan thoroughly enjoyed the play, which was about an
   American family in Berlin in the 1980s.   a noun   the sentence

B. Directions: Combine the two sentences. Use the second sentence as the adjective clause. Add commas where necessary.

Example: Anna burned the casserole. That made her family unhappy.
> *Anna burned the casserole, which made her family unhappy.*

1. Harold bought a newspaper. He read it on the train on the way to work.

   _____

2. On the way to work, Max stopped to get coffee. This was part of his morning routine.

   _____

3. After she got off the phone, Margaret typed an email. It was a message for her boss.

   _____

4. The receptionist answered the phone. It was a big part of her job.

   _____

Directions: Change the adjective clauses to adjective phrases.

Example: The woman who is sitting across the room is Jeff's aunt.
        The woman sitting across the room is Jeff's aunt.

1. The police officer who is in charge of directing traffic is very helpful.

   _____

2. Anyone who graduates this semester will get a diploma.

   _____

3. Montana, which is the fourth largest state in the U.S., is on the border with Canada.

   _____

4. The boys who are playing soccer are preparing for a big tournament.

   _____

5. Instructors who attend the workshop will learn about teaching English pronunciation.

   _____

6. How much are the tickets for the play that is showing at the New City Theater?

   _____

7. The archeologists who were digging in an area in eastern China made a significant discovery.

   _____

8. The Olympic official who presented the medals shook hands with the athletes.

   _____

9. There are more and more Americans who are driving cars that run on biodiesel.

   _____

10. Heather is the manager who oversees the accounting department.

    _____

Directions: Correct the errors.

Example: My sister, who lives in Guadalajara, ~~she~~ comes to visit every summer.

1. The book that we read it in class was about the history of jazz.

2. My best friend went to work in Indonesia, that consists of thousands of islands.

3. I like to shop at the farmers' market on Saturdays where I have a day off.

4. My DVD collection, most of who is stored at my parents' house, includes movies from the 1940s to the present.

5. Emma borrowed money from her sister whom she has to pay her back by next weekend.

6. When the weather is nice, the children like to go to the beach where is close to their house.

7. Mark doesn't get much sleep. He has a neighbor who his dog barks all night long.

8. The store manager locked the door where was at the back of the store before he went home.

9. There were fourteen students in my grammar class, seven of them were from Korea.

10. The young woman sitting across from me on the plane was listening to music and watching videos on her computer.

CHAPTER 13 – TEST 1

Part A *Directions:* Circle all the possible completions for each sentence. Do not add any commas or capital letters.

1. Jack would like to know the name of the store _____ I got my new DVD player.
   a. when   b. where   c. which   d. that

2. Philip will meet us at the bus stop _____ is on the corner of 23rd Avenue and Main Street.
   a. when   b. where   c. which   d. that

3. The travel agent needs to know some alternative dates _____ we can leave on vacation.
   a. when   b. where   c. which   d. that

4. Can you run upstairs and get my green scarf? It's in the closet _____ I keep my winter coat.
   a. when   b. where   c. which   d. that

5. The house _____ Maria is going to buy has two bedrooms and one bathroom.
   a. when   b. where   c. which   d. that

Part B *Directions:* Complete the sentences with *who, whom,* or *whose.*

1. Sarah has decided to hire the man _____ has excellent communication skills.

2. The person with _____ we were upset didn't come to the meeting.

3. I've really made a mess of the whole situation. There is no one _____ can help me now.

4. The supervisor called in the workers _____ job performance was less than satisfactory. She gave the other workers the afternoon off.

5. The interview committee read the résumés of over 200 applicants, only ten of _____ would be chosen for in-person interviews.

6. I returned the calculator to Minna, _____ had a difficult math quiz the next day.

Part C *Directions:* Combine the sentences. Use the second sentence as the adjective clause.

1. Connie finally finished typing the letters. The department supervisor needs to sign them.

   _____

2. My grandmother bought a lot of clothes. The clothes were on sale.

   _____

3. The red station wagon was driven by a drunk driver. It caused the accident.

   _____

4. The woman seemed well qualified for the position. Mr. North just interviewed her.

_____

5. Mrs. Tanaka is looking for the person. The person's car is blocking her driveway.

_____

Part D *Directions:* Change the adjective clauses to adjective phrases.

1. *Little Women,* which was published in 1868, is my sister's favorite novel.

_____

2. The science program that is showing on TV every night this week is about the brain.

_____

3. People who visit the Taj Mahal are impressed that a man built it to honor his wife.

_____

4. The director's new movie, which is opening in theaters this weekend, is sure to be entertaining.

_____

5. The manager of the French restaurant was pleased to learn that the critics who specialize in European cuisine rated his restaurant number one in the city.

_____

Part E *Directions:* Add commas where necessary.

1. Tom who lives in Port Hadlock is graduating from high school in June.

2. Mr. Parker collects toy trains which were manufactured in the 1940s and 50s.

3. Paul will call you at 5:30 P.M. when he will be home from work.

4. I have looked everywhere for my grammar book which I am sure I left on the dining room table. I can't find it anywhere.

5. There isn't any reason for the actor who is playing the part of Romeo to dye his hair.

Part A *Directions:* Circle all the possible completions for each sentence. Do not add any commas or capital letters.

1. The months _____ have 30 days are April, June, September, and November.
   a. when   b. where   c. which   d. that

2. I remember the time _____ Robert forgot to turn off the bathroom faucet and we came home to a house full of water.
   a. when   b. where   c. which   d. that

3. When we go to Atlanta, George wants to drive by the house _____ he grew up to see if it still looks the same.
   a. when   b. where   c. which   d. that

4. The office _____ you are going to be working in is down the hall, the second door to the left.
   a. when   b. where   c. which   d. that

5. The day _____ we got married was probably the happiest day of my life.
   a. when   b. where   c. which   d. that

Part B *Directions:* Complete the sentences with *who, whom,* or *whose*.

1. I recently got the autograph of J. K. Rowling, _____ is the author of the Harry Potter books.

2. Mrs. Holton, _____ son is enrolled at North Coast University, tells all her friends about her son's excellent academic record.

3. To _____ did you address the letter?

4. The students _____ had received excellent marks on the exam were honored by the National Scholastic Society.

5. Ms. Morimoto would like to find someone _____ can organize and catalog her collection of Asian art.

6. The firefighters, several of _____ had worked through the night, were exhausted from battling the fire on the hills near the city.

Part C *Directions:* Combine the sentences. Use the second sentence as the adjective clause.

1. Joe's parents don't like the music. Joe listens to the music.

   _____

2. The printer is fast and dependable. Jason bought it last week.

   _____

3. The police talked to the woman. Her car had been broken into.

   _____

4. The issue is not relevant to our current discussion. Many people are talking about the issue.

_____

5. People are in great demand in today's job market. People have advanced computer skills.

_____

Part D _Directions:_ Change the adjective clauses to adjective phrases.

1. Anyone who has grades that are above average can apply for the scholarship.

_____

2. The severe drought which is occurring in the Midwest this summer has ruined the corn crop.

_____

3. The missing man's family is desperately seeking anyone who has information about his activities.

_____

4. The lecture will most likely be attended by people who are interested in the Middle East.

_____

5. The people who watched the acrobat turn circles in the air were horrified when he fell to his death.

_____

Part E _Directions:_ Add commas where necessary.

1. The roof of my house which is already 20 years old is leaking badly and in need of repair.

2. The hunger program which Jack volunteers for feeds more than 250 families each month.

3. People who work outside at night must wear reflective clothing so they can be seen.

4. Jennifer's birthday cake which had strawberries and cream on top was enjoyed by everyone at the party.

5. The Red Cross which provides humanitarian aid to victims of wars and natural disasters is the favorite charity of the president's wife.

CHAPTER 14 Gerunds and Infinitives, Part 1

Directions: Complete each sentence with an appropriate preposition.

Example: The students are excited _____*about*_____ dissecting frogs in science class.

1. Adam and Megan are looking forward _____ going ice-skating on Saturday.

2. I'm very sorry. Will you please forgive me _____ being so rude to you?

3. Instead _____ cooking dinner last night, we went out for Mexican food.

4. Do you believe _____ trying to live in a way that protects the environment?

5. Most of the citizens at the meeting were opposed _____ closing city parks.

6. Students at the college should take advantage _____ the free tutoring available on campus.

7. The presidential candidate is committed _____ improving the country's economy.

8. Jacob is so stubborn! He always insists _____ doing things his way.

9. The police officer at the accident scene prevented drivers _____ stopping to look at what happened.

10. My co-workers are always complaining _____ working hard for low salaries.

Directions: Complete each sentence with an appropriate preposition and *-ing* form of the verb in parentheses.

Example: Margaret forgave her sister (*break*) _____*for breaking*_____ her favorite vase.

1. Are you interested (*come*) _____ to the Astronomy Center with us?

2. Mrs. Grant is devoted (*help*) _____ students learn to read and write.

3. Larry is thinking (*take*) _____ a trip to the Grand Canyon this summer.

4. My baby shows me she is hungry (*cry*) _____ .

5. Sarah is not used (*wear*) _____ a school uniform.

6. Our class is responsible (*clean*) _____ up the playground once a week.

7. I bought an energy-efficient car for the purpose (*drive*) _____ to and from work.

8. All of the students are worried (*pass*) _____ the final exams.

9. Fred fixed his broken eyeglasses (*use*) _____ Strong Bond glue.

10. Do you really think that Sonya is guilty (*rob*) _____ the jewelry store?

QUIZ 3 **Go + Gerund** (Chart 14-4)

Directions: Complete the sentences with a form of **go** + *gerund,* using the verbs in parentheses.

Example: Bowling is my favorite sport. I (*bowl*) _____go bowling_____ once a week.

1. Last Saturday Louisa (*dance*) _____ with her friends. They learned how to dance the salsa.

2. In two weeks we (*sightsee*) _____ in the area near Salzburg. If we are lucky, we may (*hike*) _____ in the Austrian Alps.

3. Guido is training for a long-distance cycling trip. He (*bike*) _____ every day after work.

4. On summer evenings, lots of people (*sail*) _____ on Lake Washington, where they can view beautiful sunsets over the city.

5. Pat caught three large trout the last time he (*fish*) _____.

6. Have you ever (*snorkel*) _____? I haven't, but I would like to.

7. I'm bored. Let's (*shop*) _____.

8. It snowed about a foot last night. The kids (*sled*) _____ as soon as they woke up this morning.

Directions: Make sentences with the given words.

Example: Claire \ spend a long time \ do homework \ usually

<u>   Claire usually spends a long time doing homework.   </u>

1. Ms. Spring \ sit at her desk \ pay bills \ last night

_____

2. Greg \ waste a lot of time \ surf the internet \ every night

_____

3. I \ catch my son \ sneak cookies from the cupboard \ when I walked into the kitchen yesterday

_____

4. Stewart \ have a hard time \ solve physics problems \ always

_____

5. Carol \ have a good time \ travel with her sisters \ last summer

_____

QUIZ 5 Common Verbs Followed by Infinitives (Chart 14-6)

Directions: Choose the correct completions.

Example: Chuck agreed ((*to visit,*) *them to visit*) his parents on Sunday.

1. Anthony is out of town this weekend, but he invited (*to come, us to come*) over for dinner next weekend.

2. My teacher offered (*to give me, me to give*) extra grammar homework, but I declined.

3. Nora has two boys. She doesn't allow (*to play, them to play*) on the computer until they do their homework.

4. My uncle plans (*to retire, him to retire*) in three to five years. His doctor advised (*to stop, him to stop*) working.

5. Our neighbor appeared (*to be, her to be*) having trouble with her car, so we offered (*to help, her to help*).

6. Teachers should always encourage (*to try, students to try*) their best in school.

7. My brother's 40th birthday is tomorrow, and I am going to surprise him. I will leave my house at 8:00 A.M. to drive to Los Angeles. I expect (*to arrive, him to arrive*) by noon. I'll meet my brother and his wife at a restaurant for lunch, but he doesn't expect (*to be, me to be*) there. I'm sure he'll be surprised to see me!

Directions: Choose the correct completions. More than one answer is possible.

Example: My sister will continue _____ at Oxford University next year.
    (a.) studying   (b.) to study

1. When my alarm clock rang at 6:30 this morning, the sky was beginning _____ light.
    a. getting   b. to get

2. I forgot _____ off the headlights on my car this morning. When I returned, my car wouldn't start.
    a. turning   b. to turn

3. I remember _____ Joe's parents at his graduation party last spring. They were very kind.
    a. meeting   b. to meet

4. Hannah regrets _____ her silver necklace. It was a gift from her grandparents.
    a. losing   b. to lose

5. Ann and Zach are trying _____ enough money to move into their own house.
    a. saving   b. to save

6. As soon as our teacher began _____ the class, the fire alarm sounded and we had to leave the building.
    a. teaching   b. to teach

7. While we were traveling through the western U.S., we stopped _____ several beautiful national parks.
    a. visiting   b. to visit

8. David can't stand _____ at his computer all day long. His eyes get tired from looking at the screen.
    a. working   b. to work

9. I'll never forget _____ the overnight train from Venice to Rome. I didn't sleep at all!
    a. taking   b. to take

10. Jay stopped _____ when he found out he had lung disease.
    a. smoking   b. to smoke

Directions: Complete each sentence with the gerund or infinitive form of the verbs in parentheses.

Example: Mr. Lee asked his wife _____*to pass*_____ the butter.

1. The young women go (*shop*) _____ almost every weekend.

2. Jada enjoys (*play*) _____ a few games of tennis on weekends.

3. Elena hopes (*celebrate*) _____ her birthday on a cruise to Hawaii.

4. Charles can't stand (*run*) _____ in the park when it rains.

5. Olga needed (*call*) _____ a plumber when her sink sprang a leak.

6. The firefighter warned the bystanders (*stay*) _____ behind the barriers and away from the flames.

7. Ann avoided (*drive*) _____ her car into the city. She was more comfortable on country roads.

8. Michiko forgot (*turn*) _____ off the heat when she left the house, so she called her husband and reminded him (*do*) _____ it.

9. London expects (*have*) _____ more than a million visitors for New Year's Eve.

10. Mrs. Alvarez suggested (*plant*) _____ flowers along the fence to cheer up the property.

11. The insurance agent encouraged Mrs. Davidson (*keep*) _____ her diamonds in a safe deposit box at the bank.

12. Kathy tried (*grow*) _____ her hair long, but long hair was too much trouble to take care of.

13. The National Press Club has invited the president of the United States (*speak*) _____ at its next meeting.

14. Paulo would like (*go*) _____ to Brazil for the holidays, but he doesn't have enough time.

15. I remember (*smell*) _____ my grandmother's perfume whenever I visited her.

16. Stefan wants (*continue*) _____ (*study*) _____ Turkish for several more years. Then he hopes (*live*) _____ in Turkey.

17. We discussed (*go*) _____ out for dinner, but we decided (*eat*) _____ at home instead.

A. ***Directions:*** Make sentences beginning with *It*. Use the given words in your sentence. Use the present tense.

Example: be enjoyable \ walk \ barefoot on the sand at the beach

       It is enjoyable to walk barefoot on the sand at the beach.

1. take a long time \ learn \ a foreign language well

   _____

2. should not be hard \ find \ a parking place \ downtown

   _____

3. might be boring \ listen \ to the politician's speech

   _____

4. cost a lot \ fly \ first class

   _____

5. be impolite \ talk \ when someone else is talking

   _____

B. ***Directions:*** Rewrite the sentences you wrote for Part A. Use gerund phrases for your subjects.

Example: *Walking barefoot on the sand at the beach is enjoyable.*

1. _____

2. _____

3. _____

4. _____

5. _____

Directions: Check (✓) the correct sentence in each pair.

Example: ✓ a. Wendy enjoys listening to Irish music.

_____ b. Wendy enjoys to listen to Irish music.

1. _____ a. My doctor told me exercising more often.

   _____ b. My doctor told me to exercise more often.

2. _____ a. I dislike eating cold eggs.

   _____ b. I dislike to eat cold eggs.

3. _____ a. Benjamin hopes to find a good job this summer.

   _____ b. Benjamin hopes finding a good job this summer.

4. _____ a. My daughter promised being home on time, but she was late.

   _____ b. My daughter promised to be home on time, but she was late.

5. _____ a. Parents want their children being happy.

   _____ b. Parents want their children to be happy.

6. _____ a. Alan is considering going to Colombia next year.

   _____ b. Alan is considering to go to Colombia next year.

7. _____ a. Many families can't afford paying the high cost of college tuition.

   _____ b. Many families can't afford to pay the high cost of college tuition.

8. _____ a. Will's friends offered to help him find a new apartment.

   _____ b. Will's friends offered helping him find a new apartment.

9. _____ a. Our teacher postponed giving us the quiz until the day after tomorrow.

   _____ b. Our teacher postponed to give us the quiz until the day after tomorrow.

10. _____ a. The bank robber threatened taking hostages if the clerk didn't hand over the money.

   _____ b. The bank robber threatened to take hostages if the clerk didn't hand over the money.

11. _____ a. Anna mentioned coming to town for a visit, but I don't know if she was serious.

   _____ b. Anna mentioned to come to town for a visit, but I don't know if she was serious.

12. _____ a. I couldn't convince my brother lending me his laptop computer.

   _____ b. I couldn't convince my brother to lend me his laptop computer.

13. _____ a. People who invest in the stock market risk losing all of their money.

   _____ b. People who invest in the stock market risk to lose all of their money.

14. _____ a. Jake's parents demanded knowing where he was going.

   _____ b. Jake's parents demanded to know where he was going.

15. _____ a. The phone quit working after the power went out.

   _____ b. The phone quit to work after the power went out.

CHAPTER 14 – TEST 1

Part A *Directions:* Check (✓) the correct sentence in each pair.

1. ___ a. The test monitor instructed the students beginning.
   ___ b. The test monitor instructed the students to begin.

2. ___ a. We always appreciate getting help with our income taxes.
   ___ b. We always appreciate to get help with our income taxes.

3. ___ a. My mom reminded me putting my dirty clothes in the laundry.
   ___ b. My mom reminded me to put my dirty clothes in the laundry.

4. ___ a. Hank claimed to know the way to Mike's house, but we got lost.
   ___ b. Hank claimed knowing the way to Mike's house, but we got lost.

5. ___ a. Athletes can't help feeling nervous before an important sports event.
   ___ b. Athletes can't help to feel nervous before an important sports event.

Part B *Directions:* Complete each sentence with an appropriate preposition.

1. Maya is worried _____ passing the test, but I'm not.

2. My little sister was so annoying! She insisted _____ going to a movie with us.

3. Eric has a good excuse _____ not coming to class. He was in a car accident on the way to school.

4. When Jan was twenty years old, she dreamt _____ living and working in Sweden.

5. The children are looking forward _____ the party on Saturday.

Part C *Directions:* Complete the sentences using a gerund or infinitive form of the verbs in parentheses. Add an appropriate preposition if needed.

1. Cynthia apologized to her sister (*borrow*) _____ her jewelry without asking permission. She promised that she would never do it again.

2. Last night Kaori was lying in bed (*study*) _____ before she went to sleep. She hopes (*get*) _____ a good grade on the next quiz.

3. Hamid remembers (*bring*) _____ his briefcase home from work, but now he can't find it.

4. (*Give*) _____ an apple to the teacher is a traditional way for a student to thank a teacher in the United States.

5. Consuela doesn't enjoy (*wait*) _____ in line at the supermarket. That's why she tries (*go*) _____ to the supermarket early in the afternoon or very late at night.

6. Nadia's allergies were very bad last spring, and she felt terrible. She couldn't help (*sneeze*) _____ all the time.

7. Jeff is interested (*learn*) _____ Russian because he is going to Moscow next summer.

8. Janice never goes (*ski*) _____ because she can't stand the cold weather.

9. When Peter decided (*buy*) _____ a new car for the family, his wife suggested (*do*) _____ some research on the internet.

10. Before a patient starts (*take*) _____ a new medicine, the doctor must prescribe the correct dosage.

11. (*Take*) _____ care of two small children is a round-the-clock job for a parent.

12. Susan took a vacation to Hawaii. She spent six days (*relax*) _____ on a white sand beach with a good book and a cold drink.

Part D *Directions:* Circle the correct completions. Pay careful attention to the meaning.

1. Oh, no! I forgot (*to send, sending*) my sister a birthday card, and her birthday is today.

2. Bruno was trying (*to snowboard, snowboarding*) for the first time when he broke his leg.

3. A: Did you remember (*to lock, locking*) the door when you left?

   B: Yes, I did. I remember (*to put, putting*) my key in the lock and (*to hear, hearing*) it click.

4. Patricia regretted (*to tell, telling*) Jane about her problems because Jane told everyone else.

5. We stopped (*to buy, buying*) a newspaper on our way to work this morning.

Part E *Directions:* Make sentences using the given words. Use the present tense. Begin the sentence with ***It*** if necessary. Use a gerund or an infinitive where necessary.

1. my dad \ always \ take his time \ choose \ a new car

   _____

2. be uncomfortable \ live \ in a hot climate \ without air-conditioning

   _____

3. my sisters and I \ go \ swim \ at the neighborhood pool \ twice a month

   _____

4. Dennis \ sometimes \ have difficulty \ express \ his opinion

   _____

5. have \ a visa \ be \ necessary \ for traveling overseas

   _____

CHAPTER 14 – TEST 2

Part A *Directions:* Check (✓) the correct sentence in each pair.

1. ___ a. There seems being a problem with his student visa.
   ___ b. There seems to be a problem with his student visa.

2. ___ a. The travel agent recommended getting our passports as soon as possible.
   ___ b. The travel agent recommended to get our passports as soon as possible.

3. ___ a. Hannah managed finishing her homework before her favorite TV program started.
   ___ b. Hannah managed to finish her homework before her favorite TV program started.

4. ___ a. Video games allow players to pretend fighting space aliens or other bad guys.
   ___ b. Video games allow players to pretend to fight space aliens or other bad guys.

5. ___ a. My supervisor doesn't tolerate employees being late for work.
   ___ b. My supervisor doesn't tolerate employees to be late for work.

Part B *Directions:* Complete each sentence with an appropriate preposition.

1. Most mothers are very devoted _____ their children.

2. After practicing hard for weeks, Adam succeeded _____ winning the 500-meter race.

3. The jury found the accountant guilty _____ cheating his clients.

4. My dad always talks _____ visiting Australia. I hope he can go there some day.

5. The traffic cones prevented us _____ driving down the street.

Part C *Directions:* Complete the sentences using a gerund or infinitive form of the verbs in parentheses. Add an appropriate preposition if needed.

1. We had a great time (*visit*) _____ the pyramids in Egypt.

2. We are considering (*buy*) _____ a new TV in June.

3. Peter said, "I fail (*see*) _____ any logic behind your argument."

4. Instead (*tell*) _____ the truth, Tom denied
   (*break*) _____ his brother's camera.

5. Mrs. Roberts taught all four of her daughters (*be*) _____
   independent.

6. Do you recommend (*eat*) _____ at the Indian restaurant on the
   corner?

7. When Ken tasted the delicious chocolate cake, he couldn't resist
   (*have*) _____ a second piece.

8. Johnny, please stop (*bother*) _____ your dad. He's trying
   (*take*) _____ a nap.

9. We thanked our neighbors (*take*) _____ care of our cat.

10. Karen prefers (*wear*) _____ her hair short and curly.

11. My teacher told us (*go*) _____ to the computer lab to get extra language practice.

12. Do you anticipate (*need*) _____ more help packing? Josh has offered (*come*) _____ by on the weekend if you need him.

Part D *Directions:* Circle the correct completions. Pay careful attention to the meaning.

1. It is fortunate that so many people have stopped (*to smoke, smoking*) for health reasons.

2. I regret (*to tell, telling*) you that you failed the test. I know you wanted to pass.

3. Helen doesn't remember (*to see, seeing*) *Romeo and Juliet* at the Shakespeare Festival, but I'm sure we did.

4. Kevin is trying (*to learn, learning*) Japanese, but he has trouble memorizing all the characters.

5. I have such a terrible memory. I sometimes do something, and then I forget (*to do, doing*) it.

6. Please remember (*to sign, signing*) the birthday card for James.

Part E *Directions:* Make sentences using the given words. Use the present tense. Begin the sentence with *it* if necessary. Use a gerund or an infinitive where necessary.

1. be terrible \ wake up \ with a headache

_____

2. live \ on their own \ be \ a good experience \ for young adults

_____

3. Jenny \ sometimes \ catch \ her children \ watch TV \ in the middle of the night

_____

4. be dangerous \ for children \ use fireworks \ without adult supervision

_____

5. the tourists \ stand \ on the corner \ try \ figure out \ where to go

_____

QUIZ 1 Infinitives of Purpose: *In Order To* (Chart 15-1)

A. Directions: Complete each sentence with *to* or *for* to express the purpose of the action.

Examples: Mike went to Chuck's Auto Supply ____to____ get some oil for his car.

Mike went to Chuck's Auto Supply ____for____ some motor oil.

1. Zachary has worked hard _____ become a successful physical therapist.

2. My parents are going to Atlanta next month _____ my sister's wedding.

3. Our teacher is extremely patient with us. She gives us many examples _____ help us understand.

4. The women drove to Vancouver _____ see an exhibit.

5. My dentist advised me to come in twice a year _____ teeth cleaning.

B. Directions: Add *in order* whenever possible. If nothing should be added, write Ø.

Examples: I wanted ____Ø____ to return my DVD to the store, but I forgot it at home.

Mary called me ____in order____ to invite me to her birthday party.

1. Jordan went to the aquarium _____ to see the new baby whale.

2. Wendy is planning _____ to spend next year traveling in South America.

3. Liz asked the taxi driver _____ to drop her off at her hotel on Tenth Avenue and Madison Street.

4. I am going to the doctor next week _____ to have my annual health checkup.

5. The chef brought the flaming dessert to the table _____ to impress his guests.

Directions: Complete the sentences with phrases from the list. More than one answer is possible. The first one is done for you.

> delighted to fortunate to relieved to
> disappointed to hesitant to surprised to
> ✓ eager to likely to unlikely to
> embarrassed to proud to

1. I am reading an exciting story. I'm _____*eager to*_____ finish the book so I can find out what happens.

2. My brother was _____ hear his girlfriend say "Yes!" when he asked her to marry him. It made him very happy.

3. Roy is _____ go to Europe next summer. He has been saving his money for a year and is planning his trip.

4. We were _____ hear that our boss refused to give us the day off on our birthday.

5. A: I know we have met before, but I am _____ admit that I can't remember your name.
   B: That's OK. I'm Julie.

6. Elizabeth's parents were _____ announce that she had been accepted to Georgetown University.

7. Jacob is very stubborn. He is _____ change his mind once he has made a decision.

8. When they arrived at school, the students were _____ find out that classes had been canceled.

9. I am very _____ have a good education. Not everyone is as lucky as I am.

10. My father is _____ let my sixteen-year-old brother drive. He is worried that my brother will have an accident.

11. Mona was _____ learn that her parents were not injured in the earthquake.

Directions: Read the first sentence. Put a check mark (✓) next to the sentence that is closest in meaning.

Example: My coffee is very hot.

   ✓ a. I can drink the coffee, but I should be careful.

   _____ b. I can't drink the coffee.

1. I'm too tired to watch a movie tonight.

   _____ a. I want to watch a movie.

   _____ b. I don't want to watch a movie.

2. It's very sunny today.

   _____ a. The sun doesn't bother me.

   _____ b. I don't like the sun.

3. This bag of groceries isn't too heavy for me.

   _____ a. I can carry it.

   _____ b. I can't carry it.

4. Melissa is too old to play with dolls.

   _____ a. Melissa plays with dolls.

   _____ b. Melissa doesn't play with dolls.

5. That problem was very difficult.

   _____ a. I solved the problem.

   _____ b. I couldn't solve the problem.

6. The coffee shop closes too early for us to go there after work.

   _____ a. We can go to the coffee shop after work.

   _____ b. We can't go to the coffee shop after work.

7. That isn't too much to pay for a leather jacket.

   _____ a. The price of the jacket is reasonable.

   _____ b. The price of the jacket is not reasonable.

8. Children are never too full to eat dessert.

   _____ a. Children always want dessert.

   _____ b. Children never want dessert.

9. I have gained five pounds. My jeans are very tight.

   _____ a. I can still wear the jeans.

   _____ b. I can't wear the jeans.

10. That car is very expensive, but it isn't too expensive.

    _____ a. I can buy that car.

    _____ b. I can't buy that car.

Directions: Choose the correct completions.

Example: A child under age 16 is ((*too young,*) *young enough*) to drive.

1. Jerry is (*too serious, serious enough*) to tell jokes. Whenever he tries to tell a joke, no one laughs.

2. The tomatoes in my garden are (*too ripe, ripe enough*) to pick. I'm going to use some for a salad.

3. This soup is (*too spicy, spicy enough*) for Bill to eat. He will enjoy it.

4. The sun is (*too bright, bright enough*) for me to see well. I need my sunglasses.

5. These shoes don't fit me, but they are (*too big, big enough*) for my brother to wear. I'll give them to him.

6. Edward isn't (*too strong, strong enough*) to move the piano by himself. He has to hire a professional mover.

7. The double chocolate cookies aren't (*too sweet, sweet enough*) for me to eat. I ate three of them.

8. This 70-degree weather is (*too warm, warm enough*) for Ruth. She doesn't like it much warmer than this.

QUIZ 5 Passive Infinitives and Gerunds (Charts 15-4 and 15-5)

Directions: Use the passive to complete the sentences with the appropriate form of the verbs in parentheses.

Examples: I didn't expect (*give*) _____ *to be given* _____ such a nice gift for my birthday.

Kelsey avoids (*invite*) _____ *being invited* _____ to parties. She hates them.

1. Jane intends (*marry*) _____ by the time she is 30.

2. Sarah was excited about (*interview*) _____ for the job.

3. The candidates enjoy (*ask*) _____ questions by the public.

4. My car needs (*repair*) _____ before we leave on our vacation.

5. The teacher warned the students (*prepare*) _____ for a difficult exam.

6. Stan appreciates (*drive*) _____ to work by his neighbor every day. They share the cost of gas.

7. When they put on their mothers' old dresses, the little girls pretended

   (*wear*) _____ beautiful evening gowns.

8. Our windows are so dirty. They really need (*wash*) _____.

9. My grandfather gives a lot of money to the poor. He wants (*remember*) _____ as a caring and generous man.

10. The summer camp counselor appreciated (*recognize*) _____ for her inspiring leadership.

QUIZ 6 Using Verbs of Perception (Chart 15-6)

Directions: Complete the sentences with an appropriate form of a verb from the list. If more than one form is appropriate, write both.

> carry   flash   ring
> discuss   go   rot
> ✓feed   park   tell

1. I watched an old lady ___*feeding / feed*___ the pigeons in Central Park.

2. When I heard the phone _____, I dropped my keys and ran to answer it.

3. Jason's little sister hurt her leg, so he carried her to the car and took her to the hospital. I was surprised when I saw Jason _____ her to the car.

4. It was exciting to hear the scientists at the conference _____ their newest discoveries.

5. We watched the strange man _____ his car and _____ into the drugstore.

6. I smelled something _____ in my refrigerator. It really stank!

7. We really enjoyed hearing Michael _____ about his Arctic adventure and seeing some amazing photographs from his trip.

8. Kate pulled over to the side of the street when she saw the ambulance's lights _____ behind her.

Directions: Choose the meaning that is closest in meaning to the verb in **bold**.

Example: The teacher **made** the students turn off their cell phones.

      (a.) gave no choice   b. requested   c. persuaded

1. Frank always **makes** his kids eat their vegetables.
    a. gave no choice   b. requested   c. persuaded

2. George **got** Mary to cut his hair.
    a. gave no choice   b. requested   c. persuaded

3. Mrs. Mikkelson always **has** her son take out the garbage.
    a. gives no choice   b. requests   c. persuades

4. The boys didn't want to clean up the backyard, so they **got** their little brother to do it by paying him $5.00.
    a. gave no choice   b. requested   c. persuaded

5. We were looking for someone to track our company's recycling practices, and we finally **had** the director of maintenance do it.
    a. gave no choice   b. requested   c. persuaded

6. When I was a teenager, my parents always **made** me finish my homework before I could call my friends.
    a. gave no choice   b. requested   c. persuaded

Directions: Choose the correct completions. More than one answer is possible.

Example: Sally got her sister _____ the dinner dishes.

    a. wash   (b.) to wash   c. washed

1. The movers helped Shane and Alicia _____ into their new home.
    a. move   b. to move   c. moved

2. Charlie wrote a letter to his lawyer to have his will _____.
    a. change   b. to change   c. changed

3. The baseball players got their coach _____ practice because it was raining.
    a. cancel   b. to cancel   c. canceled

4. Mrs. McGuiness lets her children _____ up past midnight on New Year's Eve.
    a. stay   b. to stay   c. stayed

5. Pat finally got his watch _____ after complaining about it for weeks.
    a. fix   b. to fix   c. fixed

6. The president of the company made the human resources manager _____ three people.
    a. fire   b. to fire   c. fired

7. I had my doctor _____ my blood pressure when I was in his office.
    a. check   b. to check   c. checked

8. I really like working four ten-hour days. It lets me _____ a three-day weekend every week!
  a. have   b. to have   c. had

9. Jane always helps her elderly parents _____ their bills.
  a. pay   b. to pay   c. paid

10. My brother had his car _____ to the mechanic's when it wouldn't start.
  a. take   b. to take   c. taken

QUIZ 9 Chapter Review

Directions: Correct the errors.

Example: Margaret went shopping ~~for getting~~ *to get* some new shoes.

1. I went to the gas station for to get some gas.

2. Alan has enough tall to reach the top shelf.

3. The kids were very excited to sit still.

4. Chris let his little brother borrowing his books.

5. Eddie was stunned hear that he hadn't passed his final exam in biology.

6. I am pleased introducing you to my parents, Carol and Bob Matthews.

7. It has been a long time since I've cleaned. My room really needs dusted.

8. Julia's best friend insists on be told all of her family news.

9. My cousin moved to Alaska for working in the tourist industry.

10. Toshiko got her brother-in-law pick her up at the airport.

11. Sharon is looking forward to be sent on a business trip to Hawaii.

12. Teresa saw her best friend to wave at her from across the street.

13. The advisor helped students made decisions about college.

14. My parents wanted in order to hear my reasons for not going to college, but I knew they didn't agree.

15. Reading Shakespeare takes very much concentration to read it on the subway. I prefer to read a magazine on my way to work.

CHAPTER 15 – TEST 1

Part A *Directions:* Add *in order* whenever possible to express purpose. If nothing should be added, write Ø.

1. The office staff decided _____ to have a retirement party for Norma.

2. Janice called the airport _____ to see whether her flight had been delayed.

3. Susan takes good care of her teeth _____ to prevent having to go to the dentist.

4. Please remember _____ to raise your hand if you have a question during the test.

5. Sometimes children lie to their parents _____ to avoid getting in trouble.

Part B *Directions:* Read the first sentence. Put a check mark (✓) next to the sentence that is closest in meaning.

1. Kathy is old enough to get her driver's license.

_____ a. Kathy can get her driver's license.

_____ b. Kathy can't get her driver's license.

2. The music is too loud.

_____ a. I like this music.

_____ b. I don't like this music.

3. The chocolate that Ari bought was very expensive.

_____ a. Ari spent a lot of money, but that's OK.

_____ b. Ari shouldn't have spent so much money.

4. Mitch is too young to babysit his little sisters.

_____ a. Mitch can babysit his little sisters.

_____ b. Mitch can't babysit his little sisters.

5. Jack isn't fast enough to play basketball well.

_____ a. Jack can play basketball well.

_____ b. Jack can't play basketball well.

Part C *Directions:* Use the passive to complete the sentences with an appropriate form of the verbs in parentheses.

1. Bill's car is really dirty. He hasn't washed it in three weeks. It needs

   (*wash*) _____ soon!

2. My co-worker really cares about (*see*) _____ by the "right"

   people at social events.

3. Ann didn't want (*ask*) _____ a question, so she didn't look at

   the teacher.

4. Mary was delighted (*introduce*) _____ to her sister's fiancé.

5. I don't enjoy (*laugh*) _____ at or made fun of.

Part D *Directions:* Complete the sentences with an appropriate form of a verb from the list. If more than one form is appropriate, write both.

> brush   burn   cry   fly   hide

1. The little boy noticed someone _____ in the bushes in front of the

   house, so he ran inside to tell his father.

2. Polly smelled something _____ and realized that she had forgotten

   that rice was cooking on the stove.

3. Ivan watched the other boys _____ their kites and wished that his kite

   were still in one piece.

4. Jake was eating dinner at his friend's house when he felt something

   _____ against his leg. He looked down and saw his friend's cat.

5. When I take my little daughter to the doctor, I have to wait outside because I hate to hear

   her _____ when the doctor gives her a shot.

Part E *Directions:* Circle the correct completions.

1. My parents let me (*stay, staying*) up late on weekends.

2. I'm not very strong. I always have my older brother (*move, to move*) my furniture for me.

3. I don't understand this assignment. Can you help me (*figure, figuring*) it out?

4. At the wedding, the bride even got my father (*dance, to dance*).

5. Because the jeans were too expensive, Carol's mother made her (*return, to return*) them.

Directions: Correct the errors.

1. Pete is thinking about to go to graduate school for getting a master's degree.

2. Our house needs to repair and paint before we can consider to sell it.

3. There isn't enough time to us for finishing all of the reports by Friday.

4. Tanya was sorry to being late, and she apologized for missed part of the presentation.

5. Chuck has been thinking about move out of the house and find a job.

CHAPTER 15 – TEST 2

Part A *Directions:* Add *in order* whenever possible to express purpose. If nothing should be added, write Ø.

1. Rick closed the door to his office _____ to have privacy during the phone call with his boss.

2. Cathy offered _____ to take care of my garden while I was out of town.

3. It is important _____ to take care of your health.

4. My teacher quizzed us often _____ to help us prepare for the advanced placement exam.

5. Children should be encouraged _____ to develop their individual interests.

Part B *Directions:* Read the first sentence. Put a check mark (✓) next to the sentence that is closest in meaning.

1. Bradley is too nervous to sit still because he is waiting for the test results.

_____ a. Bradley can sit calmly while he waits.

_____ b. Bradley can't sit calmly while he waits.

2. Our children aren't old enough to stay home alone.

_____ a. The parents can leave the children home alone.

_____ b. The parents can't leave the children home alone.

3. English grammar is very confusing for me.

_____ a. English grammar is confusing, but I can understand it.

_____ b. English grammar is confusing, and I can't understand it.

4. The sofa Diana wants to buy is too expensive.

_____ a. Diana will buy the sofa.

_____ b. Diana won't buy the sofa.

5. Pat is fluent enough to have a simple conversation in German.

_____ a. Pat speaks German.

_____ b. Pat doesn't speak German.

Part C *Directions:* Use the passive to complete the sentences with an appropriate form of the verbs in parentheses.

1. Instead of (*worry*) _____ about her grade on the test, Maria doesn't care about it.

2. I expected (*invite*) _____ to Tina's wedding and was disappointed when I didn't get an invitation.

3. The children were excited about (*allow*) _____ to spend the night at their friend's house.

4. These socks are so old. They have holes in both the toes and the heels. They need (*throw*) _____ away.

5. Just because he's the oldest, John expects (*treat*) _____ like a king.

Part D *Directions:* Complete the sentences with an appropriate form of a verb from the list. If more than one form is appropriate, write both.

> beep   blow   report   stand   take

1. Carlos looked at the elephant _____ in the middle of the street. He couldn't believe his eyes!

2. When I watched my baby _____ her first steps, I clapped and smiled.

3. We were listening to the news when we heard the announcer _____ that some valuable artwork had been stolen from the museum.

4. The teenagers were safe from the storm, but they could feel the wind _____ outside.

5. When Helen's food is ready, she hears the microwave oven _____ .

Part E *Directions:* Circle the correct completions.

1. If you get lost, a policeman can help you (*find, finding*) your way.

2. Do you think the teacher will let us (*use, to use*) our dictionaries during the test?

3. After three hours, Sheila finally got her computer (*to open, opening*) the document she was trying to access.

4. The coach had all of the players (*stretch, to stretch*) well before the game.

5. The bad weather might make the airline (*postpone, postponing*) our flight. We should call the airport.

Part F *Directions:* Correct the errors.

1. I heard the rain fell on the roof and realized that I needed bringing an umbrella with me.

2. My doctor made me to wait 45 minutes before he would see me.

3. Mrs. Won wouldn't let her son played football because she was worried about him gets hurt.

4. These shoes are tight enough for me. I can't wear them anymore.

5. The president had the company putting off send out its annual report.

CHAPTER 16   Coordinating Conjunctions

QUIZ 1   **Parallel Structure**   (Chart 16-1)

Directions: Choose the correct completions.

Example: George is a strong and (*health*, (*healthy*)) man.

1. Caitlin turned on her music and (*begins, began*) to dance.
2. My father is old but (*fit, fits*).
3. The kids were chasing each other around the field and (*tried, trying*) to catch one another.
4. Trust and (*forgives, forgiveness*) are necessary for a successful relationship.
5. He has difficulty understanding both (*spoken, speaking*) and written English.
6. My dog likes to jump up and (*catches, catch*) sticks in his mouth.
7. Talking on a cell phone and (*to send, sending*) text messages are inappropriate in class.
8. My teacher was shocked and (*disappointed, disappointing*) when she caught students cheating on the test.
9. Maria is an excellent musician. She plays the piano and the guitar, and (*singer, sings*) too.
10. The police officer stood in the center of the intersection and (*directed, directing*) traffic.

QUIZ 2   **Parallel Structure: Using Commas**   (Chart 16-2)

Directions: Add commas as necessary.

Example: Carrie Claire and Jordan are all graduating from high school this June.

     Carrie, Claire, and Jordan are all graduating from high school this June.

1. High school graduation is an exciting fun and rewarding time for most students and their families.
2. Students are tired of high school are ready for something new and are looking forward to college or work.
3. Parents feel proud satisfied and relieved that their children have reached this milestone in their lives.
4. There are many events leading up to graduation day. For example, most graduates get their picture taken send out graduation announcements and invite friends and family to celebrate with them.
5. On graduation day there is a ceremony that includes speeches awards and music.
6. Parents siblings and friends look on as students receive their diplomas.
7. High school graduation is a sort of "coming of age" into the adult world of opportunity independence and responsibility.

Directions: Combine the sentences into one concise sentence that contains parallel structure. Punctuate carefully.

Example: The food was tasty.
The food was cheap.
The food was plentiful.

_____*The food was tasty, cheap, and plentiful.*_____

1. Vienna, Austria, is famous for classical music.
   Vienna, Austria, is famous for opera.
   Vienna, Austria, is famous for the waltz.

   _____

   _____

2. The new magazine was colorful.
   The new magazine was glossy.
   The new magazine had lots of photographs.
   The new magazine had lots of advertising.

   _____

   _____

3. The fireman put out a fire.
   The fireman rescued a cat stuck in a tree.
   The fireman helped a man who had had a heart attack.

   _____

   _____

4. In Brazil, I saw white sand beaches.
   In Brazil, I saw beautiful young women.
   In Brazil, I saw beautiful young men.
   In Brazil, I saw crystal clear blue water.

   _____

   _____

5. When Jane got home from work, she took off her suit.
   She took off her high-heeled shoes.
   She put on an old pair of jeans.
   She put on an old pair of slippers.
   She put on a warm wool sweater.

   _____

   _____

6. For dinner, Stephan ate slices of roast beef.
   For dinner, Stephan ate rice with gravy.
   For dinner, Stephan ate string beans.

   _____

   _____

Directions: Complete the sentences with **is/are**.

Example: Not only my parents but also my grandparents ___are___ here for my birthday.

1. Both Liz and Margaret _____ teaching English at the university.

2. Neither talking nor looking around _____ tolerated in class during tests.

3. Not only the children but also their mother _____ looking forward to going on a picnic.

4. Either chips or cookies _____ an appropriate snack for the meeting.

5. Not only Cathy but also Jan _____ taking a day off tomorrow.

6. Both rats and mice _____ rodents with long thin tails.

7. Either English 100 or English 115 _____ required for graduation.

8. Not only governments but also individuals _____ responsible for taking care of the environment.

9. Julie knows that neither smoking nor eating sweets _____ good for her health, but she does both anyway.

10. The business leaders agree that either marketing their product on the internet or traveling overseas to explore new markets _____ the best strategy for increasing sales.

Directions: Combine each pair of sentences into one new sentence with parallel structure. Use the conjunctions given in parentheses.

Example: Coffee contains caffeine. Tea contains caffeine. (*both . . . and*)

<u>   Both coffee and tea contain caffeine.   </u>

1. Janice doesn't have any brothers or sisters. Erica doesn't have any brothers or sisters. (*neither . . . nor*)

   _____

2. We can have broccoli for dinner. We can have cauliflower for dinner. (*either . . . or*)

   _____

3. During her speech, Lina spoke loudly. During her speech, Lina spoke clearly. (*both . . . and*)

   _____

4. Greg is interested in studying medicine. His twin brother is interested in studying medicine. (*not only . . . but also*)

   _____

5. The New York Yankees is a great baseball team. The Boston Red Sox is a great baseball team. (*both . . . and*)

   _____

6. My husband and I will go to a movie tonight. My daughter and I will go to a movie tonight. (*either . . . or*)

   _____

7. My English teacher hadn't graded our essays. My English teacher hadn't returned our vocabulary quizzes. (*neither . . . nor*)

   _____

Directions: Punctuate the sentences by adding commas and periods. Do not add any words. Add capitalization as necessary.

Example: Sarah, Lucy, and Brian are making a cross-country road trip. They will come to visit us in two weeks.

1. My brother is an accountant he can help us with our income taxes.

2. An Australian swimmer was attacked by a shark but he scared the animal away by poking it in the eye.

3. Denny's computer crashed as he was working on his report so he took his computer to the repair shop unfortunately they were not able to save his data.

4. A woman in Michigan got a $1 parking ticket in 1976 she finally paid it in 2008 by sending a twenty-dollar bill to the local police station she also sent a note explaining the money but she told the police not to try to find her.

5. People have been playing soccer since ancient times the first soccer clubs were formed in England in the 1850s but official soccer rules were not written until 1863 many of those same rules still govern soccer today.

6. We enjoyed the movie the acting was excellent and the story was delightful it had both romance and mystery and it was exciting too.

Directions: Correct the errors.

French
Example: She speaks Italian, Spanish, and ~~France~~.

1. The students' presentation was thoughtful, intelligent, and interested.

2. Either John nor Linda will send you an email.

3. Linda has traveled by car, bus, ship, and took a plane.

4. Our English teacher speaks slowly and careful so we can understand what she says.

5. Teresa doesn't like neither spinach nor beets.

6. The young girl's father didn't approve of her painted fingernails she wore bright red nail polish.

7. Both the neighborhood committee and the city parks department works to keep Echo Lake Park clean.

8. The documentary gave interesting facts and surprising statistical on honeybees.

9. Neither cows nor horses eats meat. They are herbivores.

10. Not only vulcanologists but also geologists is interested in studying Hawaii's volcanoes.

CHAPTER 16 – TEST 1

Part A *Directions:* Circle the correct completions.

1. Both Anita and Sandra (*loves, love*) to play volleyball, but neither Betty nor Jackie (*likes, like*) sports.

2. Not only the athlete but also the spectators (*was, were*) angry about the referee's decision.

3. Either the meatballs or the chicken (*is, are*) what I will order for dinner.

4. Not only students but also their teacher (*appreciates, appreciate*) holidays.

Part B *Directions:* Combine the sentences into one concise sentence that contains parallel structure. Use the conjunctions ***and, or, but***, or ***so***.

1. Linda has traveled by car. Linda has traveled by bus. Linda has traveled by train. Linda has not traveled by ship. Linda has not traveled by plane. Linda has not traveled by balloon.

   _____

   _____

   _____

2. Thomas has read about computers. Thomas has read about the internet. Thomas has taken classes in computer programming. Thomas has taken classes in computer applications.

   _____

   _____

   _____

3. Next weekend, Shirley may visit her grandmother. She may visit her sister. She may do some shopping. She may take in a movie. She has to do the laundry. She has to clean the bathroom.

   _____

   _____

   _____

4. Last winter, Cincinnati experienced terrible storms. Cincinnati experienced terrible flooding. Cincinnati experienced unending rains. Cincinnati experienced devastating tornadoes. Cincinnati experienced devastating hail.

   _____

   _____

   _____

5. At her surprise birthday party, Gloria was surprised to see her high school friends. Gloria was surprised to see her aunt and uncle from New York City. Gloria was surprised to see her old college roommate. She was disappointed not to see her sister. She was disappointed not to see her niece.

   _____

   _____

   _____

Part C   *Directions:* Combine the sentences into one concise sentence that contains parallel structure. Use paired conjunctions (*both ... and; not only ... but also; either ... or;* or *neither ... nor*).

1. The severe rainstorm flooded basements and sewers. The severe rainstorm caused mudslides.

   _____

   _____

2. Cindy will babysit the kids this evening, or Mrs. Smith will babysit the kids this evening.

   _____

   _____

3. Arthur has never been to Disneyland. His cousins have never been to Disneyland.

   _____

   _____

4. During the holiday weekend, the parking lots at San Francisco International Airport were full. During the holiday weekend, the parking lots at San Jose Airport were full.

   _____

   _____

5. Bread should be stored in the freezer instead of the refrigerator. Flour should be stored in the freezer instead of the refrigerator.

   _____

   _____

Part D   *Directions:* Punctuate the sentences by adding commas and periods. Do not add or delete any words. Add capitalization as necessary.

1. Polly was looking for a new camera for her brother's birthday she wanted a large selection and good prices so she used the internet to do her shopping.

2. Both Silvia and her husband love the rock band Wind Tunnel but they refuse to pay $125 a ticket to attend a concert.

3. Myron has written short stories and poems for the school literary magazine and sports and feature articles for the school newspaper.

4. Acme Toy Company continues to produce dolls metal cars construction sets and action figures but it no longer makes bicycles or board games.

5. Flights 2058 and 2065 to Los Angeles have been delayed but Flight 2061 is departing on time I can get you a seat on Flight 2061.

CHAPTER 16 – TEST 2

Part A *Directions:* Circle the correct completions.

1. Both doctors and nurses (*saves, save*) people's lives every day.

2. Not only my brother but also my cousins (*lives, live*) in Orlando.

3. Neither James' new boss nor his co-workers (*has, have*) met James' wife.

4. Either emailing or phoning (*is, are*) a convenient way for most people to contact relatives who live out of town.

5. Not only the doctors but also the hospital's chief administrator (*wants, want*) to improve communication with patients.

Part B *Directions:* Combine the sentences into one concise sentence that contains parallel structure. Use the conjunctions **and, or, but**, or **so**.

1. Last night, Larry watched some TV. Larry surfed the internet. Larry listened to some music. Larry read the newspaper. Today, Larry has to do some serious work.

   _____

   _____

   _____

2. Mr. Kincaid owns real estate. Mr. Kincaid owns stocks. Mr. Kincaid owns bonds. Mr. Kincaid has to sell some stocks to pay his taxes. Mr. Kincaid has to sell some bonds to pay his taxes.

   _____

   _____

   _____

3. Craig has good computer skills and can type 70 words a minute. Jean has good computer skills and can type 70 words a minute. They both got jobs as executive assistants.

   _____

   _____

   _____

4. French is an Indo-European language. German is an Indo-European language. Chinese is not an Indo-European language. Korean is not an Indo-European language.

   _____

   _____

   _____

5. It was an extremely cold day. Mark put on a heavy sweater. Mark put on a warm jacket. Mark didn't wear a hat. Mark didn't wear a scarf.

   _____

   _____

   _____

Directions: Combine the sentences into one concise sentence that contains parallel structure. Use *both ... and; not only ... but also; either ... or;* or *neither ... nor.*

1. The earthquake knocked over several freeways. The earthquake broke gas and water lines.

   _____

   _____

2. Philip doesn't want to go to college. Philip doesn't want to find a job.

   _____

   _____

3. Oranges are a good source of vitamin C. Cabbage is a good source of vitamin C.

   _____

   _____

4. The contractor will try to repair the broken fence, or she will tear down the fence and replace it.

   _____

   _____

5. Mayoral candidate Jim Brown did not talk about the homeless problem. Mayoral candidate Alicia Taylor did not talk about the homeless problem.

   _____

   _____

Part D *Directions:* Punctuate the sentences by adding commas and periods. Do not add or delete any words. Add capitalization as necessary.

1. I have tried the pineapple diet I have tried the starch diet and the protein diet too but none of them worked.

2. The weather forecaster predicts heavy fog and light drizzle for the morning but clear skies and sunshine for the late afternoon.

3. Mary doesn't like to drink tea or decaffeinated coffee so we need to pick up some regular coffee for her.

4. Bicycles motorcycles and handicapped drivers' cars can be parked in Lot A but everyone else needs to park in Lots B or C.

5. Barbara has had many different jobs she has been a flight attendant a salesclerk a waitress and a receptionist but now she has her MBA and is the regional manager for a large multinational corporation.

QUIZ 1 Identifying Adverb Clauses of Time (Charts 17-1 and 17-2)

Directions: <u>Underline</u> the adverb clause in each sentence.

Example: <u>When Alexa came home from work</u>, she took off her shoes.

1. Bryan and Cathy went to Rome after they visited Florence.

2. As soon as my plane arrives in Jakarta, I will call you.

3. Just as I finished loading the software on my computer, the electricity went off.

4. Max was watching the news on TV while he was ironing his shirts.

5. By the time we see you next summer, you will have graduated from high school.

6. The police won't leave until the accident is cleared from the highway.

7. The first time Kevin tried to ride a motorcycle, he crashed into a fence.

8. I have been a *Star Wars* fan ever since I was a child.

9. Carol will return to her office once the meeting ends.

10. Since the 3M Company first made Post-it notes, they have been sold in eight sizes, 25 shapes, and 62 colors.

Directions: Circle the best completions.

Example: As soon as the experiment was completed, the scientists _____ their findings.

       a. analyze   b. will analyze   ⓒ analyzed   d. have analyzed

1. When James finishes weeding the garden today, he _____ the grass in the front yard.
       a. cut   b. cuts   c. has cut   d. will cut

2. Until my brother went to Brazil last year, he _____ outside of the United States.
       a. has never been   b. wasn't   c. had never been   d. won't be

3. Ever since Nina moved to Nebraska, she _____ a lot of problems with allergies.
       a. had   b. has had   c. is having   d. has

4. Podcasts on the internet allow people to listen to their favorite radio programs whenever they _____ to.
       a. want   b. wanted   c. are wanting   d. will want

5. By the time the police arrived at the bank, the robbers _____ with thousands of dollars in cash.
       a. escaped   b. had escaped   c. will have escaped   d. escapes

6. Someone's cell phone rang just as the musicians _____ to play.
       a. begin   b. are beginning   c. were beginning   d. will begin

7. After the magician finishes his show, he _____ the children some simple magic tricks.
       a. will teach   b. has taught   c. had taught   d. taught

8. The polite language of the attorney masked his frustration as he _____ the witness.
       a. questions   b. questioned   c. has questioned   d. will question

9. By the time Lisa graduates from high school, her oldest brother _____ his master's degree.
       a. is getting   b. gets   c. will have gotten   d. will had gotten

10. The last time our travel agent _____ us, the cost of airline tickets had gone up 25 percent.
       a. contacts   b. contacted   c. has contacted   d. had contacted

Directions: Combine each pair of sentences with the words in parentheses. Add commas where necessary.

Example: Jennifer checked her bank account online. She ordered a book from Books.com. (*before*)

 Before Jennifer ordered a book from Books.com, she checked her bank account online.

1. Sue comes home late. Her parents are upset. (*whenever*)

   _____

   _____

2. The chef heated up the barbecue. He grilled the steaks. (*before*)

   _____

   _____

3. I showed my passport. The customs officer let me pass into the terminal. (*after*)

   _____

   _____

4. Shelley goes jogging. She needs to drink a lot of water. (*every time*)

   _____

   _____

5. Mr. Arnold will turn off the lights. We will be able to see the screen better. (*as soon as*)

   _____

   _____

6. The crowd cheered. They saw the baseball fly over the stadium wall. (*when*)

   _____

   _____

7. I will finish my homework. It will be midnight. (*by the time*)

   _____

   _____

8. The pilot got a message from the control tower. Then the plane landed. (*just before*)

   _____

   _____

9. Karen was shutting down her computer. The computer made a strange noise. (*while*)

   _____

   _____

10. Brad and Martha got married in 1995. They play Scrabble once a week. (*since*)

   _____

   _____

Directions: Combine each pair of sentences with the words in parentheses. Add commas where necessary.

Example: Ellen took a nap when she got home from work. Ellen had had a very difficult day. (*because*)

Ellen took a nap when she got home from work because she had had a very difficult day.

1. John arrived at the airport just ten minutes before his flight's departure time. John nearly missed his plane. (*because*)

   _____

   _____

2. The price of gasoline has doubled in the last three years. The price of crude oil has risen. (*because*)

   _____

   _____

3. The rain has stopped. We can open the windows and get some fresh air. (*now that*)

   _____

   _____

4. We will have to contact Mr. Adams by mail. Mr. Adams has neither email nor a phone. (*since*)

   _____

   _____

5. Sue did not enjoy going to the movies. Sue had left her eyeglasses at home. (*because*)

   _____

   _____

6. Larry has to do a lot of traveling. Larry is the senior manager for the western division of his company. (*now that*)

   _____

   _____

7. We can stay up late and talk. We don't have to go to work tomorrow. (*since*)

   _____

   _____

8. I need to find a new place to get my hair cut. My barber has retired after 25 years. (*now that*)

_____

_____

9. Last week the two groups refused to sign the peace treaty. Today fighting between the two groups began again. (*because*)

_____

_____

10. Future funding for the space shuttle program is uncertain. The last three shuttle missions had problems. (*since*)

_____

_____

QUIZ 5 **Using *Even Though*** (Chart 17-4)

Directions: Complete the sentences with ***even though*** or ***because***.

Examples: Mark has a good job and makes a lot of money _____*even though*_____ he didn't graduate from college.

_____*Because*_____ Sue has to catch the bus at 4:59, she has to leave the meeting early.

1. Joshua is skinny _____ he eats lots of fattening junk food.

2. My husband yells at the computer _____ he gets frustrated with it.

3. _____ I have enjoyed many movies with that actor, I didn't enjoy this one.

4. Ann gives her children their own spending money _____ she wants them to learn to be responsible.

5. _____ the weather was so terrible, the soccer game was canceled.

6. Emma moved to New York _____ she was afraid of living in such a big city.

7. _____ John enjoys working with people, he still works part-time at Starbucks _____ he retired from his full-time job years ago.

8. _____ my car wouldn't start, I got to work on time _____ my neighbor gave me a ride.

Directions: Choose the best completions.

Example: While most children in the U.S. start school at age five, Charles _____.
  a. has a late birthday   c. went to school in Texas
  (b.) started school at age six   d. had a nice teacher

1. Scrabble is a word game, while Sudoku _____.
   a. looks like a crossword puzzle   c. uses paper and pencil
   b. is a number game   d. counts from one to nine

2. George drives an old Ford, while Bill drives _____.
   a. his boss crazy   c. a new Mercedes
   b. an old Ford too   d. too fast

3. While some older people have difficulty with email and text messaging, most young people _____.
   a. call their friends often   c. can't read their email
   b. do math   d. use them with ease

4. While my younger sister _____, my older sister doesn't have any children.
   a. has two daughters   c. takes her kids swimming on weekends
   b. loves children   d. is a college student

5. A gas-powered car uses only gasoline to run the engine, while a hybrid car runs on _____.
   a. four wheels   c. cheaper prices
   b. both gasoline and electric power   d. freeways

6. One candidate favors lower taxes and less spending, while the other candidate _____.
   a. is from the east coast   c. has won more votes
   b. is a female   d. plans to raise taxes

Directions: Match the first half of each sentence to the clause that best completes it. The first one is done for you as an example.

1. _*e*_ If Joe's boss doesn't give him a raise,
2. _____ Did you bring your camera? If not,
3. _____ Christine might be late for class
4. _____ If Daniel has to have knee surgery,
5. _____ Are you going to the movies tonight? If you are,
6. _____ You should study at the Art Institute
7. _____ If the bank doesn't correct the error in my account,
8. _____ If the students have time,
9. _____ Are you going to bring your camera? If so,
10. _____ My brother says he will never get married. If he does,
11. _____ If Jana passes her exam,

a. if she forgets to set her alarm clock.
b. she will be relieved.
c. Bob can take some pictures instead.
d. if you want to learn graphic design.
e̶. he will look for a new job.
f. I'm going to change banks.
g. please take some pictures of us.
h. he will miss at least a week of work.
i. they want to get some coffee before class starts.
j. my parents will be very happy.
k. I can give you a ride to the theater.

Directions: Use the given information to complete the sentences.

Examples: Maybe Andy likes his teacher, or maybe he doesn't. It doesn't matter. He has to pass the class.

Andy has to pass the class even if _____ *he doesn't like his teacher* _____.

Andy has to pass the class whether or not _____ *he likes his teacher* _____.

You probably won't need to get into the house, but maybe you will. If so, I'll give you a key.

I'll give you a house key in case _____ *you need to get into the house* _____.

1. Sometimes my four-year-old sister cries a lot. It doesn't matter. My sister is really sweet.

   My four-year-old sister is really sweet, even if _____

   _____.

2. There might be a traffic jam on the freeway. If there is, you can take Evergreen Way instead.

   In case _____,

   you can take Evergreen Way instead.

3. Sometimes the boys have a soccer game three times a week, and sometimes they don't. It doesn't matter. They never get bored.

   The boys never get bored playing soccer whether or not _____

   _____.

4. I might not see you tomorrow. If I don't, I'm going to send you an email to remind you about the meeting.

   I'm going to send you an email to remind you about the meeting in case _____

   _____.

5. Steve usually gets nine hours of sleep a night. It doesn't matter. He is always tired.

   Whether or not _____,

   he is always tired.

6. Maybe they will lower the price, and maybe they won't. I still can't afford a big screen TV.

   I can't afford a big screen TV even if _____.

Directions: Complete the sentences with **unless** or **only if**.

Examples: You won't pass the driving test _____*unless*_____ you practice parallel parking.

You will pass the driving test _____*only if*_____ you practice parallel parking.

1. I always do my homework _____ I am absent from class.

2. _____ you have a passport can you travel to foreign countries.

3. My parents will help me pay my cell phone bill _____ I promise to pay them back later.

4. The students aren't allowed to work in the computer lab _____ an instructor is with them.

5. _____ we hear from John soon, we'll assume he isn't coming.

6. Faisal can improve his English pronunciation _____ he speaks English often.

7. Our office assistant won't interrupt a managers' meeting _____ he has a good reason.

8. Pat thinks movies are worth watching _____ they have a lot of action.

Directions: Complete the sentences with your own words. Punctuate carefully.

Example: Now that my son has his driver's license, ___*he can drive to the market by himself.*___

1. If the doctor discovers that the cancer has returned _____

2. Unless the weather improves by tomorrow _____

3. Even if you aren't sure about the correct answer _____

4. Lisa can't drive us to the airport because _____

5. My apple tree didn't produce any apples this year even though _____

6. You have to stay until the end of the meeting whether or not _____

7. Now that school is out _____

8. In case you need to contact me _____

9. My father will lend me the money for a new car only if _____

10. Only if it is an emergency _____

Part A *Directions:* Combine each pair of sentences with the words in parentheses. Add commas where necessary.

1. Teresa read a lot of college catalogs. Teresa chose the college that she wants to attend. (*after*)

   _____

   _____

2. We were working on the new project. Our boss returned from his vacation on Monday. (*when*)

   _____

   _____

3. Joe will get up tomorrow at 6:00 A.M. Joe will do his exercises. (*as soon as*)

   _____

   _____

4. For her birthday, Martina is going to go out to dinner with her friends. Martina and her friends are going to go dancing at a nightclub. (*before*)

   _____

   _____

5. Kathy will move to Texas next week. Kathy's husband will return from his job in South America next month. (*by the time*)

   _____

   _____

Part B *Directions:* Complete the sentences with your own words. Punctuate carefully.

1. If it rains tomorrow _____

2. Are you going to the library? If so _____

3. My parents will be disappointed if _____

4. Do you have a flashlight? If you do _____

5. If _____ you can call me tomorrow.

Part C *Directions:* Match the first half of each sentence to the clause that best completes it. Write the letter on the line.

1. _____ The flight has been delayed because

2. _____ Even though the tuition is very low,

3. _____ John's flight has been delayed for three hours, while

4. _____ I finished reading the book although

5. _____ Kate decided to watch the movie since

a. the quality of the class offerings is good.

b. I think that it was poorly written.

c. there is heavy fog at the San Francisco airport.

d. it received a good review in the newspaper.

e. Mary's flight is going to leave on time.

Part D *Directions:* Complete the sentences with ***whether or not, even if,*** or ***in case***.

1. I'm going to the midnight movie _____ my parents don't approve.

2. John always drives his car to work _____ he can't easily find a parking place.

3. I always carry bottled water in my car _____ there's an emergency.

4. _____ you don't like her, Margaret is the new club president.

5. Joan hangs her coat near the door just _____ she has to leave in a hurry.

Part E *Directions:* Complete the sentences with ***unless*** or ***only if***.

1. _____ the meeting goes late, I will meet you at the restaurant at 6:30 P.M.

2. I will let you borrow my car _____ you promise that you will be extra careful.

3. _____ I have problems with my homework will I call you.

4. The project will be completed on time _____ there is a problem with the new design.

5. _____ your library books are returned on time, you will need to pay a fine.

Part F **Directions:** Combine each pair of sentences with the words in parentheses. Add commas where necessary.

1. The term is almost over. Students can look forward to vacation. (*now that*)

   _____

   _____

2. Shelley forgot her sister's birthday. Shelley felt terrible. (*because*)

   _____

   _____

3. The weather should improve by tomorrow. If it doesn't, we won't go camping. (*unless*)

   _____

   _____

4. I may win the lottery. I won't quit my job. (*even if*)

   _____

   _____

5. The workers refused to work on New Year's Eve. The company promised to pay them double their usual wage. (*even though*)

   _____

   _____

CHAPTER 17 – TEST 2

Part A *Directions:* Combine each pair of sentences with the words in parentheses. Add commas where necessary.

1. I am going to pick up my cousin at the airport. I am going to show him the Golden Gate Bridge. (*after*)

   _____

   _____

2. Maurice was eating lunch in a restaurant. Maurice dropped his napkin on the floor. (*when*)

   _____

   _____

3. Ann will get over her bad cold. Ann will return to work. (*as soon as*)

   _____

   _____

4. Mary rinses the food off the dishes. Mary puts the dishes in the dishwasher. (*before*)

   _____

   _____

5. Ali will graduate from high school in June. Ali's brother will get married in July. (*by the time*)

   _____

   _____

Part B *Directions:* Complete the sentences with your own words. Punctuate carefully.

1. If my neighbors don't turn down their music _____

2. Do you have a cell phone? If you do _____

3. If _____ your parents will be extremely proud.

4. Mr. Roddy will come to the sales meeting if _____

5. Is Julie driving to Seattle? If so _____

Part C *Directions:* Match the first half of each sentence to the clause that best completes it. Write the letter on the line.

1. _____ I think this book is quite interesting, while

2. _____ The flight has been delayed even though

3. _____ The weather this month has been terrible because

4. _____ While the weather this month has been rainy and cold,

5. _____ Since the tuition here is very low,

a. last month it was warm and sunny.

b. more people can take advantage of the class offerings.

c. my brother refused to read it.

d. a wet weather system has moved down from Alaska.

e. there doesn't seem to be any problem with the weather.

Part D *Directions:* Complete the sentences with *whether or not, even if,* or *in case.*

1. Chinese is a fascinating language. _____ I never go to China, I love studying Chinese.

2. _____ you need to call me, here's my number.

3. Susan will leave work at 4:00 P.M. _____ she hasn't finished the product inventory.

4. We will have a picnic in the park _____ it rains.

5. _____ Hiromi gets a low score on the next quiz, she will pass the class.

Part E *Directions:* Complete the sentences with *unless* or *only if.*

1. Christopher likes almost all kinds of ice cream. He dislikes ice cream _____ it contains walnuts.

2. _____ the store accepts credit cards, I will need to borrow some money from you.

3. I will have to retype the entire report _____ I can find the original file on my computer.

4. _____ your shoes are clean can you come into the house.

5. I forgot my key, but my sister can let us into the house _____ she is out with her friends.

Part F *Directions:* Combine each pair of sentences with the words in parentheses. Add commas where necessary.

1. The teacher will re-calculate the test grades. The teacher found an error in the answer key. (*since*)

   _____

   _____

2. The test was very easy. Patricia worked on the test for more than an hour to make sure that she didn't make any mistakes. (*even though*) _____

   _____

3. Maria is going to marry Harry. Maria doesn't really love Harry. (*even if*) _____

   _____

4. Sam needs to improve his grades in math and chemistry. If he doesn't, he won't get accepted to medical school. (*unless*) _____

   _____

5. Some people enjoy cycling for exercise. Other people enjoy walking briskly for exercise. (*while*)

   _____

   _____

CHAPTER 18

Reduction of Adverb Clauses to Modifying Adverbial Phrases

Reducing Time Clauses (Charts 18-1 and 18-2)

Directions: Check (✓) the sentences that are grammatically correct.

Examples: _____ Before playing her piano solo, the piano had to be moved to the center of the stage.

          ✓ Before playing her piano solo, Carolyn bowed to the audience.

1. _____ While playing video or computer games, Mike never hears the phone ring.
2. _____ The photographer decided to sue the newspaper after printing lies about him.
3. _____ Before calling the police, Jason's parents tried to reach him on his cell phone.
4. _____ After waiting for the bus in the rain for 30 minutes, it finally arrived.
5. _____ Since embarrassing me in public, I haven't spoken to my ex-boyfriend.
6. _____ After arriving at the scene of the accident, the reporters began asking questions.
7. _____ Beverly learned the truth about Tony's unusual family before agreeing to marry him.
8. _____ While visiting the Statue of Liberty, the wind was blowing hard.
9. _____ Since going on vacation two weeks ago, I haven't checked my email.
10. _____ Before ordering dinner at the restaurant, the waiter asked Maggie if she wanted something to drink.

Reducing Time Clauses (Charts 18-1 and 18-2)

Directions: Change the adverb clauses to modifying adverbial phrases if possible. Write *no change* if it's not possible to reduce the adverb clause.

Examples: While Nathan was chopping wood yesterday, he broke his axe.

      While chopping wood yesterday, Nathan broke his axe.

While Nathan was chopping wood yesterday, his mom called him for supper.

      no change

1. Since he moved to California a year ago, Harry has been to Disneyland five times.

_____

_____

2. Before Calum left Milwaukee for Toronto, he filled up the gas tank.

_____

_____

3. While I was driving to Boston from New York, my parents were flying to Boston from Seattle.

_____

_____

4. Usually after Katherine works an eight-hour shift at the busy restaurant, she is exhausted.

_____

_____

5. While Mary was living in Los Angeles, she often ran into famous people.

_____

_____

6. George has quit his job and started traveling around the world since he won $1,000,000 on a TV game show.

_____

_____

7. Before Derek picked up his sister at the airport, she called to let him know that she had arrived.

_____

_____

8. Mark used to watch movies on his computer while he was waiting for the bus.

_____

_____

9. Jason will do his laundry after he finishes his chemistry homework.

_____

_____

10. Before Julie and Jay go to a new restaurant, they always read reviews and look at a sample menu online.

_____

_____

A. Directions: Read each sentence. What is the meaning of the adverbial phrase? Write *because* or *while* to show the meaning.

Example: Flying in economy class, Paul finds it difficult to get comfortable because of his long legs. ___*while*___

1. Having received Alan's marriage proposal, Sue told all her friends that she was getting married. _____

2. Standing in a long line at the post office, Betty read a book to pass the time. _____

3. Working on his quiz, Ken found that his pen had run out of ink. He had to borrow one from a classmate. _____

4. Being over six feet tall, Sam is always asked to try out for the basketball team. _____

5. Knowing the basics of plumbing and electrical wiring, Carla saves a lot of money by doing her own home repairs. _____

B. Directions: Combine each pair of sentences. Change the first sentence to a modifying phrase if possible.

Example: Henry was studying at the library. He turned off his cell phone.
_____*While studying at the library, Henry turned off his cell phone.*_____

1. Phoebe is a talented singer. She often sings in local coffee houses on weekends.

   _____

   _____

2. Christine was ice-skating with her son. She fell and broke her ankle.

   _____

   _____

3. Andy was unable to finish writing his report at the office. He took some paperwork home with him.

   _____

   _____

4. Fighting fires is a very demanding job. Firefighters have to be in excellent physical condition.

   _____

   _____

5. The college administrators were attending a seminar on Friday. They discussed goals for the coming year.

   _____

   _____

Directions: Combine these sentences, using *upon + -ing*.

Example: Jeff received the good news about his new job. Jeff immediately called his family.
   Upon receiving the good news about his new job, Jeff immediately called his family.

1. The teachers heard that the meeting was canceled. They were very happy.

   _____

   _____

2. Maya finished her final exam. She breathed a sigh of relief.

   _____

   _____

3. The actor received an award for her performance. She gave a brief acceptance speech.

   _____

   _____

4. Tom found a gold coin in the sand at the beach. He couldn't believe his good luck.

   _____

   _____

5. Margaret Peters was elected mayor of the city. She set up a committee to study the public schools.

   _____

   _____

6. Tina had her sixth baby. She said, "I think this will be my last one."

   _____

   _____

7. The plumber was fired from his job. He filed a complaint with his workers' union.

   _____

   _____

8. Mrs. Alexander returned from a trip to Ecuador. She started a small business that sold Ecuadorean handicrafts.

   _____

   _____

Directions: Change the adverb clauses into modifying adverbial phrases.

Example: After James lost his wallet, he was much more careful with his things.

<u>After losing his wallet, James was much more careful with his things.</u>

1. While Joe was lying in bed feeling depressed, he wondered what he should do about his problems.

   _____

   _____

2. When Jane arrives in London, the first thing she will do is have tea at the Ritz Hotel.

   _____

   _____

3. Because Billy had no money to buy a present for his mother, he made her a birthday card.

   _____

   _____

4. After the research scientists test the drug on mice, they will test the drug on monkeys.

   _____

   _____

5. Since Alex took a course in public speaking, he has developed more self-confidence.

   _____

   _____

6. While Susan was working in her garden, she disturbed a wasp's nest and was stung several times.

   _____

   _____

7. Because Carol was confused about the directions to the party, she had to stop at a gas station to ask for help.

   _____

   _____

8. Before Brian left for India, he had to get several shots to protect him from tropical diseases.

   _____

   _____

9. While Omar was talking with his accountant, he realized that starting his own business would be quite complicated.

_____

_____

10. When Louis tasted Mrs. Wilson's blueberry pie, he said that it was the most delicious pie he had ever eaten.

_____

_____

Part A *Directions:* Change the adverb clauses to modifying adverbial phrases if possible. If not possible, write *no change*.

1. While John was cleaning out his garage, he found his old high school yearbooks.

   _____

   _____

2. After John cleaned out the garage, Mary reorganized the shelves and cabinets.

   _____

   _____

3. Before Mary threw anything away, she consulted with John to make sure it was OK.

   _____

   _____

4. Since they moved into their house in 1992, Mary and John have acquired a lot of furniture.

   _____

   _____

5. After John and Mary finished their work in the garage, they drank some cold sodas.

   _____

   _____

Part B *Directions:* Combine each pair of sentences. Change the first sentence to a modifying phrase if possible.

1. I didn't want to interrupt your meeting. I left a message with your secretary.

   _____

   _____

2. Mr. Santos became a citizen. Afterward, the first thing he did was register to vote.

   _____

   _____

3. George was standing on a ladder to change a light bulb. Suddenly, his dog ran by and knocked the ladder over.

   _____

   _____

4. First the doctor explained the medical procedure. Then the doctor asked the patient if he had any questions.

_____

_____

5. Mrs. Nguyen had no husband and three children. She had to work ten hours a day to keep them fed and clothed.

_____

_____

Part C   *Directions:*   Check (✓) the sentences that are grammatically correct.

Examples: _____ Before playing her piano solo, the piano had to be moved to the center of the stage.

    ✓ Before playing her piano solo, Carolyn bowed to the audience.

1. _____ Upon hearing about the earthquake in Japan, everyone turned on the international news channel.

2. _____ Needing money to pay the rent, Scott asked his brother for a loan.

3. _____ Before making coffee in the morning, the beans must be ground.

4. _____ Not trusting her children at home alone, Mrs. Jones hired a babysitter to stay with them.

5. _____ After having sung the baby a lullaby, she finally fell asleep in my arms.

6. _____ Jesse has been working hard since starting his new job last month.

Part A *Directions:* Change the adverb clauses to modifying adverbial phrases if possible. If not possible, write *no change*.

1. Since Joe had a car accident last summer, he had to ride his bike to work.

   _____

   _____

2. While Joe was riding to work every day, he was dreaming about buying a new car.

   _____

   _____

3. Before Joe bought a new car, his sister helped him do some research on the internet.

   _____

   _____

4. While Joe's sister was searching for information, she found two cars that she thought would interest him.

   _____

   _____

5. After Joe read all the articles that his sister had found for him, he chose which car he wanted.

   _____

   _____

Part B *Directions:* Combine each pair of sentences. Change the first sentence to a modifying phrase if possible.

1. My brother was playing basketball with his friends. He fell and sprained his ankle.

   _____

   _____

2. Sam read a book about sharks. Since then, he has been afraid to swim in the ocean.

   _____

   _____

3. First Paul finished his homework assignment. Then he was free to watch TV for the rest of the evening.

   _____

   _____

4. Luisa didn't receive a birthday package that her brother sent. She contacted the post office about tracking the package.

_____

_____

5. George graduated from the university with a degree in French history. He has been looking for a job in education.

_____

_____

Part C *Directions:* Check (✓) the sentences that are grammatically correct.

Examples: _____ Before playing her piano solo, the piano had to be moved to the center of the stage.

_✓_ Before playing her piano solo, Carolyn bowed to the audience.

1. _____ Unable to eat the large hamburger, it got cold on my plate.

2. _____ Being interested in psychology, my sister subscribes to three psychology magazines.

3. _____ After being given the prestigious award, the novelist signed copies of his newest book.

4. _____ Listening to the governor's speech, she impressed us with her energy and intelligence.

5. _____ Upon receiving the flag from her husband's coffin, the young soldier's wife began to sob.

6. _____ After giving the interesting lecture, the students thanked the visiting professor.

CHAPTER 19

Connectives That Express Cause and Effect, Contrast, and Condition

Because vs. Because Of (Chart 19-1)

Directions: Complete the sentences with either *because* or *because of*.

Examples: Sam is excited _____*because*_____ he has been accepted to Colorado State University.

Marcia decided not to send the package airmail _____*because of*_____ the high cost of postage.

1. _____ its favorable climate, southeast Washington is a rich agricultural area.

2. It takes Peter two hours to get home from work _____ he lives on Staten Island.

3. Chuck dislikes most Mexican food _____ it's too spicy and upsets his stomach.

4. _____ our offices were on the fourth floor of the building, we got a lot of exercise going up and down the stairs.

5. I can go online almost anywhere _____ the wireless capabilities of my new laptop.

6. _____ my mother's terrible snoring, my father usually sleeps on the couch.

7. Mr. Anderson worries about his elderly neighbor _____ she lives alone.

8. _____ the lack of parking on campus, I have to arrive at the college at least a half hour before my class starts to find a place to park.

9. Josh is curious about Olivia's family _____ she talks about them all the time.

10. Some animals have become extinct _____ changes in the environment.

Directions: Using the ideas given in parentheses, complete the sentences.

Example: (*The wind was blowing hard.*) Our plane couldn't take off due to <u>the strong wind</u>.

1. (*The weather was bad.*) The Wilsons had to postpone the picnic because of _____
_____ .

2. (*Sarah had a fever.*) Due to _____ ,
Sarah stayed home from school yesterday.

3. (*Marie has car problems.*) Marie had to take the bus to work today due to _____
_____ .

4. (*My mother is very ill.*) Because of _____ ,
I have to fly home tonight.

5. (*The snow was deep.*) Due to _____ ,
many roads were closed.

6. (*Carl is lazy.*) I am not very patient with Carl due to the fact that _____ .

7. (*Mark has a toothache.*) Mark is going to the dentist tomorrow because of _____
_____ .

8. (*Caffeine bothers Shelley.*) Shelley has stopped drinking coffee due to _____
_____ .

9. (*I have an 8:00 A.M. appointment tomorrow.*) Due to the fact that _____
_____ , I am going to bed early tonight.

10. (*Scientists have an increased understanding of human genetics.*) Because of _____
_____ ,
new treatments for a variety of diseases have been developed.

Directions: Punctuate the sentences. Add capital letters if necessary.

Example: Jerry wants to go to medical school so he is studying hard for entrance exams.

> <u>*Jerry wants to go to medical school, so he is studying hard for entrance exams.*</u>

1. My coffee got cold so I reheated it in the microwave.

2. Fish was on sale at the market therefore Pat bought three fillets to have for dinner.

3. Andrea was upset that her favorite team was losing the match so she turned off the TV.

4. The regular radio announcer had a sore throat consequently another announcer was on
the program.

Connectives That Express Cause and Effect, Contrast, and Condition **219**

5. Electricity, water and gas are getting more expensive people therefore are trying to conserve energy.

6. The attorneys had questioned all the witnesses so the judge called a recess in the trial.

7. Shareholders voted against the merger of the two companies consequently the merger was canceled.

8. Khanh speaks English every day his pronunciation is improving therefore.

9. The supervisor gave her employees a lot of freedom in doing their work consequently they liked working for her.

10. My doctor didn't have the right equipment for the medical test I needed he therefore sent me to a specialist.

QUIZ 4   *Because, Because Of, Due To, Therefore, Consequently, and So*   (Charts 19-1 → 19-3)

Directions: Combine the ideas by using the words in parentheses.

Example: The spring weather was too cold. My tomato plants didn't grow. (*because of*)

     Because of the cold spring weather, my tomato plants didn't grow.   OR
     My tomato plants didn't grow because of the cold spring weather.

1. The milk was left out on the table overnight. It turned sour. (*so*)

_____

_____

2. My husband doesn't like lima beans. We never eat them. (*because*)

_____

_____

3. The economy is weak. Many citizens are unhappy with the government. (*due to*)

_____

_____

4. A new book by Maggie's favorite author was just published. Maggie bought it immediately. (*consequently*)

_____

_____

5. The manager has a cold. The meeting is canceled. (*because of*)

_____

_____

6. There is a lot of damage from the windstorm. Many people have joined in the cleanup. (*therefore*)

_____

_____

7. Hannah loves sweets. She has gained back all the weight she lost. (*consequently*)

_____

_____

8. Jason dropped his cell phone in the swimming pool. His cell phone stopped working. (*therefore*)

_____

_____

9. It was very late. We decided not to go out for coffee after the play. (*due to*)

_____

_____

QUIZ 5 **Cause and Effect: *Such . . . That* and *So . . . That*** (Chart 19-4)

Directions: Complete the sentences with a word or expression from the list. Use each word/expression one time only. The first one is done for you.

> a big dog   hard   many   a silly rumor
> fast   ✓hungry   much   an ugly dress
> forgetful   little   painful

1. Adam was so _____*hungry*_____ that he ate four pieces of pizza.

2. Carlos' sprained ankle was so _____ that he couldn't walk on it.

3. Harry has so _____ money that he can't buy groceries until he gets paid.

4. It was such _____ that I laughed when I heard it.

5. James ate so _____ cake that his stomach hurt.

6. Mr. Schafer is so _____ that he often leaves his glasses at home.

7. The salesclerk brought out such _____ that I didn't even want to try it on.

8. My neighbor has such _____ that small children are afraid when they first see it.

9. My English teacher speaks so _____ that the students have trouble understanding her.

10. There were so _____ people that I couldn't see my parents in the airport.

11. Christopher laughed so _____ that he got tears in his eyes.

Directions: Combine the sentences by using *such . . . that* or *so . . . that*.

Examples: David was very tired. He fell asleep immediately after he went to bed.

_____*David was so tired that he fell asleep immediately after he went to bed.*_____

We had a delicious meal. We will go to that restaurant again.

_____*We had such a delicious meal that we will go to that restaurant again.*_____

1. Mike's motorcycle is loud. The neighbors have complained about the noise.

   _____

2. It was a heavy couch. It took three people to move it.

   _____

3. The weather in June was cold. We had to wear our winter sweaters.

   _____

4. The store has dirty windows. We can hardly see inside.

   _____

5. The Sunday paper has great comics. Nick reads them every week.

   _____

6. Patrick ate too much chocolate ice cream. He got a stomachache.

   _____

7. My essay had too many errors. I had to spend over an hour correcting it.

   _____

8. The weather is sunny and beautiful. Janet doesn't feel like going to class.

   _____

9. There were few dishes in the sink. It only took me a few minutes to wash them.

   _____

10. Nurses are in high demand in hospitals. It's easy to find a good job.

    _____

A. *Directions:* Combine the ideas by using *so that*.

Example: Max bought a bicycle. He wanted to be able to have cheap transportation.

_____Max bought a bicycle so that he would have cheap transportation._____

1. I have a part-time job. I want to be able to afford to go to college.

   _____

2. Jim will take the bus to the airport. He wants to make sure he doesn't have to pay for parking.

   _____

3. The mechanics at Sam's Garage do careful work. They want to make sure their customers come again.

   _____

4. Frank and Joan took a parenting class. They wanted to learn more about children.

   _____

5. The music director stood on a podium. He wanted to be able to see all of the musicians.

   _____

B. *Directions:* Add ***that*** to the sentence if ***so*** means *in order that*. If ***so*** means *therefore,* add a comma.

Examples: I set my alarm clock for 6:30 so I wouldn't oversleep.

  that
  I set my alarm clock for 6:30 so ∧ I wouldn't oversleep.

  James didn't know the person on the phone so he hung up.

  James didn't know the person on the phone**,** so he hung up.

1. Fahad doesn't enjoy video games so he rarely plays them.

2. Rob practices kung fu three times a week so he can stay in shape.

3. I need to get a high score on my grammar test so I will improve my grade in the class.

4. Meg is going to be gone on vacation for three months so a temporary worker will replace her.

5. Miki emails her parents in Japan almost every day so they won't worry about her while she's in the U.S.

Directions: Complete the sentences with **but**, **even though**, **nevertheless**, or **despite**. Pay close attention to the given punctuation and capitalization.

Examples: The children are very tired, ____*but*____ they don't want to go to bed.

The children don't want to go to bed ____*even though*____ they are very tired.

The children are very tired. ____*Nevertheless*____, they don't want to go to bed.

The children don't want to go to bed ____*despite*____ the fact that they are very tired.

1. The sun is shining, _____ it is still cold outside.

2. Ken studies English hard. _____, he has weak English conversation skills.

3. The chocolate cake tasted terrible _____ it looked delicious.

4. Mark had to work until he finished the report _____ he was tired and wanted to go home.

5. _____ the fact that Roberto had his car repaired last week, it is still not running smoothly.

6. The University of Washington offered Greg a great scholarship. _____, he decided to go to a different university.

7. _____ I am interested in the space program, I was bored by the astronaut's speech.

8. The vacation was more expensive than we had planned, _____ we decided to go anyway.

9. _____ his busy schedule, Ali still found time to coach his son's baseball team.

10. Millions of dollars have been spent on cancer research. _____, scientists have not found a cure for the disease.

Directions: Add commas, periods, and capital letters as necessary. Do not add, omit, or change any words.

Example: In spite of the terrible weather Mark went for a three-mile run.

      In spite of the terrible weather, Mark went for a three-mile run.

1. I wasn't really hungry but I ate lunch anyway.

2. Even though Emily skipped breakfast she still has a lot of energy.

3. Mr. Kwan is a rich man nevertheless he refuses to buy his daughter a new car.

4. In spite of the high cost of postage Omar sends a package overseas every week.

5. Rosanne really wanted to learn to drive yet she was too young to get a driver's license.

6. Helen always talks about losing weight she constantly snacks however.

7. Although Jamaal grew up in San Francisco he prefers living in Oakland.

8. Despite the fact that Anthony had already lost two cell phones his parents gave him another one.

9. Edward doesn't like to smoke nonetheless he sometimes smokes a cigar with his business partners.

10. After my house was robbed the police warned me not to go inside however I still wanted to see it for myself.

Directions: Read the information about car camping and backpacking. Using that information, write sentences with the given words to show direct contrast. Pay attention to punctuation and capitalization. Answers will vary.

PEOPLE WHO CAR CAMP . . .
    can take whatever they want with them.
    pack everything into their cars.
    usually camp in a campground they can drive to.
    often like meeting other campers.
    can enjoy fresh food prepared in camp.
    often take their pets along.

PEOPLE WHO BACKPACK . . .
    have to pack light.
    carry everything on their backs.
    have to hike into the camp area.
    often enjoy getting away from crowds.
    eat dried and canned foods in camp.
    rarely take their pets with them.

Example: (*while*)   *People who car camp can take whatever they want, while people who backpack have to pack light.*

1. (*but*) _____

_____

2. (*on the other hand*) _____

_____

3. (*while*) _____

_____

Connectives That Express Cause and Effect, Contrast, and Condition 225

4. (*however*) _____

_____

5. (*on the other hand*) _____

_____

QUIZ 11   Expressing Conditions: Using *Otherwise* and *Or (Else)*   (Chart 19-8)

A.   **Directions:** Make sentences with the same meaning by using **otherwise**.

Example: If we don't turn on the heat, we'll get cold.

          We should turn on the heat. Otherwise, we'll get cold.

1. If Maria doesn't study for her quiz, she won't get a good grade.

_____

2. If I don't find my passport, I won't be able to cross the border.

_____

3. Unless you have a reservation, you can't get a table for dinner.

_____

4. If Kathleen's flight from the Philippines doesn't arrive on time, she will miss her connecting flight to Boston.

_____

B.   **Directions:** Create sentences with the same meaning by using **or (else)**.

Example: If I don't eat more fresh vegetables, I will get sick.

          I had better eat more fresh vegetables, or else I will get sick.

1. If our teacher doesn't remember students' names, the whole class laughs.

_____

2. If Pat doesn't work hard, the repairs on the house won't get finished by winter.

_____

3. Mark can't afford a car unless he saves money every month.

_____

4. If Beth doesn't get a new car license, she'll get a ticket.

_____

Part A *Directions:* Combine ideas, using the words in parentheses.

1. The sweater Jane bought has a hole in it. She needs to return it to the store. (*so*)

   _____

   _____

2. The traffic on Highway 101 was jammed. We took Highway 280 instead. (*therefore*)

   _____

   _____

3. Ron was late for work for the third time. He was fired from his job. (*because*)

   _____

   _____

4. Bill injured his lower back. He can't lift heavy objects. (*due to*)

   _____

   _____

5. The Mars *Rover* successfully landed on Mars. Scientists had calculated everything carefully. (*consequently*)

   _____

   _____

Part B *Directions:* Complete each sentence with a word or expression from the list. Pay attention to punctuation and capitalization. Use each word/expression one time only. More than one answer is possible.

> but   even though   nevertheless
> despite   in spite of the fact that

1. Jack had planned to go to the theater, _____ he got sick and had to go to the hospital.

2. _____ I don't eat much meat at home, I enjoy going out for burgers occasionally.

3. I'm going out tonight _____ I'm exhausted.

4. Sue promised she could keep a secret. _____, she told everyone about my problems.

5. _____ being in a wheelchair, Jerry was a fantastic basketball player.

Part C   *Directions:*   Complete the sentences with *such* or *so*.

1. Mary was _____ late that she missed the first half hour of the movie.

2. James is _____ a liar that no one believes anything he says.

3. Many people in the world are _____ poor that they don't get enough to eat.

4. Tom always checks his dictionary _____ that he spells words correctly.

5. This is _____ a good book that I can't put it down!

Part D   *Directions:*   Complete each sentence with a word or expression from the list. Pay attention to punctuation and capitalization. Use each word/expression one time only. More than one answer is possible.

although	even though	such
because	nevertheless	while
because of	otherwise	
despite the fact	so	

1. I like to cook, but I hate cleaning up because I always make _____ a mess in the kitchen.

2. _____ my mother doesn't understand Italian, she loves listening to Italian opera, especially when the singer is Luciano Pavarotti.

3. The typhoon caused some damage to our house _____ that we boarded up the windows and doors.

4. Lina had to retire from her job as a medical technologist _____ problems with her hips.

5. _____ most students are motivated and care about their grades, there are others who are lazy and can't be bothered.

6. The archeologist's primary research took place in Nepal _____ he doesn't like being in the mountains.

7. The thunder during last night's storm was _____ loud that my children got really scared.

8. _____ Jordan is interested in marine biology, he got a part-time job at the Monterey Aquarium.

9. Tim's boss warned him that he might lose his job. _____, Tim was shocked when he got fired.

10. We had better get a new car soon. _____, we'll get stuck somewhere when this one breaks down.

Part E *Directions:* Combine ideas, using the words in parentheses.

1. Mary speaks Chinese and Japanese. Her sister Linda speaks Spanish and French. (*while*)

   _____

   _____

2. Botanists study plants and plant life. Zoologists study the animal kingdom.
   (*on the other hand*)

   _____

   _____

3. I really wanted to go to New York. I decided that the trip would be too expensive. (*but*)

   _____

   _____

4. My wife is always telling me we need to save money. She spends as much money as she
   wants. (*however*)

   _____

   _____

Part A *Directions:* Combine ideas, using the words in parentheses.

1. Sally doesn't like the crowds at the shopping center. She shops over the internet. (*because*)

   _____

   _____

2. The Minister of Finance raised the interest rates. He was afraid of inflation. (*therefore*)

   _____

   _____

3. The house is now quite run down. The previous owners never took care of it. (*consequently*)

   _____

   _____

4. There have been many construction delays. The subway line will not open on time. (*because of*)

   _____

   _____

5. Isaac majored in engineering. His father pressured him to do so. (*due to*)

   _____

   _____

Part B *Directions:* Complete each sentence with a word or expression from the list. Pay attention to punctuation and capitalization. Use each word/expression one time only. More than one answer is possible.

although	however	yet
despite the fact that	in spite of	

1. _____ it's raining, we're going out for a walk.

2. Elvira has a high-stress job, _____ she still likes it a lot.

3. My digital camera is only six months old. _____, it isn't working right.

4. I like spending time with Murray _____ his annoying voice.

5. Playing games on a computer is entertaining, _____ it's not as much fun as playing with another person.

Part C **Directions:** Complete the sentences with *such* or *so*.

1. I had _____ little time between classes that I never had time for lunch.

2. The economy is doing _____ well that there is very little unemployment.

3. It was _____ an important meeting that the entire staff attended.

4. Robert bought a new car _____ that he would get better gas mileage.

5. Tom has _____ poor keyboarding skills that it takes him a long time to type anything on the computer.

Part D **Directions:** Complete each sentence with a word or expression from the list. Pay attention to punctuation and capitalization. Use each word/expression one time only. More than one answer is possible.

because	in spite of	so
due to	nonetheless	such
even though	on the other hand	
however	otherwise	

1. Amy had two cups of coffee this morning. _____, she is still sleepy and is almost falling asleep at her desk.

2. School has been canceled today _____ the extremely hot weather.

3. I am _____ angry that I feel like steam is coming out of my ears.

4. _____ Lynn has to finish her research paper this weekend, she can't go out with her friends.

5. Many American high school students plan to study at a university _____ increasing tuition costs.

6. The swimmer had tried to make the Olympic team before. On his third attempt, _____, he finally succeeded.

7. My economics professor was _____ a boring lecturer that I often skipped class.

8. Teenagers should listen to music at a reasonable volume. _____, they might have some hearing loss.

9. _____ the government has been studying nuclear power for years, no one has discovered a way to make it completely safe.

10. Carpenter ants chew holes through wood to make their nests. _____, tropical weaver ants make their nests out of tree leaves.

Part E *Directions:* Combine ideas, using the words in parentheses.

1. Terry is very shy and quiet in class. Hannah is outgoing and very talkative with classmates. (*on the other hand*)

   _____

   _____

2. Jan is interested in current events and listens to the news every day. Art never listens to the news and doesn't care much about what's happening in the world. (*however*)

   _____

   _____

3. Mount McKinley, in Alaska, is the highest peak in North America. Aconcagua, in Argentina, is the highest mountain in South America and the Western Hemisphere. (*while*)

   _____

   _____

4. Coffee is made from roasted and ground beans that grow on bushes. Tea is made from the leaves and flowers of a variety of plants. (*but*)

   _____

   _____

Conditional Sentences and Wishes

True Conditionals in the Present/Future (Chart 20-2)

Directions: Decide if the sentence expresses *a habitual activity, a fact/general truth,* or *a future activity/situation.*

Examples: If we have time, we will go to the bookstore.
a. a habitual activity   b. a fact / general truth   (c.) a future activity / situation

If we have time, we go to the bookstore.
(a.) a habitual activity   b. a fact / general truth   c. a future activity / situation

1. If Melissa passes a shoe store, she usually stops to look at shoes.
a. a habitual activity   b. a fact / general truth   c. a future activity / situation

2. In most countries, if you are 18, you can get a driver's license.
a. a habitual activity   b. a fact / general truth   c. a future activity / situation

3. If my parents visit this weekend, we are going to go to the rose garden in the park.
a. a habitual activity   b. a fact / general truth   c. a future activity / situation

4. I always answer my cell phone if it rings.
a. a habitual activity   b. a fact / general truth   c. a future activity / situation

5. If children learn to read at an early age, they are more successful in school.
a. a habitual activity   b. a fact / general truth   c. a future activity / situation

6. If clothes fit well, they look good on the person wearing them.
a. a habitual activity   b. a fact / general truth   c. a future activity / situation

7. Daniel will be pleased if he finds a nice apartment in Vancouver.
a. a habitual activity   b. a fact / general truth   c. a future activity / situation

8. Jenny takes a nap in the afternoon if she's tired.
a. a habitual activity   b. a fact / general truth   c. a future activity / situation

9. If the plane arrives on time, I will be amazed.
a. a habitual activity   b. a fact / general truth   c. a future activity / situation

10. My brother usually gets upset if someone interrupts him.
a. a habitual activity   b. a fact / general truth   c. a future activity / situation

Directions: Complete the sentences with the verbs in parentheses. Some are true and some are untrue.

Examples: If Richard goes to the hardware store, he (*buy*) _____*will buy*_____ a new hammer.

If Richard went to the hardware store, he (*buy*) _____*would buy*_____ a new hammer.

1. My car is low on gas. If I run out of gas on the way to the gas station, I (*call*) _____

_____ you.

2. Jim is moving to a new apartment. He would tell us if he (*need*) _____

help.

3. If students did their homework every day, they (*pass*) _____ the

quizzes easily.

4. If Marie (*receive*) _____ an email, she always answers it promptly.

5. If the repairman (*come, not*) _____ this afternoon, I'm going to call

the electric company.

6. If I (*be*) _____ you, I (*be*) _____ angry about the

broken vase.

7. Martin needs a hammer. If he (*have*) _____ one, he

(*hang*) _____ up his painting.

8. I don't have any pets. If I (*have*) _____ a pet, it

(*be*) _____ a dog and I (*call*) _____ it Tex.

Directions: <u>Underline</u> the clause that expresses a condition. Write "T" next to statements that express a true idea. Write "U" next to statements that express an untrue idea. Then decide if the verb has a present / future or past meaning. Two are done for you as examples.

1. __T__ <u>If the coffee is ready</u>, we will drink it. (present/future) past

2. __U__ <u>If the car had started</u>, I would have driven. present/future (past)

3. _____ If children are scared, they cry. present/future past

4. _____ The police would have come if we had called. present/future past

5. _____ If Rebecca is tired, she goes to bed early. present/future past

6. _____ If the dogs had stopped barking, I would have slept. present/future past

7. _____ If I had time today, I would go rollerblading. present/future past

8. _____ If Jeremy needs more time on tests, I allow it. present/future past

9. _____ If Helena hadn't gotten sick, she would have come. present/future past

10. _____ If Ali didn't have time, he wouldn't help. present/future past

11. _____ Jason calls if he's going to be late. present/future past

12. _____ My father would have waved if he had seen us. present/future past

Directions: Answer the questions.

Example: If I had been hungry, I would have eaten breakfast.
      a. Was I hungry? ___no___
      b. Did I eat breakfast? ___no___

1. If I were rich, I would quit my job and move to an island in the Caribbean.
    a. Am I rich? _____
    b. Have I quit my job? _____
    c. Have I moved to an island in the Caribbean? _____

2. Susan wouldn't listen to country and western music if she didn't like it.
    a. Does Susan like country and western music? _____
    b. Does Susan listen to country and western music? _____

3. If Javier had thought carefully about the assignment, he wouldn't have had trouble with it.
    a. Did Javier think carefully about the assignment? _____
    b. Did Javier have trouble with the assignment? _____

4. Alicia would have avoided the traffic jam if she had listened to the traffic report before leaving home.

    a. Did Alicia get stuck in a traffic jam? _____

    b. Did Alicia listen to the traffic report? _____

5. If I didn't have a job, I would be poor.

    a. Do I have a job? _____

    b. Am I poor? _____

QUIZ 5   **Untrue Conditionals in the Past**   (Chart 20-4)

Directions: Complete the sentences with the verbs in parentheses.

Examples: If my mother (*know*) _____had known_____ the truth, she would have been upset.
          If Philip had been there, he (*enjoy*) _____would have enjoyed_____ the program very much.

1. If the doctors (*find*) _____ the problem sooner, Marie wouldn't have gotten so sick.

2. If our team hadn't won the championship, we (*be*) _____ disappointed.

3. The candidate (*win*) _____ the election if she had gotten more votes.

4. If Joseph (*bring, not*) _____ his guitar, he would have played the piano instead.

5. My cell phone battery (*die*) _____ if I had forgotten my charger at home.

6. If Jorge had been honest with me before, I (*doubt, not*) _____ him.

7. If Maya (*want*) _____ to call you last night, I (*give*) _____ her your number.

8. Ahmed (*drive, not*) _____ so fast yesterday if it (*be*) _____ an emergency.

9. When we were at the party last weekend, if I (*be*) _____ in your situation, I don't know what I (*do*) _____.

10. I bought a motorcycle. If I (*have*) _____ more money, I (*buy*) _____ a car instead.

Directions: Complete the sentences with the verbs in parentheses. Pay attention to the tense.

Examples: If it (*be*) ___is___ windy this weekend, we (*go*) ___will go___ sailing.

If it (*be*) ___were___ windy now, we (*go*) ___would go___ sailing.

If it (*be*) ___had been___ windy yesterday, we (*go*) ___would have gone___ sailing.

1. It's a beautiful day. If the weather (*stay*) _____ warm, I

   (*work*) _____ in my garden later this afternoon.

2. I'm not invisible. If I (*be*) _____ invisible, I (*enjoy*)

   _____ surprising people.

3. If William (*stay, not*) _____ up so late last night, he

   (*be, not*) _____ late for class this morning.

4. You are so unhappy at work. I (*quit*) _____ my job if I

   (*hate*) _____ mine as much as you hate yours.

5. My foot (*get, not*) _____ so swollen if I (*put*)

   _____ ice on it last night.

6. If honey bees (*exist, not*) _____, we (*have, not*)

   _____ honey.

7. If Miko (*need*) _____ a ride to school tomorrow, she

   (*call*) _____ me.

8. I always carry my umbrella, so if it (*rain*) _____, I

   (*get, not*) _____ wet.

9. If Ron (*send*) _____ an email to all employees last week, they

   (*know*) _____ that the corporate executives were coming.

10. I'm exhausted. If I (*be, not*) _____ so tired, I

    (*go*) _____ to a movie.

Directions: Complete each sentence with an appropriate auxiliary verb.

Examples: Sue doesn't live in New York, but if she ___*did*___, she would see Broadway shows often.

We already ate dinner, but if we ___*hadn't*___, we would have asked you for a snack.

1. I don't have a dictionary, but if I _____ , I would check the spelling of this word.

2. Alexander already finished his homework, but if he _____, he wouldn't have gone to his friend's house.

3. I have to go to the dentist at 3:00, but if I _____, I'd have coffee with you.

4. Paul doesn't like classical music, but if he _____, he would go to the symphony.

5. My brother is already married, but if he _____, I would try to find him a wife.

6. We didn't go to Las Vegas, but if we _____, I'm sure we would have loved it.

7. I haven't finished that book yet, but if I _____, I would lend it to you.

8. We aren't vegetarians, but if we _____, we wouldn't eat meat.

9. Mr. Lee is a good teacher, but if he _____, his students wouldn't study so hard.

10. Ted and Nadia don't have any kids, but if they _____, they wouldn't be able to travel so much.

Directions: Complete the sentences with the correct form of the verbs. Make untrue or contrary-to-fact statements.

Example: It's raining. I can't hang the laundry outside to dry.

If it ___*weren't raining*___, I could hang the laundry outside to dry.

1. Shhh! The baby is sleeping. We have to be quiet.

If the baby _____, we wouldn't have to be quiet.

2. Since Hank isn't using his dictionary, I'll borrow it.

If Hank _____ his dictionary, I wouldn't borrow it.

3. Chieko's mom was talking on the phone. She didn't smell the pizza burning.

If Chieko's mom _____ on the phone, she would have smelled the pizza burning.

4. Clara graduated from the university two months ago, but she isn't looking for a job yet.

Clara's parents would be happy if she _____ for a job.

5. Fatima went to the museum last weekend, but she left after 30 minutes. She wasn't enjoying the exhibit.

If Fatima _____ the exhibit, she wouldn't have left so soon.

Directions: Change the statements into conditional sentences.

Example: I didn't eat breakfast this morning so I'm very hungry now. But . . .

_____*If I had eaten breakfast this morning, I wouldn't be so hungry now.*_____

1. Paulo hasn't called for two weeks so his parents are worried about him. But . . .

   _____

   _____

2. I haven't finished my homework so I can't watch TV. But . . .

   _____

   _____

3. He can't drive because he didn't pass the driving test. But . . .

   _____

   _____

4. The house is too hot inside because the heat was left on. But . . .

   _____

   _____

5. The children have practiced a lot so they can sing the song by heart. But . . .

   _____

   _____

6. I can't check my email because I didn't bring my laptop computer. But . . .

   _____

   _____

7. Charles didn't feed the cats so now they are hungry. But . . .

   _____

   _____

8. Mark is tired because he flew in from Hong Kong late last night. But . . .

   _____

   _____

A. **Directions:** Make sentences with the same meaning by omitting *if*.

Example: If I had known the address, I would have written it down for you.

<u>Had I known the address, I would have written it down for you.</u>

1. If Pat were a traditional guy, he wouldn't cook or clean.

_____

2. If the phone should ring, please answer it.

_____

3. I would have called sooner if someone had told me about the accident.

_____

4. If I were you, I would look for a new hair stylist.

_____

5. If Abdul had wanted to join us for dinner, he would have been welcome.

_____

B. **Directions:** Identify the implied conditions by making sentences using *if*-clauses.

Example: Marcia would have called, but she didn't know my phone number.

<u>If she had known my phone number, she would have called.</u>

1. I would have done the dishes last night, but I was too tired.

_____

2. Bob would have bought play tickets, but the performance was sold out.

_____

3. Julio lent me $500. Otherwise, I wouldn't have been able to buy a plane ticket home.

_____

4. It wouldn't have been as much fun without Talia.

_____

5. Kate would have played the piano for us, but she has a broken finger.

_____

Directions: Choose the correct completions.

Example: I'm sorry I missed your birthday. I wish I (*remembered,* (had remembered)) it.

1. I've never been to Thailand. I wish I (*went, could go*) there to see all the old temples.

2. It's too bad Henry can't visit the museum with us. I really wish he
   (*will be going, were going*) with us.

3. Olga loves her parents, but she wishes they (*aren't, weren't*) so conservative.

4. I can't speak Chinese, but I wish I (*could, could have*).

5. I don't like it when people tell lies. I wish everyone (*will, would*) just be honest!

6. James didn't get accepted to the university he wanted to go to. Now he wishes he
   (*had studied, would studied*) harder in high school.

7. Wow! That was such a close game. I wish our team (*would win, had won*). It's
   disappointing.

8. We used to shoot off fireworks on Independence Day, but now they are illegal. I wish
   fireworks (*were, would being*) legal again.

9. Nikolai has gained a lot of weight, but he wishes he (*hadn't, wouldn't*).

10. Mrs. Archibald wishes her students (*do, did*) all of their assignments and (*turn, turned*)
    them in on time.

Directions: Answer the questions. Write complete conditional sentences.

Example: What would you do if you were a movie star?
        If I were a movie star, I would sign many autographs.

1. If you could live anywhere in the world, where would you live?

   _____

   _____

2. What would you have done if you hadn't learned English?

   _____

   _____

3. What will you do if you don't understand your next English assignment?

   _____

   _____

4. What do you wish would happen in the future?

   _____

   _____

5. What do you wish had happened in the past, but didn't?

_____

_____

6. If you were not taking this quiz, what would you be doing?

_____

_____

7. What would you be doing if you were ten years older?

_____

_____

8. What would you change about your past life if you could? What would you have done differently?

_____

_____

CHAPTER 20 – TEST 1

Part A *Directions:* Complete the sentences with the verbs in parentheses. Pay attention to the tense.

1. I (*be*) _____ very surprised if I didn't pass this test.

2. If babies cry, their parents usually (*pick*) _____ them up.

3. If Benjamin (*study, not*) _____ in the U.S. now, he would be studying in France.

4. George (*catch, not*) _____ a cold if he
   (*wear*) _____ a jacket last night.

5. If James always (*pay*) _____ his bills on time, he wouldn't be stressed about them.

6. If the price of gasoline (*go*) _____ up more, I will start taking the bus.

7. Leila (*visit*) _____ her grandchildren last summer if they
   (*visit, not*) _____ her.

8. If Byoung wins the lottery, he (*buy*) _____ a new car.

Part B *Directions:* Change the statements into conditional sentences.

1. Madeleine missed her flight, so she is feeling angry and frustrated. But . . .

   _____

   _____

2. Saya can't play the pieces for her piano lesson because she hasn't practiced all week. But . . .

   _____

   _____

3. Michael got three traffic tickets last year, so now his insurance rates are going up. But . . .

   _____

   _____

4. Tomás doesn't want to move to a different city, so he didn't accept the job offer. But . . .

   _____

   _____

5. Stacy Smith is the new mayor because she won the election. But . . .

   _____

   _____

Part C *Directions:* Identify the implied conditions by creating sentences using *if*-clauses.

1. I would stop to chat with you, but I'm in a hurry.

   _____

   _____

2. Fred had to work late. Otherwise, he would have met us for dinner.

   _____

   _____

3. I would never have completed this project on time without your help.

   _____

   _____

Part D *Directions:* Circle the correct completions.

1. Elena didn't go to the concert last weekend, but she wishes she (*had, hadn't*).

2. Mrs. Takasawa doesn't speak Japanese, but she wishes she (*did, would*).

3. My toddler can open the drawers in the kitchen, but I wish he (*can't, couldn't*).

4. Khalid's hair is turning gray, but he wishes it (*weren't, isn't*).

5. Brian isn't tall enough to ride on the roller coaster, but he wishes he (*was, were*).

6. I can't cook well, but I wish I (*could, were*).

7. My son is going to join the army, but I wish he (*wasn't, weren't*).

8. Sarah went on a blind date with Marsha's brother, but she wishes she (*hadn't, didn't*).

Part A *Directions:* Complete the sentences with the verbs in parentheses. Pay attention to the tense.

1. If Geoffrey (*lose*) _____ his job, he will look for a new job.

2. We (*go*) _____ for a hike yesterday if the weather (*be, not*) _____ terrible.

3. Leo (*visit*) _____ us more often if he had time.

4. If Lara goes to Paris for vacation this summer, she (*see*) _____ the Eiffel Tower.

5. If Tanya (*get*) _____ more exercise, she could lose weight.

6. Mr. Martinez (*pull, not*) _____ a muscle in his back if he (*be*) _____ more careful moving the sofa.

7. If I finish a good book, I always (*feel*) _____ satisfied.

8. My dad would answer the phone if he (*cook, not*) _____ dinner right now.

Part B *Directions:* Change the statements into conditional sentences.

1. Wendy didn't work hard in high school, so she isn't going to college. But . . .

_____

_____

2. Paula can't finish the marathon because she twisted her ankle. But . . .

_____

_____

3. The children are running and yelling, so they didn't hear the recess bell. But . . .

_____

_____

4. I didn't finish the report because my computer isn't working. But . . .

_____

_____

5. Roberta doesn't like cheese, so she didn't eat any pizza last night. But . . .

_____

_____

Directions: Identify the implied conditions by creating sentences using *if*-clauses.

1. I would have answered the door, but I was in the shower.

   _____

   _____

2. Lisa has a doctor's appointment. Otherwise, she wouldn't have left work early.

   _____

   _____

3. The team couldn't have won the championship without their coach's direction.

   _____

   _____

Directions: Circle the correct completions.

1. The mayor can't solve the homeless problem, but I wish she (*can, could*).

2. I don't live in California any more, but I wish I (*do, did*).

3. I have a terrible headache right now, but I wish I (*didn't, wouldn't*).

4. This blouse isn't on sale, but I wish it (*was, were*).

5. Aunt Rose couldn't come to my anniversary party, but I wish she (*had, could*).

6. The drugstore doesn't carry my favorite brand of shampoo anymore, but I wish it (*had, did*).

7. I'm not going to get an A in this class, but I wish I (*were, was*).

8. I got another parking ticket yesterday, but I wish I (*didn't, hadn't*).

Directions: Choose the correct completions.

Example: John ____ read a book quietly in his room than play tennis with his brother.
  a. prefer   (c.) would rather
  b. had better   d. had to

1. Bruce was 20 minutes late for this morning's meeting. He ____ stuck in traffic.
    a. might be   c. had to be
    b. must be   d. must have been

2. The teacher was surprised that the students needed more time. They ____ finish the quiz in 30 minutes.
    a. should have could   c. should be can
    b. should have been able to d. had better

3. When the movie actress entered the room, everyone turned and looked at ____.
    a. herself   c. her
    b. she   d. hers

4. Dogs make excellent pets. ____ provide good companionship and even protection.
    a. They   c. It
    b. Its   d. It's

5. By the time Brian ____ a parking space, he was late for the movie.
    a. was finding   c. had found
    b. was found   d. finds

6. While John ____ for a parking place, he ran out of gas.
    a. was looking   c. is looking
    b. looked   d. has looked

7. Shirley wasn't able to concentrate all morning. She ____ at all the night before and was very sleepy.
    a. wasn't sleeping   c. sleeps
    b. hadn't slept   d. hasn't been sleeping

8. Peter rarely ____ a promotion at work. He is sometimes lazy and never does more than he has to.
    a. got   c. will get
    b. is getting   d. gets

9. Mrs. Taylor is worried about the children. They ____ come home two hours ago.
    a. have got to   c. should have
    b. had better   d. didn't have to

10. ____ please answer the telephone? I'm washing the dishes, and my hands are all wet.
    a. Would you   c. May you
    b. Would you mind   d. You must

11. Can I borrow ____? I must have left mine at home.
    a. one of your pen   c. one your pen
    b. one of your pens d. one your pens

12. Maria has invited all of the students and all of the _____ parents to her birthday party.
    a. students'   c. student's
    b. students   d. students their

13. By the time William is forty years old, he _____ fifteen novels and two collections of short stories.
    a. wrote   c. has written
    b. will have written   d. will be writing

14. I'm not sure where Rob is, but he _____ to music in his room.
    a. might be listening   c. might have listened
    b. might listen   d. must have been listening

15. You _____ hungry already! You just ate a big lunch and a dish of ice cream.
    a. must not be   c. could have been
    b. can't be   d. might not be

16. _____ not smoking? I'm allergic to cigarette smoke.
    a. Would you   c. Would you mind
    b. Can you   d. Will you

17. The Chinese _____ the oldest calendar of any culture in the world today.
    a. have had   c. have
    b. has had   d. has

18. Each of _____ graduated from school and found a good job.
    a. their children have   c. their children has
    b. their child has   d. their childrens have

19. Mario _____ for four hours straight. He had better take a break to stretch and eat something.
    a. is studying   c. studied
    b. was studying   d. has been studying

20. Janice _____ a koala bear before she went to Australia last November.
    a. had never seen   c. had ever seen
    b. has never seen   d. doesn't see

21. The employees at Matrix Motors get paid _____ week.
    a. every other   c. one after the other
    b. each other   d. another

22. It looks like your cup is empty. Would you like _____ cup of coffee?
    a. other   c. one another
    b. another   d. the other

23. Babies like to talk to _____ in order to practice the sounds of a language.
    a. itself   c. itselves
    b. themself   d. themselves

24. Oh, no! _____ is missing! We have to call the police!
    a. All of the stamps   c. All of the computers
    b. All of the jewelry   d. All of the children

25. _____ a different topic. We will study Chapters 1 through 10 this semester.
    a. Each of the chapter covers
    b. Each of the chapters cover
    c. Each of the chapters covers
    d. All of the chapter cover

26. I don't think we'll need an umbrella this afternoon. The forecast is for _____ late tonight.
    a. a little rain
    b. little rain
    c. a few rain
    d. few rain

27. This chemical is very dangerous. You _____ handle it without gloves and goggles.
    a. don't have to
    b. have to
    c. could not
    d. must not

28. Philip usually doesn't take a shower while his roommate _____ the laundry.
    a. will do
    b. is doing
    c. is going to do
    d. was doing

29. I'm amazed! No one _____ any problems with the equipment since we bought it.
    a. have
    b. has
    c. have had
    d. has had

30. One hour may be enough for the midterm, but two hours _____ necessary for the final exam.
    a. was
    b. were
    c. are
    d. is

31. We enjoyed our trip to Yellowstone National Park. We saw _____ and even a black bear.
    a. several deers
    b. several deer
    c. severals deers
    d. severals deer

32. When I _____ to my country next year, I am going to visit all my friends.
    a. will return
    b. returns
    c. return
    d. am going to return

33. Every time people _____ this memorial, they will remember the soldiers who died for their country.
    a. saw
    b. see
    c. are seeing
    d. will see

34. After the hurricane has passed, people _____ to their homes to check on the damage.
    a. will be able to return
    b. could have returned
    c. will have returned
    d. return

35. The suspect will not talk to the police until his lawyer _____ present.
    a. was
    b. is going to be
    c. will have been
    d. is

36. While the children are watching a movie later this afternoon, I _____ a nap.
    a. am taking
    b. take
    c. was taking
    d. will be taking

37. I'm not sure what I'm going to do this afternoon. I might see a movie or do _____ shopping.
    a. few
    b. a few
    c. little
    d. a little

38. By this December, we _____ in this house for more than thirty years.
   a. will live
   b. had lived
   c. will have been living
   d. are going to be living

39. When Christopher went to the refrigerator for a snack, _____ many things to eat.
   a. there isn't
   b. there aren't
   c. there wasn't
   d. there weren't

40. Please don't disturb me right now. I _____ to finish the last page of this report.
   a. try
   b. am trying
   c. will try
   d. have tried

41. Nora isn't sure, but she thinks she _____ her purse in the restaurant.
   a. might leave
   b. might have been left
   c. might have left
   d. might be leaving

42. High blood pressure _____ by medication.
   a. can control
   b. has controlled
   c. can be controlling
   d. can be controlled

43. If a person _____ one foreign language, it is usually easier to learn a second one.
   a. has studied
   b. will study
   c. was studied
   d. studied

44. Don't worry. All of the reports _____ by the time you get here tomorrow morning.
   a. will complete
   b. will be completed
   c. are completed
   d. have been completed

45. These coffee beans _____ in the mountains of Colombia.
   a. were handpicked
   b. handpicked
   c. were handpicked by someone
   d. were handpicking

46. I'm sorry, but Room 1102 is not available. It _____ by another group.
   a. was using
   b. was being used
   c. is using
   d. is being used

47. Kevin didn't finish watching the movie. It _____.
   a. was bored
   b. was being bored
   c. was being boring
   d. was boring

48. You had better throw that meat away. I'm sure that it _____.
   a. is spoiling
   b. is spoiled
   c. is being spoiled
   d. spoils

49. The neighbors are very much _____ a homeless shelter in their area.
   a. opposed to
   b. opposing to
   c. opposed about
   d. opposing about

50. Mr. Patterson _____ from his job when his firm was bought out by another company.
   a. was firing
   b. fired
   c. got fired
   d. gets fired

MIDTERM EXAM 2 Chapters 1-11

Part A *Directions:* Complete the sentences. Use an appropriate form of the verbs in parentheses.
Example: Martin (*meet*) _____ will meet _____ with the committee members next Wednesday.

1. Some people (*be*) _____ very afraid of spiders. They have arachnophobia.

2. As soon as the TV program is over, Martha (*make*) _____ a salad for dinner.

3. My grandmother (*work*) _____ in the garden when we arrived at her house.

4. Do you need help with your homework? I (*help*) _____ you after lunch.

5. I have so much laundry to do. I just (*have, not*) _____ time to do it lately.

6. After I lost my third cell phone, I (*buy*) _____ a cheap one.

7. When she returns from her trip to Ecuador, Carrie (*speak*) _____ Spanish fluently.

8. Last summer, it (*rain*) _____ almost every afternoon. The weather was terrible!

9. Max (*choose*) _____ by his classmates to speak at their graduation ceremony last June.

10. Right now my cousin (*study*) _____ his astronomy notes. He has a test tomorrow.

11. By this time next year, Chris (*finish*) _____ his training and will be an electrician.

12. Steve (*surf*) _____ the internet for three hours. He needs to take a break.

13. Josef often (*have*) _____ trouble with English verbs. He gets really confused.

14. It was good to talk to Maggie yesterday. Before that, I (*talk, not*) _____ to her for months.

15. My parents' 50th wedding anniversary (*celebrate*) _____ by the entire family next month.

Directions: Decide if each sentence is correct (C) or incorrect (I). If incorrect, make the necessary changes.

Examples: C   I

                   Have

___   ✓ ~~Has~~ any of the students taken this class before?

 ✓   ___ A number of volunteers are needed to finish this cleaning project.

    C   I

___ ___ **1.** The number of the employees on the project are increasing weekly.

___ ___ **2.** We took a two-weeks vacation to Hawaii last January.

___ ___ **3.** Statistics are used in research in many fields, including social science and education.

___ ___ **4.** My son's favorite superheros are Spiderman and Batman.

___ ___ **5.** My soda is on the table. Where is your's?

___ ___ **6.** Each of the stars from the movie have been interviewed by the press.

___ ___ **7.** Suzanne speaks three languages, but she wants to learn the other one.

___ ___ **8.** Joshua had too many homeworks last weekend. He didn't have much time to relax.

___ ___ **9.** Maddy memorized the whole poem all by herself!

___ ___ **10.** One of the student in my writing class studies at the library every night.

___ ___ **11.** Todays lunch special is Spaghetti Bolognese with green salad for $5.95.

___ ___ **12.** The children fixed lunch for themselfs. They made peanut butter and jelly sandwiches.

___ ___ **13.** Let's go get some coffee. I have a little time before my next appointment.

___ ___ **14.** The *New York Times* are among the top newspapers in the U.S.

___ ___ **15.** The cucumber's at the market were reasonably priced, so I bought two of them.

Directions: Read each paragraph. Then complete the statements about it with an appropriate modal (***must, may, might, could, should***, etc.) and the given verb. More than one answer is possible.

Example: At Silvia and Robert's wedding in July, there were more than 200 guests. Silvia and Robert put off writing thank-you notes for the wedding gifts they received. Now it is December, and they still haven't sent out their thank-you notes.

The wedding guests (*be*) ___*may be*___ angry that they haven't received a thank you.

Silvia and Robert (*write*) ___*should have written*___ the thank-you notes by now.

1. Adam and his friend stayed up late watching a movie. The next morning, Adam fell asleep on the bus to work. When he woke up, he had already passed his stop. By the time he caught the next bus back, he was late for work.

   a. Adam (*stay, not*) _____ up so late.

   b. Adam's boss (*be*) _____ upset about Adam's late

   arrival.

   c. Adam (*be*) _____ more careful about arriving at work on

   time, or he will lose his job.

2. You call your friend Susan, but her mother tells you that she isn't home. You have some important news for Susan and you want to leave a message.

   a. (*leave*) _____ I please _____ a message for Susan?

   b. (*ask*) _____ you please _____ her to call me?

Directions: Using the information about each situation, complete the sentences.

Example: SITUATION: The students are taking a two-page quiz. There are five minutes left for the quiz.
Who will finish the quiz?

INFORMATION: The last two questions on **Ron**'s paper are still blank.
Sheila is working on the last question.
Wendy is still working on the first page of the quiz.

   a. ___*Wendy*___ won't finish the quiz.
   b. ___*Ron*___ might finish the quiz.
   c. ___*Sheila*___ should finish the quiz.

SITUATION 1: Hannah, James, and Wills work for the same company. They start work at 8:30 A.M. Who do you expect to be on time for work today?

INFORMATION: **Hannah** almost always arrives a few minutes late for work because she can't find a parking place.
James takes the bus to work and usually arrives by 8:20.
Will has to drop off his kids at school on the way to work. He occasionally gets to work late.

   a. _____ might be on time for work today.

   b. _____ won't be on time today.

   c. _____ should be on time for work today.

SITUATION 2: The final paper for the English 105 class is due tomorrow. Who has already completed the assignment?

INFORMATION: **Ken** hates writing assignments. He said he'll be up late tonight.

Max has already left for a semester break trip to California.

David said last night that he was almost finished writing his paper.

a. _____ must have finished his paper already.

b. _____ may have finished his paper by now.

c. _____ must not have finished writing his paper yet.

Part E **Directions:** Complete the conversations with **must, have to, must not, don't have to, could,** or **couldn't.** Use each modal one time only.

Example: A: Do you want to go to the movies tonight?

B: I'm sorry I can't. I _____*have to / must*_____ study for a test in math tomorrow.

1. A: Why didn't Karen go out for Chinese food with you last night?

   B: She hardly ever eats Chinese food. She _____ like it much.

2. A: What time does your flight leave?

   B: It leaves at 4:00. I _____ be at the airport by 2:00.

3. A: When Paul was young, he _____ run a 10K race in about 50 minutes.

   B: Really? That's pretty good. I'm sure he's much slower now, though.

4. A: It's nice to be on vacation. I _____ think about work for two weeks!

   B: That's wonderful!

5. A: Are you sure Jason is out of town this week? I thought I saw him at the soccer game today.

   B: That _____ have been Jason! He's in the Bahamas right now. It _____ have been somebody else.

Directions: Choose the correct completions.

Example: John _____ read a book quietly in his room than play tennis with his brother.
    a. prefer   (c.)would rather
    b. had better   d. had to

1. Our city _____ a record number of traffic accidents last year, so the city has worked to make streets safer.
    a. has   c. is having
    b. had   d. was having

2. Carlos _____ in the United States since he enrolled in art school three years ago.
    a. lived   c. has been living
    b. lives   d. living

3. When Linda _____ to Los Angeles next month, she will stay with her sister until she finds her own apartment.
    a. moves   c. has moved
    b. will move   d. is going to move

4. Please keep your voice down in this section of the library. If you _____ to talk loudly, I will have to ask you to leave.
    a. continued   c. will continue
    b. could continue   d. continue

5. I bought the red leather bag because it was well made, stylish, and _____.
    a. inexpensively   c. less expensive than
    b. inexpensive   d. unexpensive

6. The chemistry book _____ was a little expensive.
    a. that I bought it   c. what I bought
    b. I bought that   d. I bought

7. Why did Beth ask you _____ a bicycle?
    a. that if you had   c. that you had
    b. do you have   d. if you had

8. Eighty-five percent of the students in the class _____ brothers and sisters.
    a. has   c. have
    b. are having   d. is having

9. I got Barbara _____ her car for the weekend.
    a. to let me borrow   c. to let me to borrow
    b. let me borrow   d. let me to borrow

10. If I _____ you, I would get some rest before the game tomorrow.
    a. am   c. were
    b. could be   d. had been

11. The publishers expect that the new biography of Simón Bolívar will be bought by people _____ in Latin American history.
    a. who are interested   c. interesting
    b. are interested   d. they are interested

12. Emily is motivated to study _____ she knows that a good education can improve her life.
    a. therefore
    b. because of
    c. because
    d. so

13. Ms. Moore, the school counselor, has had years of experience dealing with student problems. _____ , she is sometimes confronted by a problem that she cannot handle by herself.
    a. Therefore
    b. Nevertheless
    c. Otherwise
    d. On the other hand

14. I have always wanted to visit Paris, _____ of France.
    a. is the capital
    b. which the capital is
    c. that is the capital
    d. the capital

15. When I went to China last September, I had _____ time for sightseeing because I was very busy attending a conference in Beijing. I would like to go there again so I can see more of the country.
    a. little
    b. a little
    c. few
    d. a few

16. Gloria never seems to get tired. I sure wish I _____ her energy.
    a. would have
    b. have
    c. have had
    d. had

17. After getting home from elementary school, _____ .
    a. our house buzzes with the children's many activities
    b. the dog greets the children at the front door with wagging tail
    c. the children have an hour to play before they begin their homework
    d. the school bus drops the children at the corner near their house

18. Jack offered to take care of my garden and _____ my mail while I was out of town.
    a. gets
    b. getting
    c. got
    d. get

19. Sonia broke her leg in two places. _____, she had to wear a cast and use crutches for three months.
    a. Nevertheless
    b. Consequently
    c. For that
    d. Because

20. Next year Nathan will attend _____ university in Germany. He's looking forward to it.
    a. a
    b. an
    c. the
    d. ∅

21. Even though a duck lives on water, it stays dry _____ the oil on its feathers, which prevents water from reaching its skin.
    a. because of
    b. since
    c. because
    d. for

22. One of the funniest _____ I saw last year was *Agent 13*. It had a crazy plot and hilarious actors.
    a. movie
    b. a movie
    c. movies
    d. the movies

23. I talked to Bob two weeks ago. I thought he wanted to know about my cat, but I misunderstood him. He asked me where _____, not my cat.
    a. is my hat
    b. my hat was
    c. my hat is
    d. was my hat

24. The voters were overwhelmingly against the candidate _____ proposals called for higher taxes.
    a. who his
    b. whose
    c. whom he had
    d. that his

25. _____ go to the beach this weekend. The weather is supposed to be hot.
    a. Let's
    c. Could we
    c. Why don't
    d. Lets

26. Please remember _____ your hand during the test if you have a question.
    a. raising
    b. to raise
    c. having raised
    d. to have raised

27. I have to go to the meeting _____ I want to or not.
    a. because
    b. whether
    c. even though
    d. only if

28. The painting was beautiful. I stood there _____ it for a long time.
    a. for admiring
    b. being admired
    c. admire
    d. admiring

29. Would you mind _____ me your email address? I'd like to get that recipe from you.
    a. to give
    b. if I gave
    c. giving
    d. give

30. My mouth is burning! This is _____ spicy food that I don't think I can finish it.
    a. such
    b. so
    c. very
    d. too

31. The customs officer opened the suitcase _____ if anything illegal was being brought into the country.
    a. seeing
    b. for seeing
    c. see
    d. to see

32. That man _____ looked before he stepped into the street. He almost got hit by a truck!
    a. should
    b. should have
    c. shouldn't
    d. shouldn't have

33. Sometimes very young children have trouble _____ fact from fiction and may believe that dragons actually exist.
    a. to separate
    b. separating
    c. to be separated
    d. for separating

34. I have to eat breakfast in the morning. _____, I get grouchy and hungry before my lunch break.
    a. Consequently
    b. And
    c. Otherwise
    d. However

35. Tony spent ____ money buying movie tickets that he didn't have enough left to buy a soft drink or candy bar.

    a. so many   c. too much

    b. a lot of   d. so much

36. Not wanting to be late my first day of class, ____ to school after I missed my bus.

    a. so I ran   c. I ran

    b. because I ran   d. therefore, I ran

37. Christopher was wet and muddy when he came home from playing soccer. It ____ during the game.

    a. must rain   c. had to rain

    b. must not rain   d. must have rained

38. Yesterday Mary left ____ backpack on the school bus.

    a. her   c. hers

    b. she   d. his

39. There ____ ten students from Korea in my English class.

    a. is   c. are

    b. be   d. being

40. The Northern Hemisphere has mostly westerly winds ____ the rotation of the earth toward the east.

    a. due to   c. therefore

    b. because   d. so

41. The police ____ whenever there is a traffic accident.

    a. calls   c. called

    b. is called   d. are called

42. When I saw my classmates at our ten-year reunion last month, I ____ most of them since graduation.

    a. didn't see   c. hadn't seen

    b. haven't seen   d. won't see

43. More than 50 buildings in the downtown area ____ in the earthquake.

    a. destroyed   c. were destroying

    b. were destroyed   d. was destroyed

44. I think I did OK in my speech last night ____ I'd had almost no sleep for 24 hours.

    a. despite the fact that   c. so that

    b. unless   d. in spite of

45. While I ____ for the train, I made three phone calls and checked my email on my cell phone.

    a. wait   c. waited

    b. am waiting   d. was waiting

46. The ____ news about robberies in the neighborhood caused everyone to be sure to lock their doors.

    a. disturbed   c. disturbs

    b. disturbing   d. disturb

47. The scientists explained how _____ insects breathe underwater.
    a. the   c. Ø
    b. an   d. a

48. Jim should have asked for help instead _____ to do it himself.
    a. of trying   c. try
    b. to try   d. from trying

49. If I _____ following that other car too closely, I would have been able to stop in time instead of running into it.
    a. wasn't   c. was
    b. would have been   d. hadn't been

50. A: Is it true that you fell asleep in class yesterday and began to snore?
    B: Unfortunately, yes. _____ is unbelievable! I'm very embarrassed.
    a. That I could do such a thing it   c. I could do such a thing it
    b. That I could do such a thing   d. I could do such a thing

Part A *Directions:* Complete the sentences. Use the appropriate form of the verbs in parentheses. More than one answer is possible.

Example: Mary (*drink*) _____drinks_____ coffee every morning before she goes to work.

1. Next week my whole family (*go*) _____ on a trip to the Grand Canyon.

2. Last year Tim (*study, not*) _____ enough, so his grades weren't very good.

3. While Fatima (*wait*) _____ in the doctor's office, the doctor suddenly had to leave for an emergency.

4. By the time we arrived at the hotel, the wedding reception (*start, already*)

    _____ .

5. The college entrance exam (*give*) _____ next Saturday in the high school auditorium.

6. I'm almost ready for my trip to Kenya. I have my plane ticket, but my new passport (*arrive, not*) _____ yet. I should get it soon.

7. We (*stay*) _____ in our tent until it stops raining. Otherwise, we'll get soaking wet!

8. Every girl, boy, woman, and man on earth (*be*) _____ affected by global warming.

9. One fourth of the students in the class (*plan, not*) _____ to go to college.

10. Thirty minutes (*be*) _____ too long to wait for a bus!

Directions: Decide if each sentence is correct (C) or incorrect (I). If incorrect, make the necessary changes.

Examples: C   I

               Have

_____ ✓ ~~Has~~ any of the students taken this class before?

✓ _____ A number of volunteers are needed to finish this cleaning project.

   C   I

____ ____ **1.** You don't have to leave a candle burning when you leave the house. It could cause a fire.

____ ____ **2.** Ninety-five percent of the professors at the university has a PhD.

____ ____ **3.** My aunt's and uncle's new baby is a sweet little girl. She's my newest cousin.

____ ____ **4.** There are several hypotheses about why some penguins may have survived when the dinosaurs died.

____ ____ **5.** The middle-school teachers always give students too many homeworks.

____ ____ **6.** I'm not sure when the bus is supposed to come. It must be here soon.

____ ____ **7.** Max is worried about his daughter. She should have call him by now.

____ ____ **8.** Even though Carol is only seven years old, she can read some novels by herself.

____ ____ **9.** John may have been gave his paycheck at work today. I'm not sure.

____ ____ **10.** I'm almost sure that story was made up. It may not be true!

Part C **Directions:** Combine each pair of sentences into one new sentence with parallel structure. Use the conjunctions given in parentheses.

Example: Coffee contains caffeine. Tea contains caffeine. (*both . . . and*)

       Both coffee and tea contain caffeine.

1. Mary got 100% on her last grammar test. John got 100% on his last grammar test. (*both . . . and*)

_____

2. Barbara can't attend the meeting on Monday. Steven can't attend the meeting on Monday. (*neither . . . nor*)

_____

3. Stewart's team won the city championship. Stewart's team won the regional championship. (*not only . . . but also*)

_____

4. We can watch a comedy film. We can watch a drama. (*either . . . or*)

_____

Directions: Complete the sentences. Either change the questions or rewrite the speaker's words to make noun clauses.

Example: (*How long has Hank lived in Memphis?*)

Do you know _____ *how long Hank has lived in Memphis* _?

1. (*What time does the train for Edinburgh leave?*)

Can you tell me _____?

2. (*"Did Kevin get his driver's license?" asked Cathy.*)

Cathy wanted to know _____.

3. (*"Whose car is that?" asked Pat.*)

Pat asked me _____.

4. (*How does that machine work?*)

_____ is explained in the instructions.

Part E *Directions:* Combine the two sentences. Use the second sentence as the adjective clause.

Example: Midori served tasty Japanese snacks. We enjoyed them very much.

_____ *Midori served tasty Japanese snacks which / that we enjoyed very much.* _____

1. Barbara wants to go to an island for her vacation. The island has warm sandy beaches and lots of sunshine.

_____

_____

2. Anne and Emily like to go shopping on Monday morning. The stores are not crowded.

_____

_____

3. The police are trying to find the man. Someone found his car near the scene of the crime.

_____

_____

Directions: Match the first half of each sentence to the clause that best completes it. The first one is done for you.

1. __e__ Michael needs to buy a new suit

2. ____ Maya didn't have enough money,

3. ____ After reading many reviews and articles on the internet,

4. ____ We could go to the museum

5. ____ While Mark loves science,

6. ____ The movie was so funny that

7. ____ I ate too much, so I have a stomachache,

8. ____ Students may not go on the class trip

9. ____ William still goes to that restaurant

10. ____ If I hadn't forgotten my phone at home,

a. even though the waiter was rude and made a mistake on the bill.

b. I would have called you sooner.

c. but I wish I didn't.

d. everyone in the audience was laughing.

e̸. because he has a job interview next Monday.

f. if it were open today.

g. so she couldn't go skiing with her friends.

h. Lori hates it.

i. unless they have permission from their parents.

j. Barry chose a new camera and bought it.

Part G *Directions:* Complete the sentences with the gerund or infinitive form of the verbs in parentheses. More than one answer is possible.

Example: I don't like (*go*) ____to go / going____ shopping on weekends. The stores are too crowded.

1. My friends and I are interested in (*study*) _____ abroad during college.

2. My cat enjoys (*play*) _____ with her mouse toy.

3. We agreed (*meet*) _____ Karen and Heather for coffee at 3:00 P.M.

4. I forgot (*get*) _____ the company's customer service number. Now I can't call them.

5. Last summer was so hot that we went (*swim*) _____ almost every day.

6. Lynne was embarrassed (*admit*) _____ that she had forgotten her student's name.

7. I'm too tired (*go*) _____ out of town this weekend. I just want to rest.

8. Jan and Maria had a good time (*travel*) _____ together last year.

9. Julie got her sister (*drive*) _____ most of the way because she doesn't like to drive.

10. Paul can't stand (*get*) _____ home from work late.

ANSWER KEY

CHAPTER 1

Quiz 1, p. 1

Answers will vary.
1. My English class **meets** . . . .
2. Today I **brought** . . . .
3. I **am going to go** . . . .
4. Last weekend I **went, did, ate, etc** . . . . (simple past)
5. (Team names) **are playing** . . . .
6. Yesterday at this time I **was studying, eating, running, etc** . . . . (past progressive)
7. Ten years from now, I **will be living** . . . .
8. I **want** to be / work / get a job as . . . .
9. I **was thinking** about . . . .
10. I **woke up** at . . . .

Quiz 2, p. 2

1. had fallen
2. has been living / has lived
3. will have finished
4. has been working / has worked
5. visited / has visited
6. had not finished
7. will have read
8. has been
9. had already begun
10. has drunk

Quiz 3, p. 3

2. have been attending / have attended
3. had gotten
4. had never taught
5. have not had
6. have been wearing
7. will have had

Quiz 4, p. 4

A.

Double the consonant	Drop the -*e*	Just add -*ing*
beginning	forgiving	learning
cutting	inviting	standing
planning	serving	studying
shopping	writing	supplying

B.
1. married
2. delayed
3. permitted
4. danced
5. hugged
6. controlled
7. studied
8. pointed
9. intensified
10. closed

Quiz 5, p. 5

1. Yesterday Clara sent an email to her friend in Hungary.
2. By the time I pay my phone bill, I will have spent most of my money.
3. Maria has been living / has lived / lived in Stockholm for three years.
4. Last Monday Mr. Williams called me at 6:00 A.M.
5. Since Jon moved to Montreal, he has made many new friends.
6. What are you going to do after the concert tomorrow night?
7. Last night while I was cooking dinner, I burned the meat.
8. Mrs. Kita has offered / offered me a job in her shop.
9. When I got to the restaurant, they had already finished their meal.
10. By this time next month, we will be in our new apartment.

TEST 1, p. 6

A.
1. ate
2. will take / is going to take / is taking
3. rides
4. has worked / has been working
5. will have finished
6. was studying
7. have been waiting
8. is going to visit / will visit / is visiting

B.
1. What did you **eat** for breakfast?
2. Right now I am **riding** the bus and talking on the phone.
3. Ruth **traveled** to Paris three times last year.
4. My brother **seems** tired this morning.
5. Grandma **fell** down and broke her arm.

C.
1. I am taking a test right now.
2. My brother has been living / has lived in the same apartment for seven years.
3. Computers will work much faster in ten years.
4. Ms. Thompson went to a play last weekend.
5. The students were eating lunch at this exact time yesterday.
6. By the time I am 80, I will have been living in Seattle for a long time.

TEST 2, p. 7

A.
1. is
2. has been teaching / has taught
3. has changed
4. used
5. developed
6. printed
7. are
8. edit
9. print
10. are
11. enjoys
12. will continue
13. will not have changed

B.
1. What **did you do** yesterday morning? OR
   What **were you doing** yesterday morning?
2. It **is going to rain** tomorrow. OR
   It **will rain** tomorrow.
3. By the time I go to work, I **will have drunk** two cups of coffee.
4. She has been **studying** for final exams all week.
5. He **has** been watching a movie since 8:00.

C.
1. By next Friday, Cathy will have written her essay for English class.
2. Last night a phone call woke me up at midnight.
3. Jake has been studying / has studied Japanese since 2006.
4. Carol lived in Kenya from 2005 to 2007.
5. Next year my parents will spend / are going to spend / are spending New Year's Day in London.
6. What will you be doing / are you going to be doing at this exact time tomorrow?

CHAPTER 2

Quiz 1, p. 9
1. stand
2. departs
3. is
4. are trying
5. are still waiting
6. takes
7. has
8. looks
9. is tapping
10. does not want

Quiz 2, p. 9
A.
2. are playing
3. is swimming
4. is enjoying

B.
1. is
2. loves
3. has
4. is talking
5. often use
6. don't understand
7. prefer

Quiz 3, p. 10
A.
1. is appearing
2. smells
3. is thinking
4. is tasting
5. love

B.
1. don't care
2. are seeing
3. do you think
4. isn't feeling
5. dislikes

Quiz 4, p. 10
1. stopped
2. made
3. caught
4. met
5. stood
6. occurred
7. read
8. preferred
9. wrote
10. slept
11. cost
12. studied
13. found
14. rang
15. spoke
16. heard
17. wore
18. quit
19. played
20. chose

Quiz 5, p. 11
1. Yes, they drove their antique car in the parade.
2. The debate started at . . . .
3. He found his passport . . . .
4. Yes, the email from my boss came earlier today.
5. Yes, they snuck / sneaked into the movie theater.
6. Yes, he paid me for the CD that he lost.
7. I lived . . . before I moved here.
8. Yes, all of the students brought their books.
9. Yes, she talked to her boyfriend last night.
10. My teacher left her keys . . . .

Quiz 6, p. 12
1. was listening
2. lost
3. was driving
4. heard
5. was rolling
6. was watching
7. was cleaning
8. ran
9. wanted
10. was traveling

Quiz 7, p. 12
A.
2. fell
3. broke
4. took
5. was not

B.
1. took
2. stayed
3. spent
4. ate
5. were having
6. was playing
7. were dancing
8. walked

Quiz 8, p. 13
1. _____ Michiko was chopping some vegetables when she **cut** her finger with the knife.
2. ✓ correct
3. _____ When Fatima woke up, she **made** a cup of tea for herself.
4. ✓ correct
5. _____ Geoff worked on his report **while** he was riding the train.
6. _____ While Faruz was shopping for a new computer, he **ran** into an old friend.
7. ✓ correct
8. _____ James **washed** the dishes when he finished reading the newspaper.
9. ✓ correct
10. _____ When Carrie **dropped** her laptop computer, she started to cry.

TEST 1, p. 14
A.
1. b, c
2. c, a
3. c, b
4. c, b

B.
1. had
2. stopped
3. is calling
4. usually goes
5. were visiting

C.
1. finds
2. is
3. reports
4. was reading / read
5. has
6. decided

D.
1. Every summer Sarah's cousin from England **visits** her.
2. Ibrahim was very upset when he **heard** the news.
3. You can't talk to Mr. James right now because he **is talking** to another student.
4. While I was **writing** my essay, I was also surfing the internet.
5. Karen is very kind and always **helps** the teachers with their work.

E.
1. Yes, I watched the evening news on TV last night.
2. They met . . . .
3. They are flying / eating / sitting . . . .
4. I was reading / talking / eating . . . .
5. Yes, Leo is planning to get the car repaired.

TEST 2, p. 16

A.
1. a, b
2. c, c
3. b, a
4. a, c

B.
1. wakes
2. worked
3. was taking
4. am taking
5. was discussing

C.
1. swim
2. live
3. move
4. is
5. is studying
6. goes
7. migrate / are migrating

D.
1. The workers were very tired and **forgot** to lock the door when they left for the day.
2. I didn't **know** about the party for me.
3. David was very busy yesterday, so today he **is taking / took** the day off.
4. Steven is in the library **reading** a book.
5. The little boy **bought** another toy because he broke the first one.

E.
1. Yes, he set the table.
2. Yes, she laid her keys on the hall table.
3. Yes, the lake froze last night.
4. Yes, he swam in the 1,000-meter race.
5. Yes, he swept the floor this morning.

CHAPTER 3

Quiz 1, p. 18
1. gone
2. seen
3. taken
4. bought
5. taught
6. flown
7. made
8. eaten
9. won
10. stolen
11. fallen
12. built
13. fed
14. ridden
15. lost
16. given
17. forgotten (*British: forgot*)
18. held
19. sung
20. told
21. shaken
22. studied
23. written
24. drunk

Quiz 2, p. 18
1. for
2. for
3. since
4. since
5. since
6. for
7. since
8. for
9. since
10. since

Quiz 3, p. 19
1. for
2. since
3. yet
4. already
5. since
6. still
7. for
8. so far
9. since
10. since

Quiz 4, p. 19
1. has won
2. has already gotten
3. have you called
4. has promised
5. have never eaten
6. haven't understood
7. has tried
8. has driven
9. hasn't been
10. has given

Quiz 5, p. 20
1. b
2. a
3. a
4. b
5. b
6. a
7. b
8. a
9. b
10. a

Quiz 6, p. 21
1. has caught
2. called, haven't called
3. has given
4. met, haven't known
5. worked
6. have changed, saw
7. has grown

Quiz 7, p. 21
1. correct
2. Sarah **has gone** to that museum four times.
3. Niko **has taken** several computer classes.
4. correct
5. Ruth **has been** sick since Monday.
6. Martha **has read** that book several times.
7. correct
8. correct
9. Faisal **has not visited** his grandmother yet.
10. correct

Quiz 8, p. 22
1. have been waiting
2. is taking, has been taking
3. is starting
4. haven't been sleeping
5. have been planning
6. is raining, is blowing

Quiz 9, p. 22
1. had not finished
2. had put
3. had forgotten
4. had broken
5. had lost
6. had had
7. had become
8. had bought
9. had never seen

Quiz 10, p. 23
1. had already finished
2. hadn't finished
3. had died, came
4. had been
5. wanted, had forgotten, was
6. hadn't called

Quiz 11, p. 24

1. had been sleeping
2. had forgotten
3. had already left
4. had been waiting
5. hadn't saved
6. had been trying
7. had lost
8. had gotten
9. hadn't stopped
10. had never had

Quiz 12, p. 25

1. b
2. a
3. a
4. b
5. a
6. b

TEST 1, p. 26

A.

1. b
2. a
3. b
4. a
5. b
6. b
7. a
8. b
9. b
10. a

B.

1. has visited
2. has enjoyed
3. has learned / has been learning
4. had never seen
5. had been looking

C.

1. for
2. still
3. yet
4. already
5. since

D.

1. has been playing / has played
2. has played
3. had been playing
4. had been
5. has played / has been playing
6. has caused
7. has become
8. have watched
9. has scored
10. has won

TEST 2, p. 28

A.

1. b
2. b
3. a
4. a
5. b
6. a
7. b
8. a
9. a
10. a

B.

A.
1. has become
2. has made
3. have been

B.
1. have been
2. had read
3. had been studying / had studied

C.

1. already
2. for
3. still
4. since
5. yet

D.

1. has been building
2. has been working / has worked
3. has been
4. had already learned
5. had won
6. had become
7. had lead
8. had been working / had worked
9. has designed / has been designing
10. have given

CHAPTER 4

Quiz 1, p. 31

1. a. will graduate   b. am going to graduate
2. a. will have   b. is going to have
3. a. will take   b. are going to take
4. a. will fly   b. are going to fly
5. a. will live   b. are going to live

Quiz 2, p. 31

1. prior plan
2. prediction
3. willingness
4. prior plan
5. prediction
6. prior plan
7. willingness
8. prediction
9. prediction
10. prior plan

Quiz 3, p. 32

1. will get
2. am going to take
3. are going to attend
4. will meet
5. is going to work
6. will work
7. will probably clean, am going to go
8. will get
9. are going to come

Quiz 4, p. 33

1. My parents won't let me drive on the freeway.
2. Teri and George aren't going to come to the wedding.
3. That dog won't stop barking.
4. Luigi isn't going to pass / won't pass his math class this semester.
5. Nathan and Lucy are not going to live in Bellingham after this year.
6. You will never get / are never going to get to the airport in this traffic jam.
7. My neighbor won't turn down his music at night.

Quiz 5, p. 33

1. rings, will take
2. finishes, is going to iron
3. will wait, park
4. arrives, is going to rent
5. boils, will make
6. get, am going to travel
7. finds, will be
8. will go, finish
9. will stop, tells
10. are going to love, hear

Quiz 6, p. 34

1. celebrate, am going to have
2. will wait, arrives
3. comes, will pay
4. will be, starts
5. buys, will give
6. is going to watch, goes

Quiz 7, p. 34

1. in the future
2. habitually
3. now
4. in the future
5. habitually
6. habitually
7. in the future
8. habitually
9. in the future
10. now

Quiz 8, p. 35

1. opens / is opening
2. is coming
3. leaves / is leaving
4. are visiting
5. is leaving
6. begins / is beginning
7. are going
8. are buying
9. closes / is closing
10. am meeting

Quiz 9, p. 35

1. will be graduating
2. will be living
3. will be traveling, will be taking
4. will be looking
5. will be enjoying
6. will be taking
7. will be cleaning, will be watching, will be relaxing

Quiz 10, p. 36

A.

1. will have eaten
2. will have finished
3. will have hit
4. will have been
5. will have played

B.

1. will have been playing
2. will have been talking
3. will have been raining
4. will have been living
5. will have been learning

Quiz 11, p. 37

1. At noon tomorrow, he **will be** attending a luncheon at the Hilton Hotel.
2. I **won't** be home until 10:00 P.M. tonight.
3. By the time Mr. Wilcox reads my email, I **will have left** the office.
4. I **am going to** finish my homework after school. (OR **will finish**)
5. After the baby **stops** crying, she will fall asleep.
6. **Will** English be an international language in 25 years?
7. The athletes will have been **training** for several years when the Olympics begin. (OR **will have trained**)
8. The TV program **is** going to start at 8:00.
9. Benjamin **is going to play** at a new golf club this weekend. (or **will play)**
10. In six months, I will **be** living in a new apartment. (OR **will live**)

Quiz 12, p. 37

1. When my brother comes home from school, he will have two cookies and a glass of milk.
2. The construction workers will have been making a lot of noise since early morning.
3. At 10:00 I will be teaching my physics class.
4. By 3:00, Junichi will have finished his essay on studying in the U.S.
5. After we eat dinner at the Ethiopian restaurant, we are going to go to a movie.
6. Carl will be really tired! By the time his favorite TV program ends, he will be falling asleep.
7. As soon as I finish my homework, I am going to call my best friend.
8. After the music stops, everyone will be waiting for the next song.
9. When the fireworks start, the onlookers will clap / are going to clap excitedly.
10. Dr. Solack is going to be seeing patients all day. She is going to be very busy.

TEST 1, p. 39

A.

1. in the future
2. in the future
3. in the future
4. now
5. habitually

B.

1. is going to rain / will rain
2. is going to give
3. will make
4. will go
5. aren't going to be

C.

1. a, b
2. b, a
3. a, c
4. a, b
5. c, a

D.

1. Barbara will be working at the computer until she goes out with her friends.
2. By the time Carol goes to bed, she will have finished correcting all her students' papers.
3. In the morning we will go to the zoo, and then we will eat lunch in the park.
4. When my daughter graduates from the university, I will be so proud.
5. Jason will have never met his girlfriends' parents.

E.

1. The movie **is** going to start at 7:45 P.M. and will end around 10:00.
2. As soon as I find my key, I will **open** the door.
3. The book sale will **help** the students raise money for their trip.
4. By the time he arrives in Boston, Bert will have **spent** three weeks cycling across the U.S.
5. I **won't** lend my brother any money. He will never pay it back! (OR **am not going to**)

TEST 2, p. 41

A.

1. now
2. now
3. in the future
4. in the future
5. habitually

B.
1. will get / am going to get
2. are going to go
3. will help
4. is going to have
5. will be / are going to be

C.
1. c, a   4. b, a
2. a, b   5. a, c
3. a, b

D.
1. Chuck will be giving a lecture in his history class.
2. She will throw her old shoes away and (will) buy some new ones.
3. By 4:00 we will have been sitting on the runway for an hour. Bad weather will have delayed our flight.
4. I will study until it is time to go to my appointment with my lawyer.
5. Michelle will have never ridden on a motorcycle.

E.
1. Tommy **will have lost** twenty pounds by December. (OR **will lose**)
2. The radio station **will be announcing** the name of the prizewinner at 4:30. (OR **will announce**)
3. My cousins **are going to send** me a postcard from Bali when they get there.
4. When you **explain** the situation, your parents will understand your problem.
5. Mr. Ballard **will be** a very good principal for our school. (OR **is going to be**)

CHAPTER 5

TEST 1, p. 43

1. c	6. a	11. a	16. c	21. b
2. a	7. c	12. b	17. a	22. c
3. b	8. c	13. a	18. c	23. a
4. a	9. b	14. c	19. a	24. c
5. b	10. c	15. a	20. c	25. c

TEST 2, p. 45

1. a	6. b	11. b	16. b	21. a
2. b	7. b	12. c	17. a	22. c
3. c	8. c	13. a	18. b	23. a
4. b	9. a	14. c	19. c	24. c
5. a	10. c	15. a	20. b	25. b

CHAPTER 6

Quiz 1, p. 47

1. churches	11. faxes
2. boys	12. salaries
3. chickens	13. lists
4. boxes	14. edges
5. tacks	15. friends
6. ends	16. dishes
7. months	17. businesses
8. glasses	18. minutes
9. ladies	19. valleys
10. coughs	20. families

Quiz 2, p. 47

1. lay	6. is
2. needs	7. require
3. is	8. make
4. aren't	9. has
5. are	10. leave

Quiz 3, p. 48

1. are	6. screams
2. do	7. has
3. has	8. are
4. like	9. requires
5. play	10. lives

Quiz 4, p. 48

1. was	6. last
2. was	7. look
3. were	8. was
4. was	9. Is
5. Do	10. don't

Quiz 5, p. 49

C	I	
	✓	1. Every one of the children **need**s love and affection.
	✓	2. Seventy-five percent of the teachers in our school **speak** Spanish.
✓		3. correct
	✓	4. A lot of my friends **recommend** this apartment complex.
✓		5. correct
	✓	6. The number of restaurants in San Francisco **exceeds** 2,000.
	✓	7. Each of these bowls **is** worth more than $150.
✓		8. correct
	✓	9. One of my **pencils** needs to be sharpened.
	✓	10. Half of the airplanes **leave** on time.

Quiz 6, p. 49

1. are	6. Were
2. have been	7. isn't
3. aren't	8. Is
4. are	9. has been
5. was	10. are

Quiz 7, p. 50

1. are	6. is
2. was	7. isn't
3. are	8. is
4. have been	9. has been
5. are	10. is

Quiz 8, p. 50

1. The news about the earthquakes in Africa **is** very upsetting.
2. correct
3. The United Nations **includes** representatives from more than 190 countries.
4. Physics and mathematics **are** really hard for him.
5. correct
6. correct

7. correct
8. Rabies **is** usually spread by infected animals.
9. correct
10. The *London Times* **reports** daily on the London Stock Exchange.

Quiz 9, p. 51

1. takes
2. come
3. are
4. is
5. have
6. is
7. are
8. is
9. has
10. are

Quiz 10, p. 51

1. rides
2. requires
3. have
4. don't remember
5. is
6. are
7. knows
8. uses
9. take
10. has

TEST 1, p. 52

A.

C	I	
✓		1. correct
	✓	2. I don't know how to correct one of the **mistakes** on my quiz.
✓		3. correct
	✓	4. Every one of my brothers and sisters **was** at my wedding.
	✓	5. The number of Spanish speakers in the United States **increases** every year.
	✓	6. My grandmother, mother, and sister **have** red hair, but my hair is brown.
✓		7. correct
	✓	8. The calls she made on her cell phone **were** expensive.
	✓	9. Some of the **speakers** in the program look interesting.
✓		10. correct

B.

1. are
2. is
3. are
4. is
5. is

C.

1. is
2. is
3. has
4. helps
5. tell
6. is
7. affects

D.

1. is
2. is
3. are
4. are
5. help
6. have
7. is
8. buys
9. spend
10. comes

TEST 2, p. 54

A.

C	I	
✓		1. correct
	✓	2. Each carry-on bag and purse **was** checked carefully at the security gate.
	✓	3. The number of crimes in the city **is** decreasing.
	✓	4. Growing roses **is** my neighbor's specialty.
✓		5. correct
✓		6. correct
	✓	7. Every one of the students **attends** class regularly.
✓		8. correct
	✓	9. Running marathons **takes** discipline, endurance, and strength.
	✓	10. The flowers in my garden **need** a lot of water every day.

B.

1. Are
2. is
3. are
4. are
5. is

C.

1. is
2. like
3. is
4. sounds
5. is
6. are
7. consists

D.

1. happens
2. take
3. leave
4. ride
5. are
6. serve
7. ride
8. make
9. increases
10. is

CHAPTER 7

Quiz 1, p. 56

-s	-es	-ves	no change
beliefs	echoes	lives	deer
cliffs	foxes	loaves	sheep
memos	heroes	shelves	species
pianos	tomatoes	wolves	shrimp
solos	bushes		

Quiz 2, p. 56

1. ladies, men
2. teeth
3. hypotheses
4. tickets
5. mice
6. children
7. phenomena

Quiz 3, p. 57

1. Mr. Jones'/Mr. Jones's
2. Marissa and George's
3. group's
4. children's
5. boss'/boss's
6. Andrea's
7. baby's
8. cousins'
9. building's
10. month's

Quiz 4, p. 57

1. woman's
2. wife's
3. Rhonda, Mick's
4. movie's
5. friends
6. parents'
7. brother's
8. forecaster's
9. Shakespeare's
10. magazines

Quiz 5, p. 58

1. Simone works at a **shoe** store.
2. The **three-week** vacation was enough for us to really relax.
3. The movie was **two hours long.**
4. There are several **seventeen-year-old students** (OR **seventeen year olds**) in our class.
5. My grandmother makes the best **tomato** sauce.
6. In many countries **eighteen years** old is the legal age for voting.
7. I needed a **steak** knife to cut the thick piece of meat.
8. The **storm** clouds were gathering in the western sky.
9. The **flower shop** has a special on roses this week.
10. The Plaza Hotel is a **well-known** hotel in New York City.

Quiz 6, p. 58

1. Our teacher gave us *suggestions* on how to be successful students. We appreciated her *advice*.
2. My dad bought new *luggage* for his trip. He got three large *suitcases* and a small duffle bag.
3. I just got today's *mail*. There are *bills* and a magazine.
4. Everyone admired the old man's *knowledge*.
5. Pat always puts *pepper* on his food. He likes spicy *dishes*.
6. David bought *coffee, butter,* and *apples* at the grocery store yesterday.
7. The queen's necklace was made of *gold* and *diamonds*.
8. Many Chinese meals include *rice, meat,* and *vegetables*.
9. Lee received twenty *dollars* from his aunt for his birthday. Now he has enough *money* to buy a new game.
10. Marcos enjoys reading *poetry* in his free time.

Quiz 7, p. 59

1. beef
2. chess
3. lights
4. luck
5. oranges
6. chickens
7. coffee
8. hair
9. homework
10. trips

Quiz 8, p. 59

1. An
2. Ø Leather
3. A
4. A
5. Ø Computers
6. Ø Baseball
7. A
8. Ø Oranges
9. An
10. Ø Children

Quiz 9, p. 60

1. a
2. b
3. a
4. a
5. c
6. a
7. b
8. b
9. a
10. c

Quiz 10, p. 61

1. the
2. Ø
3. Ø
4. the
5. the
6. Ø
7. The
8. the
9. Ø, Strawberries
10. the

Quiz 11, p. 61

1. an
2. the, a
3. a, a, The, The
4. Ø, an, a
5. Ø, a, Ø, a

Quiz 12, p. 62

1. a, the
2. Ø
3. the
4. a, Ø, an
5. Ø, Ø
6. the, an, the
7. the
8. Ø, the, the

Quiz 13, p. 63

1. many years
2. much time
3. many questions
4. much stuff
5. many theories
6. much patience
7. many reasons
8. many varieties
9. many sheep
10. much information

Quiz 14, p. 64

A.
1. little
2. a few
3. a little
4. few
5. a little

B.
1. a few
2. few
3. little
4. a few
5. a little

Quiz 15, p. 65

1. a
2. b
3. b
4. a
5. a
6. b
7. a
8. b
9. a
10. b

Quiz 16, p. 66

1. I found several ~~of~~ new movies at the video store.
2. Mr. McDonnell is unhappy about his **daughter's** wedding plans. She is too young to get married.
3. When Greg was a college student, he didn't have **much** / **any** money for going out.
4. My mom set the table with knives, forks, **salad** forks, and spoons.
5. The **flower shop** across the street has the most beautiful roses I've ever seen.
6. Mary has **a** few good friends. She enjoys spending time with them.
7. My teacher gave me some good **advice**.
8. Fifty percent of my classmates **are** from Asia.
9. Maurice doesn't like ~~the~~ fruit, but he loves vegetables.
10. I have a **sixteen-year-old** sister.
11. Two **deer** were standing near the lake in the early morning.
12. ~~The~~ English is an international language.
13. Joan needs more **bookshelves** in her room. She has lots of books.

14. One of the **students** / **One student** asked the teacher for help after class.
15. Steve loves sports. **A̶ Basketball** is his favorite game.

TEST 1, p. 67

A.
1. videos
2. feet
3. pianos
4. knives
5. roofs

B.
1. students'
2. friend's
3. Doris'/Doris's
4. men's
5. patients'

C.
1. I love *snow* in the winter, especially when it falls in big *flakes*.
2. The *information* on the internet is much more current than in printed *articles*.
3. Grace has had some good *jobs*. She really enjoys her *work* as a customer service representative.
4. *Life* is an adventure full of interesting *experiences*.
5. Baxter bought a lot of *stamps*. He was unsure about how much *postage* he needed.

D.
1. Ø, some, the, the
2. the, the, a
3. the, some, an

E.
1. When Gloria went to the zoo yesterday, she took **a̶** few pictures because it was raining.
2. My nephew is going to be **eighteen years old** on his next birthday.
3. One of the **problems** facing big cities is homelessness.
4. Brian was late for work because there were so many **cars** / **vehicles** on the road. OR Brian was late for work because **there was so much traffic**.
5. Outside the train station there is a **bicycle** rack where Ron can lock up his bike.

F.
1. some things
2. the
3. lots of
4. some
5. some
6. a few
7. the
8. vegetable
9. meat
10. the
11. the

TEST 2, p. 69

A.
1. sheep
2. thieves
3. mice
4. crises
5. teeth

B.
1. this morning's
2. ladies'
3. Louis'/Louis's
4. city's
5. Patty and Mike's

C.
1. Tim spent a lot of time on his *homework*. He had to finish *assignments* in chemistry and math.
2. Nina has fun trying on *dresses* and *shoes*. She loves to shop for *clothing*.
3. The *garbage* didn't fit in the trash can. **(no change)**

4. The police found several *hairs* at the crime scene while they were gathering *evidence*.
5. It was difficult to lose *weight*, but I lost twenty *pounds*.

D.
1. Ø, a, Ø, a
2. an, The, a
3. an, a, some

E.
1. Mr. Johnson sent his lawyer a **six-page** letter about his estate.
2. When I asked him for advice, he didn't have **many** suggestions.
3. I have only a **few** minutes to finish my homework.
4. Most of **the** parking spaces in the parking lot are full.
5. This store accepts both **o̶f̶** credit cards and traveler's checks.

F.
1. a
2. many things
3. a little
4. some
5. a lot of
6. a few
7. a
8. some
9. the
10. all my

CHAPTER 8

Quiz 1, p. 71
1. Maria
2. Sean and Adam
3. cats
4. the championship game
5. My parents and I
6. caffeine
7. Coffee, tea, and cola
8. the point of the lecture OR the lecture
9. James
10. My sister

Quiz 2, p. 71
1. She, her
2. they, them
3. it, He, us
4. he, him, him
5. they

Quiz 3, p. 72
1. mine, yours
2. Their, ours
3. her
4. His
5. Your, my
6. Their, It's
7. Her, their
8. Our, its

Quiz 4, p. 72
1. Its
2. mine
3. His
4. my
5. her
6. yours
7. Their
8. Our
9. her
10. his

Quiz 5, p. 73
1. his / her / his or her
2. They are
3. his / her / his or her
4. his / her / his or her
5. they practice OR he / she practices

6. his / her / his or her
7. It has
8. forgets his / her / his or her
9. They
10. his / her / his or her

Quiz 6, p. 74

1. yourself
2. themselves
3. himself
4. ourselves
5. themselves
6. itself
7. herself
8. himself
9. myself

Quiz 7, p. 74

1. themselves
2. herself
3. himself
4. myself
5. yourself
6. ourselves
7. himself
8. themselves
9. herself
10. myself

Quiz 8, p. 75

1. others
2. another
3. the other
4. others
5. another
6. another, the others
7. the others
8. Another, other

Quiz 9, p. 75

1. each other
2. one after another
3. every other
4. another
5. one another
6. the other
7. In other words
8. other than

Quiz 10, p. 76

1. A good employee does **his / her / his or her** job well.
2. Anna and **I** will fly to Toronto on Sunday.
3. Everybody on the bus was talking on **his / her / his or her** cell phone.
4. I was happy when I saw **myself** in the picture. I looked good!
5. Ted worked there for two years. The first year was in accounting and **the other** was in marketing.
6. In my grammar class, some students are from Korea, ~~the~~ others are from China, and the others are from Vietnam.
7. Maria wanted to use my phone, so I lent it to **her**.
8. Mr. Carlson forgot **his** jacket on the bus yesterday.
9. My family travels to Japan every **other** year.
10. Susan's family **is** large. She has five brothers and three sisters.
11. The businessmen introduced **themselves** at the meeting.
12. The support staff in our company **consists** of 50 people.
13. **We** and our parents have dinner together every week.
14. Where did you park **your** car?
15. Willy repaired the computer by **himself** and saved a lot of money.

TEST 1, p. 77

A.
1. I, my, he, me
2. her, she
3. her, She, him, his
4. their, They, him
5. his, hers

B.
1. class
2. family
3. bus driver
4. couple
5. committee
6. somebody

C.
1. himself
2. myself
3. herself
4. themselves
5. yourself
6. ourselves
7. itself

D.
1. others
2. the others
3. other
4. another
5. the other

E.
1. every other
2. one another
3. the other
4. Other than
5. one after the other
6. another
7. In other words

F.
1. he, He, his
2. they, their
3. We, our
4. his / her, He / She
5. they, they, them

TEST 2, p. 80

A.
1. We, our, us
2. her, She, him, hers
3. her, them
4. you, your, you
5. I, our, They

B.
1. public
2. dentist
3. audience
4. everyone
5. team
6. faculty

C.
1. myself
2. ourselves
3. himself
4. themselves
5. herself
6. itself
7. yourself

D.
1. The other
2. the others
3. others

E.
1. another
2. each other
3. one after the other
4. the other
5. other than
6. In other words
7. every other

F.
1. they, them, they
2. it, It
3. They, they, their
4. it, It
5. he / she / he or she, he / she / he or she, his / her / his or her

CHAPTER 9

Quiz 1, p. 83

1. request
2. permission
3. permission
4. request
5. request
6. request
7. permission
8. request
9. permission
10. permission

Quiz 2, p. 83

1. you
2. I
3. I
4. you
5. you
6. I
7. you
8. you
9. you
10. I

Quiz 3, p. 84

A.
1. if I ate
2. lending
3. if I borrowed
4. telling
5. if I gave

B.
1. helping me with my homework
2. if I went to a café
3. if I took a nap
4. carrying the box
5. waiting for me

Quiz 4, p. 85

1. a
2. b
3. c
4. a
5. b
6. a
7. c
8. a
9. b
10. c

Quiz 5, p. 86

1. must / has to go
2. must / have to study
3. don't have to go
4. must / has to take
5. must not smoke
6. must / have to do
7. doesn't have to worry
8. must / have to finish
9. must / has to pay
10. must not cross

Quiz 6, p. 87

1. advice
2. duty
3. warning
4. advice
5. advice
6. duty
7. warning
8. advice
9. duty
10. warning

Quiz 7, p. 87

1. had better OR must
2. must / have to
3. had to
4. should
5. should OR must / has to
6. must / have to
7. should OR had better
8. had better OR have to / must
9. should, should OR have to / must

Quiz 8, p. 88

1. should have
2. shouldn't have
3. shouldn't have
4. should have
5. shouldn't have
6. should have
7. shouldn't have
8. should have
9. shouldn't have
10. should have
11. should have
12. shouldn't have

Quiz 9, p. 89

1. No
2. Yes
3. Yes
4. No
5. Yes
6. No
7. Yes
8. Yes

Quiz 10, p. 89

1. Ø, I / we
2. I
3. You, you
4. Ø, we
5. you
6. we
7. you

Quiz 11, p. 90

1. could
2. could, should
3. should
4. could
5. should
6. should
7. could, could, should

Quiz 12, p. 91

2. should have
3. could have
4. should
5. should have
6. could
7. should have
8. could
9. could have
10. should
11. should have

Quiz 13, p. 92

1. May I **borrow** your grammar book?
2. Could you please ~~to~~ turn the air-conditioning off? I'm cold.
3. Mr. Sutherland is rich. He **doesn't have to** work for a living.
4. I should have **studied** for the quiz, but I didn't.
5. Why don't you ~~will~~ call me tomorrow?
6. Olivia and Robert should **get** / **have gotten** married.
7. If you lose your credit card, you should ~~to~~ **cancel** the card immediately.
8. John must **go** to bed at 8:30 tonight.
9. When Mark **is** sick, he should stay home. OR When Mark was sick, he **should have stayed** home.
10. Let's ~~we~~ go to the grocery store. I need some milk.

TEST 1, p. 93

A.
1. if I opened the window
2. you help me wash the dishes
3. taking me to the airport
4. I go to a movie tonight
5. you vacuum the carpet

B.
1. had to
2. do (we) have to
3. must not
4. have to
5. don't have to

C.
1. should (not) have
2. could
3. should have
4. could have
5. should

D.
1. must, could, should
2. don't have to, Why don't, have to, could, have to, had better, should have

E.
1. Silvia must **send** out her thank-you notes soon.
2. In the United States, children are **supposed** to go to school until age sixteen.
3. **Could** you please help me move this table?
4. Tony shouldn't have **come** to school with the flu.
5. Would you mind **calling** me tomorrow?

TEST 2, p. 95

A.
1. you put the laundry away
2. if I got a drink of water
3. you tell me what time it is
4. I go shopping
5. emptying the garbage

B.
1. have to
2. must not
3. must / have to, had to
4. don't have to, don't have to

C.
1. should have
2. could have
3. could
4. should
5. should (not) have

D.
1. could, Should, Let's, would, had better
2. have to, should, Why don't, Would, have to

E.
1. Matthew should not **have** fallen asleep at work yesterday.
2. I must ~~to~~ help my parents in their store after school, so I can't play basketball.
3. Lindsay **had better** ~~to~~ call me tonight.
4. Would you mind if I **left** work early today?
5. When does Ben **have** to be at the airport?

CHAPTER 10

Quiz 1, p. 97
1. must
2. may
3. couldn't
4. may
5. might not
6. might
7. must
8. must not
9. could, might

Quiz 2, p. 98
1. must
2. may / could / might
3. must
4. may / could / might
5. must
6. could / must
7. may / might / could
8. may / might / could, may / might
9. must

Quiz 3, p. 99
1. may / might / could have gone
2. can't / couldn't have gotten
3. may / might / could have had
4. must have been
5. must not have slept
6. may / might / could have hit
7. may / might / could have missed

8. must not / couldn't / can't have been
9. may / might / could have been
10. must have been

Quiz 4, p. 100
1. Joyce may / might / could have forgotten her cell phone at home.
2. Joyce can't / couldn't have forgotten our meeting.
3. Joyce must have left her office late.
4. George may / might / could have parked on a different street.
5. The police must have towed the car away.
6. George may / might not have parked the car legally.
7. George may / might / could have had many unpaid parking tickets before this.

Quiz 5, p. 101
1. a. Jane
   b. Martha
   c. Mark
2. a. Alice's
   b. Kay's
   c. Jack's
3. a. Ms. Callahan
   b. Mr. Anton
   c. Mrs. Chu
4. a. Megan
   b. Holly
   c. Esther

Quiz 6, p. 102
1. may / might / could be talking
2. should have been listening
3. may / might / could have been taking
4. must be eating
5. should be cleaning
6. could / may / must have been driving
7. should have been sleeping
8. may / might / could be washing
9. must have been crying
10. should be paying

Quiz 7, p. 103
1. possibility
2. an acquired skill
3. permission
4. a physical ability
5. an acquired skill
6. a physical ability
7. possibility
8. permission
9. a physical ability
10. possibility

Quiz 8, p. 104
1. can
2. couldn't
3. can't / couldn't
4. can't / couldn't
5. can
6. can / could
7. can't
8. could
9. could
10. can

Quiz 9, p. 105

C   I

✓   ___   1. correct

___   ✓   2. Lisa **used to** be able to speak Chinese when she was younger, but she can't anymore.

✓   ___   3. correct

✓   ___   4. correct

✓   ___   5. correct

✓   ___   6. correct

___   ✓   7. Alex **used to** work for Microsoft last year, but now he is working for Apple Computer.

___   ✓   8. I **used to** study at the University of Florida before I transferred to the University of Georgia.

✓   ___   9. correct

___   ✓   10. In 2007 Mary **used to** live in a chic apartment in midtown Manhattan. She loved it!

Quiz 10, p. 106

1. would rather take
2. would rather have
3. would rather not cook
4. would rather be sleeping
5. would rather have gone
6. would rather visit
7. would rather plant / would rather have planted
8. would rather have gotten
9. would rather not be taking, would rather be playing

Quiz 11, p. 107

1. Alice must have **forgotten** her phone at home. She doesn't have it with her.
2. Children **have** got to go to bed early on school nights.
3. The meeting with our attorney is **supposed** to start at 9:30 A.M.
4. Dan had better not ~~to~~ use bad language around his parents.
5. I might **be able to** meet you at the airport.
6. Jason should **have** spent less money on my birthday present.
7. Maxine would rather **drink** coffee than tea.
8. May I **borrow** your dictionary?
9. Students may **leave** the examination room when they finish the test. It's allowed.
10. That couldn't **be** true! I don't believe it!
11. Charles must be ~~to~~ at work by 5:30 A.M. every morning.
12. My uncle Willy will not **be able to** come for a visit this summer.
13. Emily, **will** / **can** you lend me twenty dollars until Saturday?
14. We haven't seen John since summer. We **may** / **might** / **could** get together with him this weekend.
15. When I was growing up, we could **ride** our bicycles all over my hometown.

TEST 1, p. 108

A.
1. could / may / might be
2. must be / must have been
3. can / could change, could / may / might be
4. could / may / might need
5. should finish

B.
1. a. Linda   2. a. Mr. French
   b. Liz   b. Mrs. White
   c. Sam   c. Ms. Adams

C.
1. should be leaving
2. could / may / might be raining
3. must / could / may / might be leaking
4. should be cleaning
5. could / may / might be meeting

D.
1. couldn't   4. can't
2. can   5. could, can
3. can

E.
1. would call   4. would play
2. would rather be eating   5. would rather live
3. would give

TEST 2, p. 111

A.
1. may / might / could / would rather go, should do
2. may / might / could change
3. must be / must have been
4. can / could leave, may / might be able to
5. can / may / might / not get

B.
1. a. Eva   2. a. Kevin
   b. Ken   b. Julie
   c. Jeff   c. Mr. Chang
              d. Tom

C.
1. must be looking
2. may / might / could be playing, may / might / could be reading
3. may / might / could be studying
4. should / must be going, should / must be getting

D.
1. Can   4. couldn't
2. could   5. can
3. can't

E.
1. would take   4. would rather pass
2. would rather take   5. would study
3. would rather have seen

CHAPTER 11

Quiz 1, p. 113

1. P   6. P
2. P   7. A
3. A   8. A
4. P   9. P
5. A   10. P

Quiz 2, p. 113

1. a   4. a
2. b   5. b
3. a   6. b

Quiz 3, p. 114

1. were stolen
2. is going to be discussed
3. has been found, will be given
4. is enjoyed
5. had already been helped, was taken
6. will have been given
7. are being analyzed
8. was woken up

Quiz 4, p. 115

1. My car **was hit** by a speeding truck.
2. no change
3. Several of the downtown office buildings **have been damaged** by an earthquake.
4. The rock band's first CD **was recorded** last year. OR The first CD **was recorded** by the rock band last year.
5. no change
6. The reservations are going to **be made** by the travel agent very soon.
7. no change
8. All of the windows **were washed** last weekend.
9. The artist's masterpiece **was completed** when she was only 25 years old. OR The masterpiece **was completed** by the artist when she was only 25 years old.
10. Many scientists believe that global warming **has been caused** by humans. OR It **is believed** by many scientists that humans have caused global warming. OR It **is believed** by many scientists that global warming **has been caused** by humans.

Quiz 5, p. 116

1. are eaten
2. was invented
3. will be finished / is going to be finished
4. has not been elected
5. was hit, was given / has been given
6. is being shown / will be shown / is going to be shown
7. were given
8. is taught, are introduced

Quiz 6, p. 117

2. are read
3. (are) studied
4. were written
5. were performed
6. had not been published
7. have been translated
8. have been printed
9. are seen
10. are being kept / have been kept
11. will be enjoyed

Quiz 7, p. 117

1. The east coast of Florida **was hit** by Hurricane Betty two days ago.
2. The storm winds **reached** speeds of 150 miles per hour.
3. Many houses **were damaged** in the storm.
4. Many people **went** to stay with friends and relatives.
5. Injured people **were taken care of** by aid workers.
6. Many coastal towns **lost** electricity during the storm.
7. The damage **was assessed** in the morning after the storm.
8. Some people **were not allowed** to go back to their homes.

Quiz 8, p. 118

1. must be checked
2. ought not to be fired
3. has to be finished
4. can't be identified
5. should sit
6. must have been started
7. should be split / should split
8. had better be fixed
9. may have been injured
10. may be given / may have been given

Quiz 9, p. 119

Sample answers:
1. All food must be rinsed from plastics, glass, and cans. Plastics, glass, and cans should be rinsed clean.
2. Clean boxes and paper items can / should be pressed flat.
3. Paper with food on it must not be recycled. It should be put in the trash. Paper with food on it should not be put in the recycle bin. It must be put in the trash.
4. All clean recyclable items can / should be put into your recycling bin.
5. Recycling bins should / must be put out for pick up by 7:00 A.M. on collection day.

Quiz 10, p. 119

1. with / by
2. about
3. to
4. with
5. for
6. to
7. of
8. to
9. to
10. with / by

Quiz 11, p. 120

2. is terrified by
3. is limited by
4. are crowded with
5. is located in
6. Are (you) done with
7. is composed of
8. am annoyed by
9. is remembered for
10. are excited about
11. is prepared for

Quiz 12, p. 121

1. b, c
2. a, d
3. b, d
4. b, d
5. a, b
6. a
7. a, c, d
8. a, b, d

Quiz 13, p. 122

2. got arrested
3. have gotten killed
4. got done
5. am getting worried
6. got damaged
7. get (it) fixed
8. got finished
9. gets taken / will get taken
10. am getting accustomed
11. get arrested

Quiz 14, p. 123

1. depressing
2. surprised
3. thrilling
4. excited
5. embarrassing
6. annoyed
7. shocked
8. frustrating
9. disappointing
10. injured

Quiz 15, p. 123

1. entertaining
2. embarrassed
3. frightening
4. boring
5. confusing
6. frustrated
7. fascinating
8. surprised
9. satisfying
10. annoyed

Quiz 16, p. 124

1. a
2. c
3. c
4. d
5. c
6. a
7. c
8. b
9. a
10. c
11. b
12. d
13. a
14. d
15. d

TEST 1, p. 126

A.
1. was taken, was arrested
2. was made / will be made
3. are encouraged / have been encouraged / are being encouraged / were encouraged
4. has been given / was given / is going to be given / will be given
5. is being played

B.
1. Cell phones are being used by nearly everyone these days.
2. The snow will be cleared from the roof by Rick and Dennis later today.
3. The old book was lent to the university by the museum. OR
   The university was lent the old book by the museum.
4. Government offices, schools, and many businesses are closed on holidays.
5. Our car is being fixed (by the mechanic) at Maher's Auto Repair.

C.
1. should be obeyed
2. could have been given
3. should arrive
4. must be finished
5. can be seen

D.
1. of
2. in
3. to
4. in / with
5. with
6. with / by
7. for

E.
1. interesting
2. exciting
3. fascinated, amazing
4. frightening
5. embarrassed

F.
1. d
2. a
3. c
4. a
5. c
6. a
7. c
8. c
9. a
10. d

TEST 2, p. 129

A.
1. has been asked / was asked / is being asked / will be asked
2. will be given
3. is scheduled
4. were agreed / have been agreed
5. is being loaded, will be finished

B.
1. Scholarships are being given to many students from low-income families. OR
   Many students from low-income families are being given scholarships.
2. Michael was hit on the head by a falling pine cone.
3. Each computer is checked five times before they put it in a box for shipping. OR
   Each computer is checked five times before it is put in a box for shipping.
4. The weeds on the hill are going to be cut down.
5. The Cancer Foundation was given $2 million. OR
   The Cancer Foundation was given $2 million by an anonymous donor.
   Two million dollars was given to the Cancer Foundation.

C.
1. should have been eaten
2. must have left
3. can always be counted
4. should be baked / should have been baked
5. may be invited / may have been invited

D.
1. about
2. with
3. to
4. for
5. from
6. with / by
7. to

E.
1. embarrassing
2. expected, surprising
3. balanced
4. Experienced
5. thrilling

F.
1. c
2. b
3. a
4. b
5. b
6. a
7. b
8. a
9. c
10. c

CHAPTER 12

Quiz 1, p. 132

1. how much the tickets are.
2. when the final exam is.
3. if her dad would give her a ride to school.
4. what happened.
5. That we start on time
6. what time it is?
7. who the man was OR why he had come to the meeting.
8. that we had to pay $90 to take the exam.
9. what the weather forecast for tomorrow is.
10. that carpooling to work was a good idea.

Quiz 2, p. 132

1. what the purpose of your visit is.
2. who the mayor of Shoreline is?
3. How much Sue's car cost

4. how much time we have left.
5. who left the door unlocked.
6. which pages we are supposed to study.
7. where the nearest post office is?
8. why there is so much traffic today.
9. How they will solve their financial problems
10. whose dictionary that is.

Quiz 3, p. 133

1. A: did your digital camera cost
   B: I paid
2. A: he parked / he had parked
   B: I can't find
3. A: did you sell / have you sold
   B: Ted sold / Ted has sold
4. does it say
5. A: the key is
   B: is it
   A: it is

Quiz 4, p. 134

Sample answers:

1. I don't know if / whether Mandy is going to pass her chemistry class.
2. We can ask the mail clerk if / whether an overnight mail package arrived today or not.
3. Whether or not Andy likes the new basketball coach is unknown.
4. Let's find out if / whether anyone has seen the new show at the Paramount.
5. I meant to ask you if / whether Jim was at the party last night or not.
6. Please let me know if / whether you prefer coffee or tea for breakfast.
7. I wonder if / whether Ken had ever been to an opera before last night or not.
8. Whether / Whether or not Tom minds when his brother practices the drums is unimportant.
9. I need to know if / whether the Smiths are coming over for dinner on Saturday or not.
10. Liz isn't sure if / whether she will be going to Orlando with us or not.

Quiz 5, p. 135

A.
1. Mick showed me how to solve a Sudoku puzzle.
2. I can't decide whether or not to travel over the holidays.
3. Julie wanted to know when to start the barbecue.
4. I had several huge flowerpots that I didn't want. I wondered what to do with them.
5. Sandy and Jack discussed where to go on vacation.

B. *Possible answers:*
1. how to do / how to solve / how to figure out
2. how to get / how to go / how to drive
3. where to find / where to get
4. what to do
5. whether to paint / whether to make

Quiz 6, p. 136

A.
1. Are you sure **that** you didn't leave your cell phone in the car?

2. It's a fact **that** pirates captured a boat off the coast of Africa recently.
3. **That** Steve failed his driving test is unfortunate.
4. Did I remind you **that** we are going shopping after work?
5. Ginger is excited **that** she will go to Costa Rica in March.

B.
1. That Sarah won't be able to attend the ceremony is unfortunate.
2. It is unlikely that the doctor gave you the wrong prescription.
3. It's a miracle that the little boy survived the plane crash.
4. That Rosa didn't finish the project on time surprises me.
5. That no one will pass this class without additional help from the teacher is clear.

Quiz 7, p. 137

Sample answers:

2. That Martha and Jim will arrive tomorrow is wonderful.
3. It's wonderful that Mary got an award for Teacher of the Year.
4. I'm lucky that I have a very loving and supportive family.
5. Martin is confident that our soccer team is going to do well this season.
6. Scientists believe (that) a meteorite hit the earth 65 million years ago.
7. It is unfortunate that a number of the tests were graded incorrectly.
8. That my daughter got a job as a flight attendant with Amazon Airlines is wonderful.
9. I promise that I will pay back the money I borrowed by the end of the month.

Quiz 8, p. 138

1. "Where are you going on your vacation?" Ruth asked.
2. "We are going on a road trip to Alaska," replied Anne.
3. "Wow." said Ruth, "That sounds like fun. How long will you be gone?"
4. "Around three weeks," answered Anne. "We are going to tour the southeast coast and visit a glacier. We also hope to go to one of the national parks."
5. "I hear Alaska is beautiful," commented Ruth, "so you're sure to have a wonderful vacation."
6. "Yes," added Anne, "and we're sure to put lots of miles on our car."

Quiz 9, p. 138

1. what time the meeting started
2. (that) the earth has seven continents and five oceans
3. if I played golf
4. (that) they had forgotten to pick up their dry cleaning
5. (that) she had a lot of work to do today / that day
6. if we had ever been to Mexico
7. that he will / would be here in fifteen minutes
8. if there were any new magazines available
9. (that) he thought that was an excellent book
10. why the sky is blue

Quiz 10, p. 139

Sample answers:

1. David's mom asked him how his English test had been, and he replied that it hadn't been too hard.
2. When Harry said that he was so tired, Max told him that he should get more sleep.
3. Doug asked a clerk where the shoe department was, and she / he told him it was on the second floor. Doug thanked the clerk for his / her help.
4. Susan said that she had her first accounting class, and Carol asked her who her instructor was. Susan told her that her instructor was Professor Nelson. Carol replied that she had been in her class last year and thought she was great.
5. My brother Jim asked me if I had any plans for the weekend. I told him I didn't have anything special planned and asked why he wanted to know. He told me that he had some tickets for the baseball game on Saturday, and he asked me if I wanted to go. I agreed that it sounded like fun, and asked what time the game was. Jim told me the game started at two, but that we should probably leave by one or so. I accepted his offer and told him I would love to go with him, and I offered to buy the hot dogs.

Quiz 11, p. 140

1. wherever
2. Whenever
3. whatever
4. Whoever
5. whichever
6. however
7. Whenever
8. whoever
9. whichever
10. whatever

Quiz 12, p. 141

1. The student asked her counselor which class she should ~~to take~~. OR
   The student asked her counselor which class to take.
2. I'm not sure **if** we will buy a new car this year (**or not**). OR
   I'm not sure **whether** we will buy a new car this year (**or not**). OR
   I'm not sure **whether or not** we will buy a new car this year.
3. Can you tell me what time ~~does~~ the concert **starts**?
4. I know Nellie will be accepted to **whichever** college she chooses.
5. Marcos knows ~~if~~ that I am going to ride to Vancouver with him.
6. Marcy asked the clerk how much the bag ~~does~~ cost.
7. How many times a month **do** you visit your grandparents?
8. That Jordan was angry ~~it~~ was obvious.
9. I wonder **if it is** supposed to rain tomorrow.
10. Whenever ~~time~~ you want to go is fine with me.

TEST 1, p. 142

A.
1. when Flight 2803 arrives
2. if the mail has already been picked up
3. how the fire started
4. what grade I got on the last quiz
5. if Jim would prefer a sweater or a shirt

B.
1. don't know what else to say
2. didn't know which way to go or whom to ask for help
3. wasn't sure what to do or how to begin

4. can't decide whether to go on a trip or visit his family during the holidays

C.
1. That James is lying is a shame. OR
   It is a shame that James is lying.
2. I am amazed that Sophie got 100% on the vocabulary quiz.
3. It is a fact that women live longer than men. OR
   That women live longer than men is a fact.
4. I agree that the coffee at the Campus Café is terrible.
5. That Max's father has six names is unusual. OR
   It is unusual that Max's father has six names.

D.
1. "I don't want to waste time," said Mary, "so let's hurry."
2. **"W**hy did the mother bird fly away from the nest**?"** asked Jimmy.
3. Valerie told the tour group, **"P**lease stay close together so no one gets lost**."**
4. "Mr. Donovan is our attorney," Margaret said. **"H**e is very good**."**
5. When he saw the car coming towards them, James shouted, **"**Look out!**"**

E.
Sample answer:

When Anita asked the clerk if they sold computer accessories, he asked what she was looking for. Anita said she needed a wireless mouse for her laptop. The clerk asked Anita what kind of computer she had. When she said she had a Sony Notebook, he showed her those that should work with her computer. Anita thanked him.

F.
1. whenever / wherever
2. whatever
3. whichever
4. whoever
5. however

TEST 2, p. 144

A.
1. how often you go to the gym
2. if / whether Teresa stayed after school for the meeting
3. what time the movie starts
4. where she went after the lecture
5. if / whether her meetings usually end on time

B.
1. can't decide which one to invite to the school dance
2. asked the doctor how often to take the medicine
3. told us how many words to write, what type size to use, and when to turn it in
4. told the actors to rehearse their lines more before the performance

C.
1. That Mischa needs to study harder is the truth. OR
   It is the truth that Mischa needs to study harder.
2. It is too bad that Emma had to take her driving test three times before she passed.
3. Many Chinese are proud that the Chinese have used traditional medicines for thousands of years.
4. That too much sun can cause skin cancer is a well-known fact. OR
   It is a well-known fact that too much sun can cause skin cancer.
5. Jason is glad that the library is a quiet place to study.

D.
1. "**A**re you ready to order?" asked the waiter.
2. "**P**lease help me," Doug begged. "**T**his box is too heavy for me to carry."
3. "I don't want to go home!" cried the angry child.
4. "**I**t is an unusual problem," said the scientist, "but I think we can find a solution."
5. Ms. Bell said to the students, "**P**lease talk quietly in the library."

E.
Sample answer:
Mr. Thomas told Mary that she hadn't done well on the quiz, and he asked her what had happened. She said that she really hadn't had enough time to study, so Mr. Thomas asked her why. She told him that her mother had been sick and she had been taking care of her. Mr. Thomas said that Mary should have told him because she could have taken the quiz on a different day.

F.
1. however	4. whatever
2. wherever	5. Whoever
3. whichever	

CHAPTER 13

Quiz 1, p. 146
1. a, b, c	6. d
2. c, d	7. a, b, c
3. a, c	8. c, d
4. c, d	9. a, b, c
5. b	10. c, d

Quiz 2, p. 147
1. Robin told the children a story that / which made them laugh.
2. Jason met a famous baseball player who / that had hit many homeruns during his career.
3. The pianist played a Mozart concerto that / which was one of Mark's favorite pieces of music.
4. My roommate invited her brother who(m) / that / Ø I had never met before to our party.
5. The new computer that / which / Ø I just bought last week makes my work easier.
6. Angela, who has three younger sisters and a younger brother, is the oldest child in her family.
7. The elderly woman who(m) / that / Ø Anne helped with yard work was grateful.
8. Julia's husband gave her a beautiful bouquet of roses that / which / Ø he bought at the flower market.

Quiz 3, p. 147
1. who	6. who
2. whose	7. who
3. who	8. whose
4. whose	9. whose
5. whose	10. whose

Quiz 4, p. 148
1. The boy whose father is a dentist has beautiful teeth.
2. We want to do business with that company whose products are top quality.
3. Sarah feels sorry for her neighbors whose car was stolen last night.
4. The student whose homework was never done came to class late every day.
5. I have never met Meg's brother, whose wife is the conductor of the symphony orchestra.
6. The dog whose back leg is injured always begs for food.
7. Ellen met a kind man whose parents died when he was very young.
8. The Johnsons, whose son goes to Stanford University, live in the apartment upstairs.

Quiz 5, p. 149
1. where	6. when
2. when	7. where
3. where	8. when
4. where	9. where
5. when	10. when

Quiz 6, p. 150
1. My favorite season is spring when the daffodils and tulips bloom.
2. That is the furniture store where we bought our couch and coffee table.
3. The store where they sell many Scandinavian products is near our house.
4. Jim remembers a time when gasoline cost $1.25 per gallon.
5. The Chinese restaurant where we ate dinner served delicious seafood.
6. Do you know the name of the city where the Olympic games will be held?
7. Every student looks forward to the day when school gets out.
8. I last saw Jerry on that day when he got his new car.

Quiz 7, p. 151
2. f	
3. h	
4. a	
5. c	
6. d	
7. k	
8. e	
9. j	
10. g	
11. b	

Quiz 8, p. 152
1. b	4. a
2. a	5. a
3. a	

Quiz 9, p. 152
1. The city of Dubrovnik, which is on the Adriatic coast, is surrounded by an ancient stone wall.
2. no change
3. On our last family vacation we went to Disneyland, where we shook hands with Mickey Mouse.
4. I saw Alex and Alice, who are twins, at the shopping center.
5. The Mississippi River, which is one of the most important rivers in the United States, has an interesting history.
6. Mr. Mitchell, with whom we shared our back fence, was a fantastic gardener.

7. no change
8. *The Marriage of Figaro,* which is one of Mozart's comedic operas, is performed regularly on stages around the world.
9. Jason has two brothers. His older brother, who lives in New York, is a financial advisor, and his younger brother is a police officer.
10. The book that I'm reading is from the Everett Public Library, where you can borrow books for up to three weeks.

Quiz 10, p. 153

1. This story has three main characters, all of whom are interesting and funny.
2. My school employs 60 teachers, more than half of whom have master's degrees.
3. I bought a pound of strawberries, a few of which are still green.
4. The building caretaker found two jackets, neither of which was Josh's.
5. Peter advises many students, most of whose questions are easy to answer.
6. The students, several of whom were half asleep, listened to the boring professor talk.
7. Mr. Carter talked to the large group of college students, some of whom did not know that he used to be the president.
8. The workers, many of whose jobs were in danger because of consolidation and cost cutting, attended the meeting about the merger of the two companies.

Quiz 11, p. 154

A.
1. a noun
2. the sentence
3. the sentence
4. a noun
5. the sentence
6. a noun

B.
1. Harold bought a newspaper which he read on the train on the way to work.
2. On the way to work, Max stopped to get coffee, which was part of his morning routine.
3. After she got off the phone, Margaret typed an email which was a message for her boss.
4. The receptionist answered the phone, which was a big part of her job.

Quiz 12, p. 155

1. The police officer in charge of directing traffic is very helpful.
2. Anyone graduating this semester will get a diploma.
3. Montana, the fourth largest state in the U.S., is on the border with Canada.
4. The boys playing soccer are preparing for a big tournament.
5. Instructors attending the workshop will learn about teaching English pronunciation.
6. How much are the tickets for the play showing at the New City Theater?
7. The archeologists digging in an area in eastern China made a significant discovery.
8. The Olympic official presenting the medals shook hands with the athletes.
9. There are more and more Americans driving cars that run on biodiesel.
10. Heather is the manager overseeing the accounting department.

Quiz 13, p. 156

1. The book that we read ~~it~~ in class was about the history of jazz.
2. My best friend went to work in Indonesia, **which** consists of thousands of islands.
3. I like to shop at the farmers' market on Saturdays **when** I have a day off.
4. My DVD collection, most of **which** is stored at my parents' house, includes movies from the 1940s to the present.
5. Emma borrowed money from her sister whom she has to pay ~~her~~ back by next weekend.
6. When the weather is nice, the children like to go to the beach **that / which** is close to their house.
7. Mark doesn't get much sleep. He has a neighbor **whose** dog barks all night long.
8. The store manager locked the door **that / which** was at the back of the store before he went home.
9. There were fourteen students in my grammar class, seven of **whom** were from Korea.
10. The young woman **who / Ø** was sitting across from me on the plane was listening to music and watching videos on her computer.

TEST 1, p. 157

A.
1. b
2. c, d
3. a, d
4. b
5. c, d

B.
1. who
2. whom
3. who
4. whose
5. whom
6. who

C.
1. Connie finally finished typing the letters that / which the department supervisor needs to sign.
2. My grandmother bought a lot of clothes that / which were on sale.
3. The red station wagon which / that caused the accident was driven by a drunk driver.
4. The woman who / whom Mr. North just interviewed seemed well qualified for the position.
5. Mrs. Tanaka is looking for the person whose car is blocking her driveway.

D.
1. *Little Women,* published in 1868, is my sister's favorite novel.
2. The science program showing on TV every night this week is a series about the brain.
3. People visiting the Taj Mahal are impressed that a man built it to honor his wife.
4. The director's new movie, opening in theaters this weekend, is sure to be entertaining.
5. The manager of the French restaurant was pleased to learn that the critics specializing in European cuisine rated his restaurant number one in the city.

E.
1. Tom, who lives in Port Hadlock, is graduating from high school in June.
2. no change
3. Paul will call you at 5:30 P.M., when he will be home from work.
4. I have looked everywhere for my grammar book, which I am sure I left on the dining room table. I can't find it anywhere.
5. no change

TEST 2, p. 159

A.

1. c, d
2. a, d
3. b
4. c, d
5. a, d

B.

1. who
2. whose
3. whom
4. who
5. who
6. whom

C.

1. Joe's parents don't like the music that / which Joe / he listens to.
2. The printer that / which Jason bought last week is fast and dependable.
3. The police talked to the woman whose car had been broken into.
4. The issue that / which many people are talking about is not relevant to our current discussion.
5. People who have advanced computer skills are in great demand in today's job market.

D.

1. Anyone having grades that are above average can apply for the scholarship.
2. The severe drought occurring in the Midwest this summer has ruined the corn crop.
3. The missing man's family is desperately seeking anyone having information about his activities.
4. The lecture will most likely be attended by people interested in the Middle East.
5. The people watching the acrobat turn circles in the air were horrified when he fell to his death.

E.

1. The roof of my house, which is already 20 years old, is leaking badly and in need of repair.
2. no change
3. no change
4. Jennifer's birthday cake, which had strawberries and cream on top, was enjoyed by everyone at the party.
5. The Red Cross, which provides humanitarian aid to victims of wars and natural disasters, is the favorite charity of the president's wife.

CHAPTER 14

Quiz 1, p. 161

1. to
2. for
3. of
4. in
5. to
6. of
7. to
8. on
9. from
10. about

Quiz 2, p. 161

1. in coming
2. to helping
3. about / of taking
4. by crying
5. to wearing
6. for cleaning
7. of driving
8. about passing
9. by using
10. of robbing

Quiz 3, p. 162

1. went dancing
2. will go sightseeing, go hiking
3. goes biking
4. go sailing
5. went fishing
6. gone snorkeling
7. go shopping
8. went sledding

Quiz 4, p. 163

1. Ms. Spring sat at her desk paying bills last night.
2. Every night Greg wastes a lot of time surfing the internet.
3. I caught my son sneaking cookies from the cupboard when I walked into the kitchen yesterday. OR When I walked into the kitchen yesterday, I caught my son sneaking cookies from the cupboard.
4. Stewart always has a hard time solving physics problems.
5. Carol had a good time traveling with her sisters last summer.

Quiz 5, p. 163

1. us to come
2. to give me
3. them to play
4. to retire, him to stop
5. to be, to help
6. students to try
7. to arrive, me to be

Quiz 6, p. 164

1. b
2. b
3. a
4. a
5. b
6. a, b
7. b
8. a, b
9. a
10. a

Quiz 7, p. 165

1. shopping
2. playing
3. to celebrate
4. to run / running
5. to call
6. to stay
7. driving
8. to turn, to do
9. to have
10. planting
11. to keep
12. growing
13. to speak
14. to go
15. smelling
16. to continue, studying / to study, to live
17. going, to eat

Quiz 8, p. 166

A.

1. It takes a long time to learn a foreign language well.
2. It should not be hard to find a parking place downtown.
3. It might be boring to listen to the politician's speech.
4. It costs a lot to fly first class.
5. It is impolite to talk when someone else is talking.

B.

1. Learning a foreign language well takes a long time.
2. Finding a parking place downtown should not be hard.
3. Listening to the politician's speech might be boring.

4. Flying first class costs a lot.
5. Talking when someone else is talking is impolite.

Quiz 9, p. 167

1. b	6. a	11. a
2. a	7. b	12. b
3. a	8. a	13. a
4. b	9. a	14. b
5. b	10. b	15. a

TEST 1, p. 168

A.

1. b	4. a
2. a	5. a
3. b	

B.

1. about	4. about / of
2. on	5. to
3. for	

C.

1. for borrowing	7. in learning
2. studying, to get	8. skiing
3. bringing	9. to buy, doing
4. Giving	10. to take / taking
5. waiting, to go	11. Taking
6. sneezing	12. relaxing

D.

1. to send
2. snowboarding
3. to lock, putting, hearing
4. telling
5. to buy

E.

1. My dad always takes his time choosing a new car.
2. It is uncomfortable to live in a hot climate without air-conditioning.
3. My sisters and I go swimming at the neighborhood pool twice a month.
4. Dennis sometimes has difficulty expressing his opinion.
5. Having a visa is necessary for traveling overseas.

TEST 2, p. 170

A.

1. b	4. b
2. a	5. a
3. b	

B.

1. to	4. about
2. in	5. from
3. of	

C.

1. visiting	7. having
2. buying	8. bothering, to take
3. to see	9. for taking
4. of telling, breaking	10. to wear / wearing
5. to be	11. to go
6. eating	12. needing, to come

D.

1. smoking	4. to learn
2. to tell	5. doing
3. seeing	6. to sign

E.

1. It is terrible to wake up with a headache.
2. Living on their own is a good experience for young adults.
3. Jenny sometimes catches her children watching TV in the middle of the night.
4. It is dangerous for children to use fireworks without adult supervision.
5. The tourists are standing on the corner trying to figure out where to go.

CHAPTER 15

Quiz 1, p. 172

A.

1. to	4. to
2. for	5. for
3. to	

B.

1. in order	4. in order
2. Ø	5. in order
3. Ø	

Quiz 2, p. 173

2. delighted to
3. likely to
4. disappointed to
5. embarrassed to
6. proud to
7. unlikely to / hesitant to
8. surprised to
9. fortunate to
10. hesitant to / unlikely to
11. relieved to

Quiz 3, p. 174

1. b	6. b	
2. a	7. a	
3. a	8. a	
4. b	9. a	
5. a	10. a	

Quiz 4, p. 175

1. too serious	5. big enough
2. ripe enough	6. strong enough
3. spicy enough	7. too sweet
4. too bright	8. warm enough

Quiz 5, p. 175

1. to be married
2. being interviewed
3. being asked
4. to be repaired / repairing
5. to be prepared
6. being driven
7. to be wearing
8. to be washed / washing
9. to be remembered
10. being recognized

Quiz 6, p. 176

2. ring / ringing
3. carry / carrying
4. discuss / discussing
5. park, go
6. rotting
7. tell
8. flashing

Quiz 7, p. 177

1. a
2. c
3. b
4. c
5. b
6. a

Quiz 8, p. 177

1. a, b
2. c
3. b
4. a
5. c
6. a
7. a
8. a
9. a, b
10. c

Quiz 9, p. 178

1. I went to the gas station **for** some gas. OR
   I went to the gas station **to get** some gas.
2. Alan has enough **height** to reach the top shelf. OR
   Alan **is tall enough** to reach the top shelf.
3. The kids were **too** excited to sit still.
4. Chris let his little brother **borrow** his books.
5. Eddie was stunned **to** hear that he hadn't passed his final exam in biology.
6. I am pleased **to introduce** you to my parents, Carol and Bob Matthews.
7. It has been a long time since I've cleaned. My room really needs **to be** dusted. OR
   It has been a long time since I've cleaned. My room really needs **dusting**.
8. Julia's best friend insists on **being** told all of her family news.
9. My cousin moved to Alaska **to work** in the tourist industry.
10. Toshiko got her brother-in-law **to** pick her up at the airport.
11. Sharon is looking forward to **being** sent on a business trip to Hawaii.
12. Teresa saw her best friend ~~to~~ **waving** / **wave** at her from across the street.
13. The advisor helped students **make** / **to make** decisions about college.
14. My parents wanted ~~in order~~ **to hear** my reasons for not going to college, but I knew they didn't agree.
15. Reading Shakespeare takes **too** much concentration to read it on the subway. I prefer to read a magazine on my way to work.

TEST 1, p. 179

A.
1. Ø
2. in order
3. in order
4. Ø
5. in order

B.
1. a
2. b
3. a
4. b
5. b

C.
1. to be washed
2. being seen
3. to be asked
4. to be introduced
5. being laughed

D.
1. hiding
2. burning
3. flying
4. brushing / brush
5. crying / cry

E.
1. stay
2. move
3. figure
4. to dance
5. return

F.
1. Pete is thinking about **going** to graduate school **to get** / **for** a master's degree.
2. Our house needs to **be repaired** and **painted** before we can consider **selling** it.
3. There isn't enough time **for us to finish** all of the reports by Friday.
4. Tanya was sorry to **be** late, and she apologized for **missing** part of the presentation.
5. Chuck has been thinking about **moving** out of the house and **finding** a job.

TEST 2, p. 182

A.
1. in order
2. Ø
3. Ø
4. in order
5. Ø

B.
1. b
2. b
3. a
4. b
5. a

C.
1. being worried
2. to be invited
3. being allowed
4. to be thrown
5. to be treated

D.
1. standing
2. take / taking
3. report / reporting
4. blowing
5. beep / beeping

E.
1. find
2. use
3. to open
4. stretch
5. postpone

F.
1. I heard the rain **falling** on the roof and realized that I needed **to bring** an umbrella with me.
2. My doctor made me **wait** ~~to~~ 45 minutes before he would see me.
3. Mrs. Won wouldn't let her son **play** football because she was worried about him **getting** hurt.
4. These shoes are **too tight** for me to wear anymore.
5. The president had the company **put off sending** out its annual report.

CHAPTER 16

Quiz 1, p. 184

1. began
2. fit
3. trying
4. forgiveness
5. spoken
6. catch
7. sending
8. disappointed
9. sings
10. directed

Quiz 2, p. 184

1. High school graduation is an exciting, fun, and rewarding time for most students and their families.
2. Students are tired of high school, are ready for something new, and are looking forward to college or work.
3. Parents feel proud, satisfied, and relieved that their children have reached this milestone in their lives.
4. There are many events leading up to graduation day. For example, most graduates get their picture taken, send out graduation announcements, and invite friends and family to celebrate with them.
5. On graduation day there is a ceremony that includes speeches, awards, and ceremonial music.
6. Parents, siblings, and friends look on as students receive their diplomas.
7. High school graduation is a sort of "coming of age" into the adult world of opportunity, independence, and responsibility.

Quiz 3, p. 185

1. Vienna, Austria, is famous for classical music, opera, and the waltz.
2. The new magazine was colorful and glossy and had lots of photographs and advertising.
3. The fireman put out a fire, rescued a cat stuck in a tree, and helped a man who had had a heart attack.
4. In Brazil, I saw white sand beaches, beautiful young women and men, and crystal clear blue water.
5. When Jane got home from work, she took off her suit and her high-heeled shoes and put on an old pair of jeans, an old pair of slippers, and a warm wool sweater.
6. For dinner, Stephan ate slices of roast beef, rice with gravy, and string beans.

Quiz 4, p. 186

1.	are	6.	are
2.	is	7.	is
3.	is	8.	are
4.	are	9.	is
5.	is	10.	is

Quiz 5, p. 187

1. Neither Janice nor Erica has any brothers or sisters.
2. We can have either broccoli or cauliflower for dinner.
3. During her speech, Lina spoke both loudly and clearly.
4. Not only Greg but also his twin brother is interested in studying medicine.
5. Both the New York Yankees and the Boston Red Sox are great baseball teams.
6. Either my husband or my daughter and I will go to a movie tonight. OR
   Either my husband and I or my daughter and I will go to a movie tonight.
7. My English teacher had neither graded our essays nor returned our vocabulary quizzes.

Quiz 6, p. 188

1. My brother is an accountant. **H**e can help us with our income taxes.
2. An Australian swimmer was attacked by a shark, but he scared the animal away by poking it in the eye.
3. Denny's computer crashed as he was working on his report, so he took his computer to the repair shop. **U**nfortunately they were not able to save his data.
4. A woman in Michigan got a $1 parking ticket in 1976. **S**he finally paid it in 2008 by sending a twenty-dollar bill to the local police station. **S**he also sent a note explaining the money, but she told the police not to try to find her.
5. People have been playing soccer since ancient times. **T**he first soccer clubs were formed in England in the 1850s, but official soccer rules were not written until 1863. **M**any of those same rules still govern soccer today.
6. We enjoyed the movie. **T**he acting was excellent, and the story was delightful. **I**t had both romance and mystery, and it was exciting too.

Quiz 7, p. 189

1. The students' presentation was thoughtful, intelligent, and **interesting**.
2. **Either** John **or** Linda will send you an email. OR
   Neither John **nor** Linda will send you an email.
3. Linda has traveled by car, bus, ship, and ~~took a~~ plane.
4. Our English teacher speaks slowly and **carefully** so we can understand what she says.
5. Teresa **likes** neither spinach nor beets. OR
   Teresa doesn't like **either** spinach **or** beets.
6. The young girl's father didn't approve of her painted fingernails. **S**he wore bright red nail polish.
7. Both the neighborhood committee and the city parks department **work** to keep Echo Lake Park clean.
8. The documentary gave interesting facts and surprising **statistics** on honeybees.
9. Neither cows nor horses **eat** meat. They are herbivores.
10. Not only vulcanologists but also geologists **are** interested in studying Hawaii's volcanoes.

TEST 1, p. 190

A.

1.	love, likes	3.	is
2.	were	4.	appreciates

B.

1. Linda has traveled by car, bus, **and** train, **but** she has not traveled by ship, plane, **or** balloon.
2. Thomas has read about computers **and** the internet, **and** he has taken classes in computer programming **and** applications.
3. Next weekend, Shirley may visit her grandmother **or** her sister, do some shopping **or** take in a movie, **but** she has to do the laundry **and** clean the bathroom.
4. Last winter, Cincinnati experienced terrible storms **and** flooding, unending rain, **and** devastating tornadoes **and** hail.
5. At her surprise birthday party, Gloria was surprised to see her high school friends, her aunt and uncle from New York City, **and** her old college roommate, **but** she was disappointed not to see her sister **or** her niece.

C.

1. The severe rainstorm not only flooded basements and sewers but also caused mudslides. OR
   The severe rainstorm both flooded basements and sewers and caused mudslides.
2. Either Cindy or Mrs. Smith will babysit the kids this evening.
3. Neither Arthur nor his cousins have ever been to Disneyland. OR
   Not only Arthur but also his cousins have never been to Disneyland.
4. During the holiday weekend, the parking lots at both San Francisco International Airport and San Jose Airport were full. OR
   During the holiday weekend, the parking lot at not only San Francisco International Airport but also at San Jose Airport was full.
5. Both bread and flour should be stored in the freezer instead of the refrigerator. OR
   Not only bread but also flour should be stored in the freezer instead of the refrigerator.

D.

1. Polly was looking for a new camera for her brother's birthday. **S**he wanted a large selection and good prices, so she used the internet to do her shopping.
2. Both Silvia and her husband love the rock band Wind Tunnel, but they refuse to pay $125 a ticket to attend a concert.
3. Myron has written short stories and poems for the school literary magazine, and sports and feature articles for the school newspaper.
4. Acme Toy Company continues to produce dolls, metal cars, construction sets, and action figures, but it no longer makes bicycles or board games.
5. Flights 2058 and 2065 to Los Angeles have been delayed, but Flight 2061 is departing on time. I can get you a seat on Flight 2061.

TEST 2, p. 192

A.

1. save	4. is
2. live	5. wants
3. have	

B.

1. Last night, Larry watched some TV, surfed the internet, listened to some music, **and** read the newspaper, **but** today he has to do some serious work.
2. Mr. Kincaid owns real estate, stocks, **and** bonds, **but** he has to sell some stocks **and** bonds to pay his taxes.
3. Both Craig and Jean have good computer skills and can type 70 words a minute, **so** they both got jobs as executive assistants.
4. Both French and German are Indo-European languages, but Chinese and Korean are not.
5. It was an extremely cold day, **so** Mark put on a heavy sweater **and** a warm jacket, **but** he didn't wear a hat **or** a scarf.

C.

1. The earthquake both knocked over several freeways and broke gas and water lines. OR
   The earthquake not only knocked over several freeways but also broke gas and water lines.
2. Philip wants neither to go to college nor find a job.
3. Both oranges and cabbage are good sources of vitamin C.

4. The contractor will either try to repair the broken fence or tear it down and replace it.
5. Neither mayoral candidate Jim Brown nor mayoral candidate Alicia Taylor talked about the homeless problem.

D.

1. I have tried the pineapple diet, the starch diet, and the protein diet too, but none of them worked.
2. The weather forecaster predicts heavy fog and light drizzle for the morning, but clear skies and sunshine for the late afternoon.
3. Mary doesn't like to drink tea or decaffeinated coffee, so we need to pick up some regular coffee for her.
4. Bicycles, motorcycles, and handicapped drivers' cars can be parked in Lot A, but everyone else needs to park in Lots B or C.
5. Barbara has had many different jobs. **S**he has been a flight attendant, a salesclerk, a waitress, and a receptionist, but now she has her MBA and is the regional manager for a large multinational corporation.

CHAPTER 17

Quiz 1, p. 194

1. Bryan and Cathy went to Rome <u>after they visited Florence</u>.
2. <u>As soon as my plane arrives in Jakarta</u>, I will call you.
3. <u>Just as I finished loading the software on my computer</u>, the electricity went off.
4. Max was watching the news on TV <u>while he was ironing his shirts</u>.
5. <u>By the time we see you next summer</u>, you will have graduated from high school.
6. The police won't leave <u>until the accident is cleared from the highway</u>.
7. <u>The first time Kevin tried to ride a motorcycle</u>, he crashed into a fence.
8. I have been a *Star Wars* fan <u>ever since I was a child</u>.
9. Carol will return to her office <u>once the meeting ends</u>.
10. <u>Since the 3-M Company first made Post-It Notes</u>, they have been sold in eight sizes, 25 shapes, and 62 colors.

Quiz 2, p. 195

1. d		6. c	
2. c		7. a	
3. b		8. b	
4. a		9. c	
5. b		10. b	

Quiz 3, p. 196

1. Whenever Sue comes home late, her parents are upset. OR
   Sue's parents are upset whenever she comes home late.
2. The chef heated up the barbecue before he grilled the steaks. OR
   Before the chef grilled the steaks, he heated up the barbecue.
3. After I showed my passport, the customs officer let me pass into the terminal. OR
   The customs officer let me pass into the terminal after I showed my passport.

4. Every time Shelley goes jogging, she needs to drink a lot of water. OR
Shelley needs to drink a lot of water every time she goes jogging.
5. As soon as Mr. Arnold turns off the lights, we will be able to see the screen better. OR
We will be able to see the screen better as soon as Mr. Arnold turns off the lights.
6. The crowd cheered when they saw the baseball fly over the stadium wall. OR
When the crowd saw the baseball fly over the stadium wall, they cheered.
7. By the time I finish my homework, it will be midnight. OR
It'll be midnight by the time I finish my homework.
8. The pilot got a message from the control tower just before the plane landed. OR
Just before the plane landed, the pilot got a message from the control tower.
9. While Karen was shutting down her computer, the computer made a strange noise. OR
Karen's computer made a strange noise while she was shutting it down.
10. Since Brad and Martha got married in 1995, they have played Scrabble once a week. OR
Brad and Martha have played Scrabble once a week since they got married in 1995.

Quiz 4, p. 197

1. Because John arrived at the airport just ten minutes before his flight's departure time, he nearly missed his plane. OR
John nearly missed his plane because he arrived at the airport just ten minutes before his flight's departure time.
2. Because the price of crude oil has risen, the price of gasoline has doubled in the last three years. OR
The price of gasoline has doubled in the last three years because the price of crude oil has risen.
3. Now that the rain has stopped, we can open the windows and get some fresh air. OR
We can open the windows and get some fresh air now that the rain has stopped.
4. We will have to contact Mr. Adams by mail since he has neither email nor a phone. OR
Since Mr. Adams has neither email nor a phone, we will have to contact him by mail.
5. Sue did not enjoy going to the movies because she had left her eyeglasses at home. OR
Because Sue had left her eyeglasses at home, she did not enjoy going to the movies.
6. Larry has to do a lot of traveling now that he is the senior manager for the western division of his company. OR
Now that Larry is the senior manager for the western division of his company, he has to do a lot of traveling.
7. We can stay up late and talk since we don't have to go to work tomorrow. OR
Since we don't have to go to work tomorrow, we can stay up late and talk.
8. I need to find a new place to get my hair cut now that my barber has retired after 25 years. OR
Now that my barber has retired after 25 years, I need to find a new place to get my hair cut.

9. Because the two groups refused to sign the peace treaty last week, fighting between them began again today. OR
Fighting between the two groups began again today because they refused to sign the peace treaty last week.
10. Future funding for the space shuttle program is uncertain since the last three shuttle missions had problems. OR
Since the last three shuttle missions had problems, future funding for the space shuttle program is uncertain.

Quiz 5, p. 198

1. even though
2. because
3. Even though
4. because
5. Because
6. even though
7. Because, even though
8. Even though, because

Quiz 6, p. 199

1. b
2. c
3. d
4. a
5. b
6. d

Quiz 7, p. 199

2. c
3. a
4. h
5. k
6. d
7. f
8. i
9. g
10. j
11. b

Quiz 8, p. 200

1. she cries a lot.
2. there is a traffic jam on the freeway
3. they have a game three times a week
4. I don't see you tomorrow
5. Steve gets nine hours of sleep a night
6. they lower the price

Quiz 9, p. 201

1. unless
2. Only if
3. only if
4. unless
5. Unless
6. only if
7. unless
8. only if

Quiz 10, p. 201

Sample answers:
1. , you will have to have more treatment.
2. , we will have to cancel the hike.
3. , you should make your best guess.
4. her car is in the repair shop.
5. it had lots of blossoms.
6. you have other things to do.
7. I can sleep in every morning.
8. , here is my cell phone number.
9. I promise to drive carefully.
10. should you call 911.

TEST 1, p. 202

A.
1. After Teresa read a lot of college catalogs, she chose the college that she wants to attend. OR

Teresa chose the college that she wants to attend after she read a lot of college catalogs.

2. We were working on the new project when our boss returned from his vacation on Monday. OR
When our boss returned from his vacation on Monday, we were working on the new project.

3. As soon as Joe gets up tomorrow at 6:00 A.M., he will do his exercises. OR
Joe will do his exercises as soon as he gets up tomorrow at 6 A.M.

4. For her birthday, Martina is going to go out to dinner with her friends before they go dancing at a nightclub. OR
Before Martina and her friends go dancing at a nightclub, they are going to go out to dinner for her birthday.

5. Kathy will have moved to Texas by the time her husband returns from his job in South America next month. OR
By the time Kathy's husband returns from his job in South America next month, Kathy will have moved to Texas.

B.
Sample answers:
1. , we will not go to the baseball game.
2. , please return this book for me.
3. I don't do well in my classes.
4. , I would like to borrow it.
5. you need more information,

C.
1. c   4. b
2. a   5. d
3. e

D.
1. even if   4. Even if
2. even if   5. in case
3. in case / whether or not

E.
1. Unless   4. unless
2. only if   5. Unless
3. Only if

F.
1. Now that the term is almost over, students can look forward to vacation. OR
Students can look forward to vacation now that the term is almost over.

2. Because Shelley forgot her sister's birthday, she felt terrible. OR
Shelley felt terrible because she forgot her sister's birthday.

3. Unless the weather improves by tomorrow, we won't go camping. OR
We won't go camping unless the weather improves by tomorrow.

4. Even if I win the lottery, I won't quit my job. OR
I won't quit my job even if I win the lottery.

5. The workers refused to work on New Year's Eve even though the company promised to pay them double their usual wage. OR
Even though the company promised to pay them double their usual wage, the workers refused to work on New Year's Eve.

TEST 2, p. 205

A.
1. After I pick up my cousin at the airport, I am going to show him the Golden Gate Bridge. OR
I am going to show my cousin the Golden Gate Bridge after I pick him up at the airport.

2. Maurice was eating lunch in a restaurant when he dropped his napkin on the floor. OR
When Maurice dropped his napkin on the floor, he was eating lunch in a restaurant.

3. As soon as Ann gets over her bad cold, she will return to work. OR
Ann will return to work as soon as she gets over her bad cold.

4. Mary rinses the food off the dishes before she puts them in the dishwasher. OR
Before Mary puts the dishes in the dishwasher, she rinses the food off them.

5. Ali will have graduated from high school by the time his brother gets married in July. OR
By the time Ali's brother gets married in July, Ali will have graduated from high school.

B.
Sample answers:
1. , I'm going to complain to the building manager.
2. , I will call you later.
3. you complete your bachelor's degree,
4. he's in town that day.
5. I will ask her for a ride.

C.
1. c   4. a
2. e   5. b
3. d

D.
1. Even if   4. whether or not / even if
2. In case   5. Whether or not / Even if
3. even if

E.
1. only if   4. Only if
2. Unless   5. unless
3. unless

F.
1. The teacher will re-calculate the test grades since he / she found an error in the answer key. OR
Since the teacher found an error in the answer key, he / she will re-calculate the test grades.

2. Even though the test was very easy, Patricia worked on it for more than an hour to make sure that she didn't make any mistakes. OR
Patricia worked on the test for more than an hour to make sure that she didn't make any mistakes even though the test was easy.

3. Maria is going to marry Harry even if she doesn't really love him. OR
Even if Maria doesn't really love Harry, she is going to marry him.

4. Unless Sam improves his grades in math and chemistry, he won't get accepted to medical school. OR
Sam won't get accepted to medical school unless he improves his grades in math and chemistry.

5. While some people enjoy cycling for exercise, other people enjoy walking briskly. OR
While some people enjoy walking briskly for exercise, other people enjoy cycling.

CHAPTER 18

Quiz 1, p. 208

1. ✓
2. incorrect
3. ✓
4. incorrect
5. incorrect
6. ✓
7. ✓
8. incorrect
9. ✓
10. incorrect

Quiz 2, p. 208

1. Since moving to California a year ago, Harry has been to Disneyland five times.
2. Before leaving Milwaukee for Toronto, Calum filled up the gas tank.
3. no change
4. Usually after working an eight-hour shift at the busy restaurant, Katherine is exhausted.
5. While living in Los Angeles, Mary often ran into famous people.
6. George has quit his job and started traveling around the world since winning $1,000,000 on a TV game show.
7. no change
8. Mark used to watch movies on his computer while waiting for the bus.
9. Jason will do his laundry after finishing his chemistry homework.
10. Before going to a new restaurant, Julie and Jay always read reviews and look at a sample menu online.

Quiz 3, p. 210

A.
1. because
2. while
3. while
4. because
5. because

B.
1. Being a talented singer, Phoebe often sings in local coffee houses on weekends.
2. While ice-skating with her son, Christine fell and broke her ankle.
3. Unable to finish writing his report at the office, Andy took some paperwork home with him.
4. Because fighting fires is a very demanding job, firefighters have to be in excellent physical condition.
5. While attending a seminar on Friday, the college administrators discussed goals for the coming year.

Quiz 4, p. 211

1. Upon hearing that the meeting was canceled, the teachers were very happy.
2. Upon finishing her final exam, Maya breathed a sigh of relief.
3. Upon receiving an award for her performance, the actor gave a brief acceptance speech.
4. Upon finding a gold coin in the sand at the beach, Tom couldn't believe his good luck.
5. Upon being elected mayor of the city, Margaret Peters set up a committee to study the public schools.
6. Upon having her sixth baby, Tina said, "I think this will be my last one."
7. Upon being fired from his job, the plumber filed a complaint with his workers' union.
8. Upon returning from a trip to Ecuador, Mrs. Alexander started a small business that sold Ecuadorean handicrafts.

Quiz 5, p. 212

1. While lying in bed feeling depressed, Joe wondered what he should do about his problems.
2. Upon arriving in London, the first thing Jane will do is have tea at the Ritz Hotel.
3. Having no money to buy a present for his mother, Billy made her a birthday card.
4. After testing the drug on mice, the research scientists will test the drug on monkeys.
5. Since taking a course in public speaking, Alex has developed more self-confidence.
6. While working in her garden, Susan disturbed a wasp's nest and was stung several times.
7. (Being) confused about the directions to the party, Carol had to stop at a gas station to ask for help.
8. Before leaving for India, Brian had to get several shots to protect him from tropical diseases.
9. While talking with his accountant, Omar realized that starting his own business would be quite complicated.
10. Upon tasting Mrs. Wilson's blueberry pie, Louis said that it was the most delicious pie he had ever eaten.

TEST 1, p. 214

A.
1. While cleaning out his garage, John found his old high school yearbooks.
2. no change
3. Before throwing anything away, Mary consulted with John to make sure it was OK.
4. Since moving into their house in 1992, Mary and John have acquired a lot of furniture.
5. After finishing / Having finished their work in the garage, John and Mary drank some cold sodas.

B.
1. Not wanting to interrupt your meeting, I left a message with your secretary.
2. After / Upon becoming a citizen, the first thing Mr. Santos did was register to vote.
3. While George was standing on a ladder to change a light bulb, his dog ran by and knocked the ladder over.
4. After explaining the medical procedure, the doctor asked the patient if he had any questions.
5. Having no husband and three children, Mrs. Nguyen had to work ten hours a day to keep them fed and clothed.

C.
1. ✓
2. ✓
3. incorrect
4. ✓
5. incorrect
6. ✓

TEST 2, p. 216

A.
1. Having had a car accident last summer, Joe had to ride his bike to work.
2. Riding to work every day, Joe was dreaming about buying a new car.
3. no change
4. While searching for information, Joe's sister found two cars that she thought would interest him.
5. After reading / Having read all the articles that his sister had found for him, Joe chose which car he wanted.

B.

1. While playing basketball with his friends, my brother fell and sprained his ankle.
2. Since reading a book about sharks, Sam has been afraid to swim in the ocean.
3. After finishing his homework assignment, Paul was free to watch TV for the rest of the evening.
4. Not having received a birthday package that her brother sent, Luisa contacted the post office about tracking the package.
5. Since graduating from the university with a degree in French history, George has been looking for a job in education.

C.

1. incorrect	4. incorrect
2. ✓	5. ✓
3. ✓	6. incorrect

CHAPTER 19

Quiz 1, p. 218

1. Because of	6. Because of
2. because	7. because
3. because	8. Because of
4. Because	9. because
5. because of	10. because of

Quiz 2, p. 219

Sample answers:

1. the bad weather
2. her fever
3. (her) car problems
4. my mother's illness
5. the deep snow
6. he is lazy
7. a toothache
8. the caffeine
9. I have an 8:00 A.M. appointment tomorrow
10. scientists' increased understanding of human genetics

Quiz 3, p. 219

1. My coffee got cold, so I reheated it in the microwave.
2. Fish was on sale at the market. **T**herefore, Pat bought three fillets to have for dinner.
3. Andrea was upset that her favorite team was losing the match, so she turned off the TV.
4. The regular radio announcer had a sore throat. **C**onsequently, another announcer was on the program.
5. Electricity, water, and gas are getting more expensive. **P**eople, therefore, are trying to conserve energy.
6. The attorneys had questioned all the witnesses, so the judge called a recess in the trial.
7. Shareholders voted against the merger of the two companies. **C**onsequently, the merger was canceled.
8. Khanh speaks English every day. **H**is pronunciation is improving, therefore.
9. The supervisor gave her employees a lot of freedom in doing their work. **C**onsequently, they liked working for her.
10. My doctor didn't have the right equipment for the medical test I needed. **H**e, therefore, sent me to a specialist.

Quiz 4, p. 220

1. The milk was left out on the table overnight, so it turned sour.
2. Because my husband doesn't like lima beans, we never eat them.
3. Due to the weak economy, many citizens are unhappy with the government.
4. A new book by Maggie's favorite author was just published. Consequently, Maggie bought it immediately.
5. Because of the manager's cold, the meeting is canceled.
6. There is a lot of damage from the windstorm. Therefore, many people have joined in the cleanup.
7. Hannah loves sweets. Consequently, she has gained back all the weight she lost.
8. Jason dropped his cell phone in the swimming pool. Therefore, his cell phone stopped working.
9. Due to the fact that it was very late, we decided not to go out for coffee after the play.

Quiz 5, p. 221

2. painful	7. an ugly dress
3. little	8. a big dog
4. a silly rumor	9. fast
5. much	10. many
6. forgetful	11. hard

Quiz 6, p. 222

1. Mike's motorcycle is so loud that the neighbors have complained about the noise.
2. It was such a heavy couch that it took three people to move it.
3. The weather in June was so cold that we had to wear our winter sweaters.
4. The store has such dirty windows that we can hardly see inside.
5. The Sunday paper has such great comics that Nick reads them every week.
6. Patrick ate so much chocolate ice cream that he got a stomachache.
7. My essay had so many errors that I had to spend over an hour correcting it.
8. The weather is so sunny and beautiful that Janet doesn't feel like going to class.
9. There were so few dishes in the sink that it only took me a few minutes to wash them.
10. Nurses are in such high demand in hospitals that it's easy to find a good job.

Quiz 7, p. 223

A.

1. I have a part-time job so that I can afford to go to college.
2. Jim will take the bus to the airport so that he doesn't have to pay for parking.
3. The mechanics at Sam's Garage do careful work so that their customers will come again.
4. Frank and Joan took a parenting class so that they would / could learn more about children.
5. The music director stood on a podium so that he could see all of the musicians.

B.
1. Fahad doesn't enjoy video games, so he rarely plays them.
2. Rob practices kung fu three times a week so **that** he can stay in shape.
3. I need to get a high score on my grammar test so **that** I will improve my grade in the class.
4. Meg is going to be gone on vacation for three months, so a temporary worker will replace her.
5. Miki emails her parents in Japan almost every day so **that** they won't worry about her while she's in the U.S.

Quiz 8, p. 224

1. but
2. Nevertheless
3. even though
4. even though
5. Despite
6. Nevertheless
7. Even though
8. but
9. Despite
10. Nevertheless

Quiz 9, p. 225

1. I wasn't really hungry, but I ate lunch anyway.
2. Even though Emily skipped breakfast, she still has a lot of energy.
3. Mr. Kwan is a rich man. **N**evertheless, he refuses to buy his daughter a new car.
4. In spite of the high cost of postage, Omar sends a package overseas every week.
5. Rosanne really wanted to learn to drive, yet she was too young to get a driver's license.
6. Helen always talks about losing weight. **S**he constantly snacks, however.
7. Although Jamaal grew up in San Francisco, he prefers living in Oakland.
8. Despite the fact that Anthony had already lost two cell phones, his parents gave him another one.
9. Edward doesn't like to smoke. **N**onetheless, he sometimes smokes a cigar with his business partners.
10. After my house was robbed, the police warned me not to go inside. **H**owever, I still wanted to see it for myself.

Quiz 10, p. 225

Sample answers:
1. People who car camp pack everything into their cars, but backpackers carry everything on their backs.
2. People who backpack hike into their camp. On the other hand, people who car camp usually camp in a campground they can drive to.
3. People who prefer car camping often like meeting other campers, while backpackers often enjoy getting away from crowds.
4. Car campers can enjoy fresh food prepared in camp. However, backpackers eat mostly dried and canned foods in camp.
5. People who car camp often take their pets along. On the other hand, people who backpack rarely take their pets with them.

Quiz 11, p. 226

Sample answers:

A.
1. Maria had better study for her quiz. Otherwise, she won't get a good grade.

2. I have to find my passport. Otherwise, I won't be able to cross the border.
3. You must have a reservation. Otherwise, you can't get a table for dinner.
4. Kathleen's flight from the Philippines had better arrive on time. Otherwise, she will miss her connecting flight to Boston.

B.
1. Our teacher has to remember students' names, or (else) the whole class laughs.
2. Pat should work hard, or (else) the repairs on the house won't get finished by winter.
3. Mark must save money every month, or (else) he won't be able to afford a car.
4. Beth has to get a new car license, or (else) she'll get a ticket.

TEST 1, p. 227

A.
1. The sweater Jane bought has a hole in it, so she needs to return it to the store.
2. The traffic on Highway 101 was jammed. Therefore, we took Highway 280 instead.
3. Because Ron was late for work for the third time, he was fired from his job.
4. Due to injuring his lower back, Bill can't lift heavy objects. OR
   Due to a lower back injury, Bill can't lift heavy objects.
5. Scientists had calculated everything carefully. Consequently, the Mars *Rover* successfully landed on Mars.

B.
1. but
2. In spite of the fact that / Even though
3. even though / in spite of the fact that
4. Nevertheless
5. Despite

C.
1. so
2. such
3. so
4. so
5. such

D.
1. such
2. Even though / Although
3. despite the fact
4. because of
5. While
6. Although / Even though
7. so
8. Because
9. Nevertheless
10. Otherwise

E.
1. Mary speaks Chinese and Japanese, while her sister Linda speaks Spanish and French.
2. Botanists study plants and plant life. On the other hand, zoologists study the animal kingdom.
3. I really wanted to go to New York, but I decided that the trip would be too expensive.
4. My wife is always telling me we need to save money. However, she spends as much money as she wants.

TEST 2, p. 230

A.
1. Because Sally doesn't like the crowds at the shopping center, she shops over the internet.
2. The Minister of Finance was afraid of inflation. Therefore, he raised the interest rates.
3. The previous owners of the house never took care of it. Consequently, it is now quite run down.
4. Because of many construction delays, the subway line will not open on time.
5. Isaac majored in engineering due to pressure from his father.

B.
1. Although / Despite the fact that
2. yet
3. However
4. in spite of
5. Despite the fact that / Although

C.

1. so	4. so
2. so	5. such
3. such	

D.
1. Nonetheless
2. due to
3. so
4. Because
5. in spite of
6. however
7. such
8. Otherwise
9. Even though
10. On the other hand

E.
1. Terry is very shy and quiet in class. On the other hand, Hannah is outgoing and very talkative with classmates.
2. Jan is interested in current events and listens to the news every day. However, Art never listens to the news and doesn't care much about what's happening in the world.
3. Mount McKinley, in Alaska, is the highest peak in North America, while Aconcagua, in Argentina, is the highest peak in South America and the Western Hemisphere.
4. Coffee is made from roasted and ground beans that grow on bushes, but tea is made from the leaves and flowers of a variety of plants.

CHAPTER 20

Quiz 1, p. 233
1. a
2. b
3. c
4. a
5. b
6. b
7. c
8. a
9. c
10. a

Quiz 2, p. 234
1. will call
2. needed
3. would pass
4. receives
5. doesn't come
6. were, would be
7. had, would hang
8. had, would be, would call

Quiz 3, p. 235
3. **T**, If children are scared, they cry. present / future
4. **U**, The police would have come if we had called. past
5. **T**, If Rebecca is tired, she goes to bed early. present / future
6. **U**, If the dogs had stopped barking, I would have slept. past
7. **U**, If I had time today, I would go rollerblading. present / future
8. **T**, If Jeremy needs more time on tests, I allow it. present / future
9. **U**, If Helena hadn't gotten sick, she would have come. past
10. **U**, If Ali didn't have time, he wouldn't help. present / future
11. **T**, Jason calls if he's going to be late. present / future
12. **U**, My father would have waved if he had seen us. past

Quiz 4, p. 235

1. a. no		4. a. yes	
b. no		b. no	
c. no			
2. a. yes		5. a. yes	
b. yes		b. no	
3. a. no			
b. yes			

Quiz 5, p. 236
1. had found
2. would have been
3. would have won
4. hadn't brought
5. would have died
6. wouldn't have doubted
7. had wanted, would have given
8. wouldn't have driven, hadn't been
9. had been, would have done
10. had had, would have bought

Quiz 6, p. 237
1. stays, will work
2. were, would enjoy
3. hadn't stayed, wouldn't have been
4. would quit, hated
5. wouldn't have gotten, had put
6. didn't exist, wouldn't have
7. needs, will call
8. rains, don't get
9. had sent, would have known
10. weren't, would go

Quiz 7, p. 238

1. did
2. hadn't
3. didn't
4. did
5. weren't
6. had
7. had
8. were
9. weren't
10. did

Quiz 8, p. 238

1. weren't sleeping
2. were using
3. hadn't been talking
4. were looking
5. had been enjoying

Quiz 9, p. 239

1. If Paulo had called his parents, they wouldn't be worried about him.
2. If I had finished my homework, I could watch TV.
3. He could drive if he had passed the driving test.
4. The house wouldn't be too hot if the heat hadn't been left on.
5. If the children hadn't practiced a lot they couldn't sing the song by heart.
6. I could check my email if I had brought my laptop computer.
7. If Charles had fed the cats, they wouldn't be hungry now.
8. Mark wouldn't be tired if he hadn't flown in from Hong Kong late last night.

Quiz 10, p. 240

A.
1. Were Pat a traditional guy, he wouldn't cook or clean.
2. Should the phone ring, please answer it.
3. I would have called sooner had someone told me about the accident.
4. Were I you, I would look for a new hair stylist.
5. Had Abdul wanted to join us for dinner, he would have been welcome.

B.
1. If I hadn't been so tired, I would have done the dishes last night.
2. Bob would have bought play tickets if the performance hadn't been sold out.
3. If Julio hadn't lent me $500, I wouldn't have been able to buy a plane ticket home.
4. It wouldn't have been as much fun if Talia hadn't been there.
5. Kate would have played the piano for us if she didn't have a broken finger.

Quiz 11, p. 241

1. could go
2. were going
3. weren't
4. could
5. would
6. had studied
7. had won
8. were
9. hadn't
10. did, turned

Quiz 12, p. 241

Sample answers:
1. If I could live anywhere in the world, I would live in Seattle.
2. If I hadn't learned English, I would have studied Italian.

3. If I don't understand my next English assignment, I will ask my teacher for help.
4. I wish all wars would end.
5. I wish I had known my grandparents better before they died.
6. If I were not taking this quiz, I would be drinking coffee with my friends.
7. If I were ten years older, I would be working at an interesting job.
8. If I could change anything about my past life, I would change the way I treated my little brother. I would have been nicer and more helpful.

TEST 1, p. 243

A.
1. would be
2. pick
3. weren't studying
4. wouldn't have caught, had worn
5. paid
6. goes
7. would have visited, hadn't visited
8. will buy

B.
1. If Madeleine hadn't missed her flight, she wouldn't be feeling angry and frustrated.
2. If she had practiced, Saya could play the pieces for her piano lesson.
3. If Michael hadn't gotten three traffic tickets last year, his insurance rates wouldn't be going up.
4. If Tomas wanted to move to a different city, he would have accepted the job offer.
5. If Stacy Smith hadn't won the election, she wouldn't be the new mayor.

C.
1. If I weren't in a hurry, I would stop to chat with you.
2. If Fred hadn't had to work late, he would have met us for dinner.
3. If you hadn't helped me, I would never have completed this project on time.

D.
1. had
2. did
3. couldn't
4. weren't
5. were
6. could
7. weren't
8. hadn't

TEST 2, p. 245

A.
1. loses
2. would have gone, hadn't been
3. would visit
4. will see
5. got
6. wouldn't have pulled, had been
7. feel
8. were not cooking

B.
1. If Wendy had worked hard in high school, she would be going to college.
2. If Paula hadn't twisted her ankle, she would / could finish the marathon.
3. If the children weren't running and yelling, they would have heard the recess bell.

4. If my computer were working, I would have finished the report.
5. If Roberta liked cheese, she would have eaten some pizza.

C.
1. If I hadn't been in the shower, I would have answered the door.
2. If Lisa didn't have a doctor's appointment, she wouldn't have left work early.
3. If the coach hadn't directed the team, they couldn't have won the championship.

D.
1. could
2. did
3. didn't
4. were
5. had
6. did
7. were
8. hadn't

MIDTERM EXAM 1, p. 247

1. d	11. b	21. a	31. b	41. c
2. b	12. a	22. b	32. c	42. d
3. c	13. b	23. d	33. b	43. a
4. a	14. a	24. b	34. a	44. b
5. c	15. b	25. c	35. d	45. a
6. a	16. c	26. a	36. d	46. d
7. b	17. c	27. d	37. d	47. d
8. d	18. c	28. b	38. c	48. b
9. c	19. d	29. d	39. d	49. a
10. a	20. a	30. c	40. b	50. c

MIDTERM EXAM 2, p. 251

A.
1. are
2. will make / is going to make
3. was working
4. will help
5. haven't had
6. bought
7. will speak / will be speaking
8. rained
9. was chosen
10. is studying
11. will have finished
12. has been surfing
13. has
14. hadn't talked
15. will be celebrated

B.

C	I	
	✓	1. The number of the employees on the project **is** increasing weekly.
	✓	2. We took a **two-week** vacation to Hawaii last January.
✓		3. correct
	✓	4. My son's favorite **superheroes** are Spiderman and Batman.
	✓	5. My soda is on the table. Where is **yours**?
	✓	6. Each of the stars from the movie **has** been interviewed by the press.
	✓	7. Suzanne speaks three languages, but she wants to learn **another** one.
	✓	8. Joshua had too **much homework** last weekend. He didn't have much time to relax.
✓		9. correct
	✓	10. One of the **students** in my writing class studies at the library every night.
	✓	11. **Today's** lunch special is Spaghetti Bolognese with green salad for $5.95.
	✓	12. The children fixed lunch for **themselves**. They made peanut butter and jelly sandwiches.
	✓	13. correct
	✓	14. The *New York Times* **is** among the top newspapers in the U.S.
	✓	15. The **cucumbers** at the market were reasonably priced, so I bought two of them.

C.
1. a. shouldn't have stayed
   b. may / might / could / must have been
   c. should / must / has to be
2. a. Can / Could / May leave
   b. Would / Could / Will ask

D.
1. a. Will
   b. Hannah
   c. James
2. a. Max
   b. David
   c. Ken

E.
1. must not
2. have to / must
3. could
4. don't have to
5. couldn't, must

FINAL EXAM 1, p. 255

1. b	11. a	21. a	31. d	41. d
2. c	12. c	22. c	32. b	42. c
3. a	13. b	23. b	33. b	43. b
4. d	14. d	24. b	34. c	44. a
5. b	15. a	25. a	35. d	45. d
6. d	16. d	26. b	36. c	46. b
7. d	17. c	27. b	37. d	47. c
8. c	18. d	28. d	38. a	48. a
9. a	19. b	29. c	39. c	49. d
10. c	20. a	30. a	40. a	50. b

FINAL EXAM 2, p. 260

A.
1. is going to go / will go / is going
2. didn't study
3. was waiting
4. had already started
5. will be given / is going to be given
6. hasn't arrived
7. will stay / are going to stay
8. is / will be
9. don't plan / aren't planning
10. is

B.

C	I	
____	✓	1. You **must not / shouldn't** leave a candle burning when you leave the house. It could cause a fire.
____	✓	2. Ninety-five percent of the professors at the university **have** a PhD.
____	✓	3. My **aunt** and uncle's new baby is a sweet little girl. She's my newest cousin.
✓	____	4. correct
____	✓	5. The middle-school teachers always give students too **much homework**.
____	✓	6. I'm not sure when the bus is supposed to come. It **should / could / may / might** be here soon.
____	✓	7. Max is worried about his daughter. She should have **called** him by now.
✓	____	8. correct
____	✓	9. John may have been **given** his paycheck at work today. I'm not sure.
____	✓	10. I'm almost sure that story was made up. It **couldn't / can't** be true!

C.
1. Both Mary and John got 100% on their last grammar test.
2. Neither Barbara nor Steven can attend the meeting on Monday.
3. Stewart's team won not only the city championship but also the regional championship.
4. We can watch either a comedy film or a drama.

D.
1. what time the train for Edinburgh leaves
2. if / whether Kevin had gotten his driver's license
3. whose car that was
4. How that machine works

E.
1. Barbara wants to go to an island that has warm sandy beaches and lots of sunshine for her vacation.
2. Anne and Emily like to go shopping on Monday morning when the stores are not crowded.
3. The police are trying to find the man whose car was found near the scene of the crime.

F.

2. g		7. c	
3. j		8. i	
4. f		9. a	
5. h		10. b	
6. d			

G.

1. studying		6. to admit	
2. playing		7. to go	
3. to meet		8. traveling	
4. to get		9. to drive	
5. swimming		10. getting / to get	